DESIGNERS' GUIDES TO THE EUROCODES

DESIGNERS' GUIDE TO EN 1994-1-1 EUROCODE 4: DESIGN OF COMPOSITE STEEL AND CONCRETE STRUCTURES

PART 1.1: GENERAL RULES AND RULES FOR BUILDINGS

DESIGNERS' GUIDES TO THE EUROCODES

DESIGNERS' GUIDE TO EN 1994-1-1 EUROCODE 4: DESIGN OF COMPOSITE STEEL AND CONCRETE STRUCTURES

PART 1.1: GENERAL RULES AND RULES FOR BUILDINGS

R. P. JOHNSON and D. ANDERSON

Published by Thomas Telford Publishing, Thomas Telford Ltd, 1 Heron Quay, London E14 4JD
URL: http://www.thomastelford.com

Distributors for Thomas Telford books are
USA: ASCE Press, 1801 Alexander Bell Drive, Reston, VA 20191-4400
Japan: Maruzen Co. Ltd, Book Department, 3–10 Nihonbashi 2-chome, Chuo-ku, Tokyo 103
Australia: DA Books and Journals, 648 Whitehorse Road, Mitcham 3132, Victoria

First published 2004

Also available from Thomas Telford Books
Designers' Guide to EN 1990. Eurocode: Basis of Structural Design. H. Gulvanessian, J.-A.Calgaro and M. Holický. ISBN 0 7277 3011 8

Eurocodes Expert

Structural Eurocodes offer the opportunity of harmonized design standards for the European construction market and the rest of the world. To achieve this, the construction industry needs to become acquainted with the Eurocodes so that the maximum advantage can be taken of these opportunities

Eurocodes Expert is a new ICE and Thomas Telford initiative set up to assist in creating a greater awareness of the impact and implementation of the Eurocodes within the UK construction industry

Eurocodes Expert provides a range of products and services to aid and support the transition to Eurocodes. For comprehensive and useful information on the adoption of the Eurocodes and their implementation process please visit our website on or email eurocodes@thomastelford.com

---

A catalogue record for this book is available from the British Library

ISBN: 0 7277 3151 3

Typeset by Helius, Brighton and Rochester
Printed and bound in Great Britain by MPG Books, Bodmin

Preface

EN 1994, also known as *Eurocode 4*, is one standard of the Eurocode suite and describes the principles and requirements for safety, serviceability and durability of composite steel and concrete structures. It is subdivided into three parts:

- *Part 1.1: General Rules and Rules for Buildings*
- *Part 1.2: Structural Fire Design*
- *Part 2: Bridges.*

It is intended to be used in conjunction with EN 1990, *Basis of Structural Design*, EN 1991, *Actions on Structures*, and the other design Eurocodes.

Aims and objectives of this guide

The principal aim of this book is to provide the user with guidance on the interpretation and use of EN 1994-1-1 and to present worked examples. The guide explains the relationship with the other Eurocode parts to which it refers and with the relevant British codes. It also provides background information and references to enable users of Eurocode 4 to understand the origin and objectives of its provisions.

Layout of this guide

EN 1994-1-1 has a foreword and nine sections, together with three annexes. This guide has an introduction which corresponds to the foreword of EN 1994-1-1, and Chapters 1 to 9 of the guide correspond to Sections 1 to 9 of the Eurocode. Chapters 10 and 11 correspond to Annexes A and B of the Eurocode, respectively. Appendices A to C of this guide include useful material from the draft Eurocode ENV 1994-1-1.

The numbering and titles of the sections in this guide also correspond to those of the clauses of EN 1994-1-1. Some subsections are also numbered (e.g. 1.1.2). This implies correspondence with the subclause in EN 1994-1-1 of the same number. Their titles also correspond. There are extensive references to lower-level clause and paragraph numbers. The first significant reference is in **bold italic** type (e.g. *clause 1.1.1(2)*). These are in strict numerical sequence throughout the book, to help readers to find comments on particular provisions of the code. Some comments on clauses are necessarily out of sequence, but use of the index should enable these to be found.

All cross-references in this guide to sections, clauses, subclauses, paragraphs, annexes, figures, tables and equations of EN 1994-1-1 are in *italic* type, which is also used where text from a clause in EN 1994-1-1 has been directly reproduced (conversely, cross-references to and quotations from other sources, including other Eurocodes, are in roman type).

Expressions repeated from EN 1994-1-1 retain their number; other expressions have numbers prefixed by D (for *Designers' Guide*), e.g. equation (D6.1) in Chapter 6.

Acknowledgements

The authors are deeply indebted to the other members of the four project teams for Eurocode 4 on which they have worked: Jean-Marie Aribert, Gerhard Hanswille, Bernt Johansson, Basil Kolias, Jean-Paul Lebet, Henri Mathieu, Michel Mele, Joel Raoul, Karl-Heinz Roik and Jan Stark; and also to the Liaison Engineers, National Technical Contacts, and others who prepared national comments. They thank the University of Warwick for the facilities provided for Eurocode work, and, especially, their wives Diana and Linda for their unfailing support.

R. P. Johnson
D. Anderson

Contents

Introduction

The provisions of EN 1994-1-1[1] are preceded by a foreword, most of which is common to all Eurocodes. This *Foreword* contains clauses on:

- the background to the Eurocode programme
- the status and field of application of the Eurocodes
- national standards implementing Eurocodes
- links between Eurocodes and harmonized technical specifications for products
- additional information specific to EN 1994-1-1
- National Annex for EN 1994-1-1.

Guidance on the common text is provided in the introduction to the *Designers' Guide to EN 1990, Eurocode: Basis of Structural Design*,[2] and only background information essential to users of EN 1994-1-1 is given here.

EN 1990[3] lists the following structural Eurocodes, each generally consisting of a number of parts which are in different stages of development at present:

EN 1990   *Eurocode: Basis of Structural Design*
EN 1991   *Eurocode 1: Actions on Structures*
EN 1992   *Eurocode 2: Design of Concrete Structures*
EN 1993   *Eurocode 3: Design of Steel Structures*
EN 1994   *Eurocode 4: Design of Composite Steel and Concrete Structures*
EN 1995   *Eurocode 5: Design of Timber Structures*
EN 1996   *Eurocode 6: Design of Masonry Structures*
EN 1997   *Eurocode 7: Geotechnical Design*
EN 1998   *Eurocode 8: Design of Structures for Earthquake Resistance*
EN 1999   *Eurocode 9: Design of Aluminium Structures*

The information specific to EN 1994-1-1 emphasizes that this standard is to be used with other Eurocodes. The standard includes many cross-references to particular clauses in EN 1992[4] and EN 1993.[5] Similarly, this guide is one of a series on Eurocodes, and is for use with the guide for EN 1992-1-1[6] and the guide for EN 1993-1-1.[7]

It is the responsibility of each national standards body to implement each Eurocode part as a national standard. This will comprise, without any alterations, the full text of the Eurocode and its annexes as published by the European Committee for Standardization (CEN). This will usually be preceded by a National Title Page and a National Foreword, and may be followed by a National Annex.

Each Eurocode recognizes the right of national regulatory authorities to determine values related to safety matters. Values, classes or methods to be chosen or determined at national level are referred to as Nationally Determined Parameters (NDPs), and are listed in the foreword to each Eurocode, in the clauses on National Annexes. NDPs are also indicated by notes immediately after relevant clauses. Each National Annex will give or cross-refer to the NDPs to be used in the relevant country. Otherwise the National Annex may contain only the following:[8]

- decisions on the application of informative annexes, and
- references to non-contradictory complementary information to assist the user in applying the Eurocode.

In EN 1994-1-1 the NDPs are principally the partial factors for material or product properties peculiar to this standard; for example, for the resistance of headed stud shear connectors, and of composite slabs to longitudinal shear. Other NDPs are values that may depend on climate, such as the free shrinkage of concrete.

CHAPTER I

General

This chapter is concerned with the general aspects of EN 1994-1-1, *Eurocode 4: Design of Composite Steel and Concrete Structures,* Part 1.1: *General Rules and Rules for Buildings.* The material described in this chapter is covered in *Section 1*, in the following clauses:

1.1. Scope

1.1.1. Scope of Eurocode 4

The scope of EN 1994 (all three parts) is outlined in *clause 1.1.1*. It is to be used with EN 1990, *Eurocode: Basis of Structural Design,* which is the head document of the Eurocode suite. *Clause 1.1.1(2)* emphasizes that the Eurocodes are concerned with structural behaviour and that other requirements, e.g. thermal and acoustic insulation, are not considered.

Clause 1.1.1

Clause 1.1.1(2)

The basis for verification of safety and serviceability is the partial factor method. EN 1990 recommends values for load factors and gives various possibilities for combinations of actions. The values and choice of combinations are to be set by the National Annex for the country in which the structure is to be constructed.

Eurocode 4 is also to be used in conjunction with EN 1991, *Eurocode 1: Actions on Structures*[9] and its National Annex, to determine characteristic or nominal loads. When a composite structure is to be built in a seismic region, account needs to be taken of EN 1998, *Eurocode 8: Design of Structures for Earthquake Resistance.*[10]

The Eurocodes are concerned with design and not execution, but minimum standards of workmanship are required to ensure that the design assumptions are valid. For this reason, *clause 1.1.1(3)* lists the European standards for the execution of steel structures and the execution of concrete structures. The former includes some requirements for composite construction, for example for the testing of welded stud shear connectors.

Clause 1.1.1(3)

1.1.2. Scope of Part 1.1 of Eurocode 4

EN 1994-1-1 deals with aspects of design that are common to the principal types of composite structure, buildings and bridges. This results from the CEN requirement that a provision should not appear in more than one EN standard, as this can cause inconsistency when one standard is revised before another. For example, if the same rules for resistance to bending apply for a composite beam in a building as in a bridge (as most of them do), then those rules are 'general' and must appear in EN 1994-1-1 and not in EN 1994-2 (on bridges).[11] This has been done even where most applications occur in bridges. For example, *clause 6.8* (fatigue) is in Part 1.1, with a few additional provisions in Part 2.

In EN 1994-1-1, all rules that are for buildings only are preceded by a heading that includes the word 'buildings', or, if an isolated paragraph, are placed at the end of the relevant clause, e.g. *clauses 5.3.2* and *5.4.2.3(5)*.

The coverage in this guide of the 'general' clauses of Part 1.1 is relevant to both buildings and bridges, except where noted otherwise. However, guidance provided by or related to the worked examples may be relevant only to applications in buildings.

Clause 1.1.2(2) — *Clause 1.1.2(2)* lists the titles of the sections of Part 1.1. Those for *Sections 1–7* are the same as in the other material-dependent Eurocodes. The contents of *Sections 1* and *2* similarly follow an agreed model.

The provisions of Part 1.1 cover the design of the common composite members:

- beams in which a steel section acts compositely with concrete
- composite slabs formed with profiled steel sheeting
- concrete-encased or filled composite columns
- joints between composite beams and steel or composite columns.

Sections 5 and *8* concern connected members. *Section 5*, 'Structural analysis', is needed particularly for a frame that is not of 'simple' construction. Unbraced frames and sway frames are within its scope. The provisions include the use of second-order global analysis and prestress by imposed deformations, and define imperfections.

The scope of Part 1.1 extends to steel sections that are partially encased. The web of the steel section is encased by reinforced concrete, and shear connection is provided between the concrete and the steel. This is a well-established form of construction. The primary reason for its choice is improved resistance in fire.

Fully encased composite beams are not included because:

- no satisfactory model has been found for the ultimate strength in longitudinal shear of a beam without shear connectors
- it is not known to what extent some design rules (e.g. for moment–shear interaction and redistribution of moments) are applicable.

A fully encased beam with shear connectors can usually be designed as if partly encased or uncased, provided that care is taken to prevent premature spalling of encasement in compression.

Part 2, *Bridges*, includes further provisions that may on occasion be useful for buildings, such as those on:

- composite plates (where the steel member is a flat steel plate, not a profiled section)
- composite box girders
- tapered or non-uniform composite members
- structures that are prestressed by tendons.

The omission of application rules for a type of member or structure should not prevent its use, where appropriate. Some omissions are deliberate, to encourage the use of innovative design, based on specialized literature, the properties of materials, and the fundamentals of equilibrium and compatibility; and following the principles given in the relevant Eurocodes. This applies, for example, to:

- large holes in webs of beams
- types of shear connector other than welded studs
- base plates beneath composite columns
- shear heads in reinforced concrete framed structures, and
- many aspects of 'mixed' structures, as used in tall buildings.

In addition to its nine normative sections, EN 1994-1-1 includes three informative annexes:

- *Annex A*, 'Stiffness of joint components in buildings'
- *Annex B*, 'Standard tests'
- *Annex C*, 'Shrinkage of concrete for composite structures for buildings'.

The reasons for these annexes, additional to the normative provisions, are explained in the relevant chapters of this guide.

1.2. Normative references

References are given only to other European standards, all of which are intended to be used as a package. Formally, the Standards of the International Organization for Standardization (ISO) apply only if given an EN ISO designation. National standards for design and for products do not apply if they conflict with a relevant EN standard.

It is intended that, following a period of overlap, all competing national standards will be withdrawn by around 2010. As Eurocodes may not cross-refer to national standards, replacement of national standards for products by EN or ISO standards is in progress, with a time-scale similar to that for the Eurocodes.

During the period of changeover to Eurocodes and EN standards it is likely that an EN referred to, or its National Annex, may not be complete. Designers who then seek guidance from national standards should take account of differences between the design philosophies and safety factors in the two sets of documents.

1.2.1. General reference standards

Some references here, and also in *clause 1.2.2*, appear to repeat references in *clause 1.1.1*. The difference is explained in *clause 1.2*. These 'dated' references define the issue of the standard that is referred to in detailed cross-references, given later in EN 1994-1-1.

1.2.2. Other reference standards

Eurocode 4 necessarily refers to EN 1992-1-1, *Eurocode 2: Design of Concrete Structures*, Part 1.1: *General Rules and Rules for Buildings*, and to several parts of EN 1993, *Eurocode 3: Design of Steel Structures*.

In its application to buildings, EN 1994-1-1 is based on the concept of the initial erection of a steel frame, which may include prefabricated concrete-encased members. The placing of profiled steel sheeting or other shuttering follows. The addition of reinforcement and in situ concrete completes the composite structure. The presentation and content of EN 1994-1-1 therefore relate more closely to EN 1993-1-1 than to EN 1992-1-1.

1.3. Assumptions

The general assumptions are those of EN 1990, EN 1992 and EN 1993. Commentary on them will be found in the relevant guides in this series.

1.4. Distinction between principles and application rules

Clauses in the Eurocodes are set out as either principles or application rules. As defined by EN 1990:

- 'Principles comprise general statements for which there is no alternative and requirements and analytical models for which no alternative is permitted unless specifically stated'
- 'Principles are distinguished by the letter 'P' following the paragraph number'
- 'Application Rules are generally recognised rules which comply with the principles and satisfy their requirements'.

There are relatively few principles. It has been recognized that a requirement or analytical model for which 'no alternative is permitted unless specifically stated' can rarely include a numerical value, because most values are influenced by research and/or experience, and may change over the years. (Even the specified elastic modulus for structural steel is an approximate value.) Furthermore, a clause cannot be a principle if it requires the use of another clause that is an application rule; effectively that clause also would become a principle.

It follows that, ideally, the principles in all the codes should form a consistent set, referring only to each other, and intelligible if all the application rules were deleted. This over-riding principle has strongly influenced the drafting of EN 1994.

1.5. Definitions

1.5.1. General

In accordance with the model for *Section 1*, reference is made to the definitions given in clauses 1.5 of EN 1990, EN 1992-1-1, and EN 1993-1-1. Many types of analysis are defined in clause 1.5.6 of EN 1990. It is important to note that an analysis based on the deformed geometry of a structure or element under load is termed 'second order' rather than 'non-linear'. The latter term refers to the treatment of material properties in structural analysis. Thus, according to EN 1990 'non-linear analysis' includes 'rigid plastic'. This convention is not followed in EN 1994-1-1, where the heading 'Non-linear global analysis' (*clause 5.4.3*) does not include 'rigid plastic global analysis' (*clause 5.4.5*).

Clause 1.5.1

References from *clause 1.5.1* include clause 1.5.2 of EN 1992-1-1, which defines prestress as an action caused by the stressing of tendons. This applies to EN 1994-2 but not to EN 1994-1-1, as this type of prestress is outside its scope. Prestress by jacking at supports, which is outside the scope of EN 1992-1-1, is within the scope of EN 1994-1-1.

The definitions in clauses 1.5.1 to 1.5.9 of EN 1993-1-1 apply where they occur in clauses in EN 1993 to which EN 1994 refers. None of them uses the word 'steel'.

1.5.2. Additional terms and definitions

Clause 1.5.2

Most of the 13 definitions in *clause 1.5.2* of EN 1994-1-1 include the word 'composite'. The definition of 'shear connection' does not require the absence of separation or slip at the interface between steel and concrete. Separation is always assumed to be negligible, but explicit allowance may need to be made for effects of slip, e.g. in *clauses 5.4.3, 7.2.1, 9.8.2(7)* and *A.3*.

The definition 'composite frame' is relevant to the use of *Section 5*. Where the behaviour is essentially that of a reinforced or prestressed concrete structure, with only a few composite members, global analysis should generally be in accordance with Eurocode 2.

These lists of definitions are not exhaustive, because all the codes use terms with precise meanings that can be inferred from their contexts.

Concerning use of words generally, there are significant differences from British codes. These arose from the use of English as the base language for the drafting process, and the need to improve precision of meaning and to facilitate translation into other European languages. In particular:

- 'action' means a load and/or an imposed deformation
- 'action effect' (*clause 5.4*) and 'effect of action' have the same meaning: any deformation or internal force or moment that results from an action.

1.6. Symbols

The symbols in the Eurocodes are all based on ISO standard 3898: 1987.[12] Each code has its own list, applicable within that code. Some symbols have more than one meaning, the particular meaning being stated in the clause.

There are a few important changes from previous practice in the UK. For example, an x–x axis is along a member, a y–y axis is parallel to the flanges of a steel section (clause 1.7(2) of EN 1993-1-1), and a section modulus is W, with subscripts to denote elastic or plastic behaviour.

Wherever possible, definitions in EN 1994-1-1 have been aligned with those in EN 1990, EN 1992 and EN 1993; but this should not be assumed without checking the list in *clause 1.6*. Some quite minor differences are significant.

The symbol f_y has different meanings in EN 1992-1-1 and EN 1993-1-1. It is retained in EN 1994-1-1 for the nominal yield strength of structural steel, though the generic subscript for that material is 'a', based on the French word for steel, 'acier'. Subscript 'a' is not used in EN 1993-1-1, where the partial factor for steel is not γ_A, but γ_M; and this usage is followed in EN 1994-1-1. The characteristic yield strength of reinforcement is f_{sk}, with partial factor γ_S.

CHAPTER 2

Basis of design

The material described in this chapter is covered in *Section 2* of EN 1994-1-1, in the following clauses:

- Requirements   *Clause 2.1*
- Principles of limit states design   *Clause 2.2*
- Basic variables   *Clause 2.3*
- Verification by the partial factor method   *Clause 2.4*

The sequence follows that of EN 1990, Sections 2–4 and 6.

2.1. Requirements

Design is to be in accordance with the general requirements of EN 1990. The purpose of *Section 2* is to give supplementary provisions for composite structures.

Clause 2.1(3) reminds the user again that design is based on actions and combinations of actions in accordance with EN 1991 and EN 1990, respectively. The use of partial safety factors for actions and resistances (the 'partial factor method') is expected but is not a requirement of Eurocodes. The method is presented in Section 6 of EN 1990 as one way of satisfying the basic requirements set out in Section 2 of that standard. This is why use of the partial factor method is given 'deemed to satisfy' status in *clause 2.1(3)*. To establish that a design was in accordance with the Eurocodes, the user of any other method would normally have to demonstrate, to the satisfaction of the regulatory authority and/or the client, that the method satisfied the basic requirements of EN 1990.

Clause 2.1(3)

2.2. Principles of limit states design

The clause provides a reminder that the influence of sequence of construction on action effects must be considered. It does not affect the bending resistance of beams that are in Class 1 or 2 (as defined in *clause 5.5*) or the resistance of a composite column, as these are determined by rigid plastic theory, but it does affect the resistances of beams in Class 3 or 4.

2.3. Basic variables

The classification of effects of shrinkage and temperature in *clause 2.3.3* into 'primary' and 'secondary' will be familiar to designers of continuous beams, especially for bridges.

Clause 2.3.3

Secondary effects are to be treated as 'indirect actions', which are 'sets of imposed deformations' (clause 1.5.3.1 of EN 1990), not as action effects. This distinction appears to have no consequences in practice, for the use of EN 1994-1-1.

2.4. Verification by the partial factor method

2.4.1. Design values

Clause 2.4.1.1
Clause 2.4.1.2

Clauses 2.4.1.1 and *2.4.1.2* illustrate the treatment of partial factors. Recommended values are given in Notes, in the hope of eventual convergence between the values for each partial factor that will be specified in the National Annexes. This process was adopted because the regulatory bodies in the member states of CEN, rather than CEN itself, are responsible for setting safety levels. The Notes are informative, not normative (i.e., not part of the preceding provision), so that there are no numerical values in the principles of *clause 2.4.1.2*, as explained earlier.

The Notes also link the partial factors for concrete, reinforcing steel and structural steel to those recommended in EN 1992 and EN 1993. Design would be more difficult if the factors for these materials in composite structures differed from the values in reinforced concrete and steel structures.

The remainder of EN 1994-1-1 normally refers to design strengths, rather than characteristic or nominal values with partial factors. The design strength for concrete is given by

$$f_{cd} = f_{ck}/\gamma_C \qquad (2.1)$$

where f_{ck} is the characteristic cylinder strength. This definition is stated algebraically because it differs from that of EN 1992-1-1, in which an additional coefficient α_{cc} is applied:

$$f_{cd} = \alpha_{cc} f_{ck}/\gamma_C \qquad (D2.1)$$

The coefficient is explained by EN 1992-1-1 as taking account of long-term effects and of unfavourable effects resulting from the way the load is applied. The recommended value is 1.0, but a different value could be chosen in a National Annex. This possibility is not appropriate for EN 1994-1-1 because the coefficient has been taken as 1.0 in calibration of composite elements.

Clause 2.4.1.3

Clause 2.4.1.3 refers to 'product standards hEN'. The 'h' stands for 'harmonized'. This term from the *Construction Products Directive*[13] is explained in the *Designers' Guide to EN 1990.*[2]

Clause 2.4.1.4

Clause 2.4.1.4, on design resistances, refers to expressions (6.6a) and (6.6c) given in clause 6.3.5 of EN 1990. Resistances in EN 1994-1-1 often need more than one partial factor, and so use expression (6.6a), which is

$$R_d = R\{(\eta_i X_{k,i}/\gamma_{M,i}); a_d\} \qquad i \geq 1 \qquad (D2.2)$$

For example, *clause 6.7.3.2(1)* gives the plastic resistance to compression of a cross-section as the sum of terms for the structural steel, concrete and reinforcement:

$$N_{pl,Rd} = A_a f_{yd} + 0.85 A_c f_{cd} + A_s f_{sd} \qquad (6.30)$$

In this case, there is no separate term a_d based on geometrical data, because uncertainties in areas of cross-sections are allowed for in the γ_M factors.

In terms of characteristic strengths, from *clause 2.4.1.2, equation (6.30)* becomes:

$$N_{pl,Rd} = A_a f_y/\gamma_M + 0.85 A_c f_{ck}/\gamma_C + A_s f_{sk}/\gamma_S \qquad (D2.3)$$

in which:

- the characteristic material strengths $X_{k,i}$ are f_y, f_{ck} and f_{sk}
- the conversion factors, η_i in EN 1990, are 1.0 for steel and reinforcement and 0.85 for concrete
- the partial factors $\gamma_{M,i}$ are γ_M, γ_C and γ_S.

Expression (6.6c) of EN 1990 is $R_d = R_k/\gamma_M$. It applies where characteristic properties and a single partial factor can be used; for example, in expressions for the shear resistance of a headed stud (*clause 6.6.3.1*).

2.4.2. Combination of actions

No comment is necessary.

2.4.3. Verification of static equilibrium (EQU)

The abbreviation EQU appears in EN 1990, where four types of ultimate limit state are defined in clause 6.4.1:

- EQU, for loss of static equilibrium
- FAT, for fatigue failure
- GEO, for failure or excessive deformation of the ground
- STR, for internal failure or excessive deformation of the structure.

This guide covers ultimate limit states only of types STR and FAT. Use of type GEO arises in design of foundations to EN 1997.[14]

CHAPTER 3

Materials

This chapter concerns the properties of materials needed for the design of composite structures. It corresponds to *Section 3*, which has the following clauses:

- Concrete   *Clause 3.1*
- Reinforcing steel   *Clause 3.2*
- Structural steel   *Clause 3.3*
- Connecting devices   *Clause 3.4*
- Profiled steel sheeting for composite slabs in buildings   *Clause 3.5*

Rather than repeating information given elsewhere, *Section 3* consists mainly of cross-references to other Eurocodes and EN standards. The following comments relate to provisions of particular significance for composite structures.

3.1. Concrete

Clause 3.1(1) refers to EN 1992-1-1 for the properties of concrete. For lightweight-aggregate concrete, several properties are dependent on the oven-dry density, relative to 2200 kg/m³.

Clause 3.1(1)

Complex sets of time-dependent properties are given in its clause 3.1 for normal concrete and clause 11.3 for lightweight-aggregate concrete. For composite structures built unpropped, with several stages of construction, simplification is essential. Specific properties are now discussed. (For thermal expansion, see Section 3.3.)

Strength and stiffness

Strength and deformation characteristics are summarized in EN 1992-1-1, Table 3.1 for normal concrete and Table 11.3.1 for lightweight-aggregate concrete.

Strength classes for normal concrete are defined as Cx/y, where x and y are respectively the cylinder and cube compressive strengths in units of newtons per square millimetre. All compressive strengths in design rules in Eurocodes are cylinder strengths, so an unsafe error occurs if a specified cube strength is used in calculations. It should be replaced at the outset by the equivalent cylinder strength, using the relationships given by the strength classes.

Classes for lightweight concrete are designated LCx/y. The relationships between cylinder and cube strengths differ from those of normal concrete.

Except where prestressing by tendons is used (which is outside the scope of this guide), the tensile strength of concrete is rarely used in design calculations for composite members. The mean tensile strength f_{ctm} appears in the definitions of 'cracked' global analysis in *clause 5.4.2.3(2)*, and in *clause 7.4.2(1)* on minimum reinforcement. Its value and the 5 and 95% fractile values are given in Tables 3.1 and 11.3.1 of EN 1992-1-1. The appropriate fractile value should be used in any limit state verification that relies on either an adverse or beneficial effect of the tensile strength of concrete.

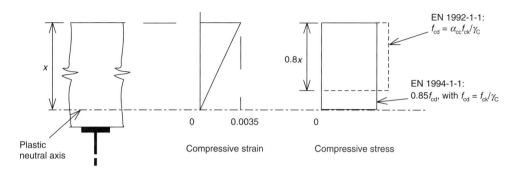

Fig. 3.1. Stress blocks for concrete at ultimate limit states

Values of the modulus of elasticity are given in Tables 3.1 and 11.3.1. Clause 3.1.3 of EN 1992-1-1 points out that these are indicative, for general applications. The short-term elastic modulus E_{cm} increases for ages greater than 28 days. The influence of this small change on the effective modulus is negligible compared with the uncertainties in the modelling of creep, so it should be ignored.

Stress/strain properties
The design compressive strength of concrete, f_{cd}, is defined in clause 3.1.6(1)P of EN 1992-1-1 as

$$f_{cd} = \alpha_{cc} f_{ck}/\gamma_C$$

where

α_{cc} is the coefficient taking account of long term effects on the compressive strength and of unfavourable effects resulting from the way the load is applied.

Note: The value of α_{cc} for use in a Country should lie between 0.8 and 1.0 and may be found in its National Annex. The recommended value is 1.

The reference in *clause 3.1(1)* to EN 1992-1-1 for properties of concrete begins '*unless otherwise given by Eurocode 4*'. Resistances of composite members given in EN 1994-1-1 are based on extensive calibration studies (e.g. see Johnson and Huang[15,16]). The numerical coefficients given in resistance formulae are consistent with the value $\alpha_{cc} = 1.0$ and the use of either elastic theory or the stress block defined in *clause 6.2.1.2*. Therefore, there is no reference in EN 1994-1-1 to a coefficient α_{cc} or to a choice to be made in a National Annex. The symbol f_{cd} always means f_{ck}/γ_C, and for beams and most columns is used with the coefficient 0.85, as in *equation (6.30)* in *clause 6.7.3.2(1)*. An exception, in that clause, is when the value of 0.85 is replaced by 1.0 for concrete-filled column sections, based on calibration.

The approximation made to the shape of the stress–strain curve is also relevant. Those given in clause 3.1 of EN 1992-1-1 are mainly curved or bilinear, but in clause 3.1.7(3) there is a simpler rectangular stress distribution, similar to the stress block given in the British Standard for the structural use of concrete, BS 8110.[17] Its shape, for concrete strength classes up to C50/60, and the corresponding strain distribution are shown in Fig. 3.1.

This stress block is inconvenient for use with composite cross-sections, because the region near the neutral axis assumed to be unstressed is often occupied by a steel flange, and algebraic expressions for resistance to bending become complex.

In composite sections, the contribution from the steel section to the bending resistance reduces the significance of that from the concrete. It is thus possible[18] for EN 1994 to allow the use of a rectangular stress block extending to the neutral axis, as shown in Fig. 3.1.

For a member of unit width, the moment about the neutral axis of the EN 1992 stress block ranges from $0.38f_{ck}x^2/\gamma_C$ to $0.48f_{ck}x^2/\gamma_C$, depending on the value chosen for α_{cc}. The value for beams in EN 1994-1-1 is $0.425f_{ck}x^2/\gamma_C$. Calibration studies have shown that this overestimates the bending resistance of cross-sections of columns, so a correction factor α_{M} is given in *clause 6.7.3.6(1)*. See also the comments on *clauses 6.2.1.2(2)* and *6.7.3.6*.

Clause 3.1(2) limits the scope of EN 1994-1-1 to the strength range C20/25 to C60/75 for normal concrete and from LC20/22 to LC60/66 for lightweight concrete. These ranges are narrower than those given in EN 1992-1-1 because there is limited knowledge and experience of the behaviour of composite members with weak or very strong concrete. This applies, for example, to the load/slip properties of shear connectors, the redistribution of moments in continuous beams and the resistance of columns. The use of rectangular stress blocks for resistance to bending (*clause 6.2.1.2(d)*) relies on the strain capacity of the materials. The relevant property of concrete, $\varepsilon_{\mathrm{cu3}}$ in Table 3.1 of EN 1992-1-1, is −0.0035 for classes up to C50/60, but is only −0.0026 for class C90/105.

Clause 3.1(2)

Shrinkage

The shrinkage of concrete referred to in **clause 3.1(3)** is the drying shrinkage that occurs after setting. It does not include the plastic shrinkage that precedes setting, nor autogenous shrinkage. The latter develops during hardening of the concrete (clause 3.1.4(6) of EN 1992-1-1), and is that which occurs in enclosed or sealed concrete, as in a concrete-filled tube, where no loss of moisture occurs. **Clause 3.1(4)** permits its effect on stresses and deflections to be neglected, but does not refer to crack widths. It has little influence on cracking due to direct loading, and the rules for initial cracking (*clause 7.4.2*) take account of its effects.

Clause 3.1(3)

Clause 3.1(4)

The shrinkage strains given in clause 3.1.4(6) of EN 1992-1-1 are significantly higher than those given in BS 8110. Taking grade C40/50 concrete as an example, with 'dry' environment (relative humidity 60%), the final drying shrinkage could be −400 × 10^{-6}, plus autogenous shrinkage of −75 × 10^{-6}.

The value in ENV 1994-1-1 was −325 × 10^{-6}, based on practice and experience. In the absence of adverse comment on the ENV, this value is repeated in *Annex C* (informative) of EN 1994-1-1, with a Note below *clause 3.1* that permits other values to be given in National Annexes. In the absence of this Note, a design using a value from *Annex C*, confirmed in a National Annex, would not be in accordance with the Eurocodes. This is because normative clause 3.1.4(6) of EN 1992-1-1 takes precedence over an informative National Annex, and all variations in National Annexes have to be permitted in this way.

In typical environments in the UK, the influence of shrinkage of normal-weight concrete on the design of composite structures for buildings is significant only in:

- very tall structures
- very long structures without movement joints
- the prediction of deflections of beams with high span/depth ratios (*clause 7.3.1 (8)*).

There is further comment on shrinkage in Chapter 5.

Creep

The provisions of EN 1992-1-1 on creep of concrete can be simplified for composite structures for buildings, as discussed in comments on *clause 5.4.2.2*.

3.2. Reinforcing steel

Clause 3.2(1) refers to EN 1992-1-1, which states in clause 3.2.2(3)P that its rules are valid for specified yield strengths f_{yk} up to 600 N/mm².

Clause 3.2(1)

The scope of clause 3.2 of EN 1992-1-1, and hence of EN 1994-1-1, is limited to reinforcement, including wire fabrics with a nominal bar diameter of 5 mm and above, that is, 'ribbed' (high bond) and weldable. There are three ductility classes, from A (the lowest) to C. The requirements include the characteristic strain at maximum force, rather than the elongation at fracture used in past British standards. *Clause 5.5.1(5)* of EN 1994-1-1 excludes the use of Class A reinforcement in any composite cross-section in Class 1 or 2.

The minimum ductility properties of wire fabric given in Table C.1 of EN 1992-1-1 may not be sufficient to satisfy *clause 5.5.1(6)* of EN 1994-1-1, as this requires demonstration of sufficient ductility to avoid fracture when built into a concrete slab.[19] It has been found in tests on continuous composite beams with fabric in tension that the cross-wires initiate cracks in concrete, so that tensile strain becomes concentrated at the locations of the welds in the fabric.

Clause 3.2(2)

For simplicity, *clause 3.2(2)* permits the modulus of elasticity of reinforcement to be taken as 210 kN/mm^2, the value given in EN 1993-1-1 for structural steel, rather than 200 kN/mm^2, the value in EN 1992-1-1.

3.3. Structural steel

Clause 3.3(1)

Clause 3.3(2)

Clause 3.3(1) refers to EN 1993-1-1. This lists in its Table 3.1 steel grades with nominal yield strengths up to 460 N/mm^2, and allows other steel products to be included in National Annexes. *Clause 3.3(2)* sets an upper limit of 460 N/mm^2 for use with EN 1994-1-1. There has been extensive research[20–23] on the use in composite members of structural steels with yield strengths exceeding 355 N/mm^2. It has been found that some design rules need modification for use with steel grades higher than S355, to avoid premature crushing of concrete. This applies to:

- redistribution of moments (*clause 5.4.4(6)*)
- rotation capacity (*clause 5.4.5(4a)*)
- plastic resistance moment (*clause 6.2.1.2(2)*)
- resistance of columns (*clause 6.7.3.6(1)*).

Thermal expansion

For the coefficient of linear thermal expansion of steel, clause 3.2.6 of EN 1993-1-1 gives a value of 12×10^{-6} 'per °C' (also written in Eurocodes as /K or K^{-1}). This is followed by a Note that for calculating the 'structural effects of unequal temperatures' in composite structures, the coefficient may be taken as 10×10^{-6} per °C, which is the value given for normal-weight concrete in clause 3.1.3(5) of EN 1992-1-1 'unless more accurate information is available'.

Thermal expansion of reinforcement is not mentioned in EN 1992-1-1, presumably because it is assumed to be the same as that of normal-weight concrete. For reinforcement in composite structures the coefficient should be taken as 10×10^{-6} K^{-1}. This was stated in ENV 1994-1-1, but is not in the EN.

Coefficients of thermal expansion for lightweight-aggregate concretes can range from 4×10^{-6} to 14×10^{-6} K^{-1}. Clause 11.3.2(2) of EN 1992-1-1 states that

The differences between the coefficients of thermal expansion of steel and lightweight aggregate concrete need not be considered in design,

but 'steel' here means reinforcement, not structural steel. The effects of the difference from 10×10^{-6} K^{-1} should be considered in design of composite members for situations where the temperatures of the concrete and the structural steel could differ significantly.

3.4. Connecting devices

3.4.1. General

Reference is made to EN 1993, *Eurocode 3: Design of Steel Structures,* Part 1.8: *Design of Joints,*[24] for information relating to fasteners, such as bolts, and welding consumables. Provisions for 'other types of mechanical fastener' are given in clause 3.3.2 of EN 1993-1-3.[25] Commentary on joints is given in Chapters 8 and 10.

3.4.2. Stud shear connectors

Headed studs are the only type of shear connector for which detailed provisions are given in EN 1994-1-1, in *clause 6.6.5.7*. Any other method of connection must satisfy *clause 6.6.1.1*. The use of adhesives on a steel flange is unlikely to be suitable.

Clause 3.4.2 refers to EN 13918, *Welding – Studs and Ceramic Ferrules for Arc Stud Welding.*[26] This gives minimum dimensions for weld collars. Other methods of attaching studs, such as spinning, may not provide weld collars large enough for the resistances of studs given in *clause 6.6.3.1(1)* to be applicable.

Shear connection between steel and concrete by bond or friction is permitted only in accordance with *clause 6.7.4*, for columns, and *clauses 9.1.2.1* and *9.7*, for composite slabs.

Clause 3.4.2

3.5. Profiled steel sheeting for composite slabs in buildings

The title includes 'in buildings', as this clause and other provisions for composite slabs are not applicable to composite bridges.

The materials for profiled steel sheeting must conform to the standards listed in *clause 3.5*. There are at present no EN standards for the wide range of profiled sheets available. Such standards should include tolerances on embossments and indentations, as these influence resistance to longitudinal shear. Tolerances on embossments, given for test specimens in *clause B.3.3(2)*, provide guidance.

The minimum bare metal thickness has been controversial, and in EN 1994-1-1 is subject to National Annexes, with a recommended minimum of 0.70 mm. The total thickness of zinc coating in accordance with *clause 4.2(3)* is about 0.05 mm.

Clause 3.5

CHAPTER 4

Durability

This chapter concerns the durability of composite structures. It corresponds to *Section 4*, which has the following clauses:

- General   *Clause 4.1*
- Profiled steel sheeting for composite slabs in buildings   *Clause 4.2*

4.1. General

Almost all aspects of the durability of composite structures are covered by cross-references to EN 1990, EN 1992 and EN 1993. The material-independent provisions, in clause 2.4 of EN 1990, require the designer to take into account 10 factors. These include the foreseeable use of the structure, the expected environmental conditions, the design criteria, the performance of the materials, the particular protective measures, the quality of workmanship and the intended level of maintenance.

Clauses 4.2 and 4.4.1 of EN 1992-1-1 define exposure classes and cover to reinforcement. A Note defines structural classes. These and the 'acceptable deviations' (tolerances) for cover may be modified in a National Annex. *Clause 4.4.1.3* recommends an addition of 10 mm to the minimum cover to allow for the deviation.

As an example, a concrete floor of a multi-storey car park will be subject to the action of chlorides in an environment consisting of cyclic wet and dry conditions. For these conditions (designated class XD3) the recommended structural class is 4, giving a minimum cover for a 50 year service life of 45 mm plus a tolerance of 10 mm. This total of 55 mm can be reduced, typically by 5 mm, where special quality assurance is in place.

Section 4 of EN 1993-1-1 refers to execution of protective treatments for steelwork. If parts will be susceptible to corrosion, there is need for access for inspection and maintenance. This will not be possible for shear connectors, and *clause 4.1(2)* of EN 1994-1-1 refers to *clause 6.6.5*, which includes provisions for minimum cover.

4.2. Profiled steel sheeting for composite slabs in buildings

For profiled steel sheeting, *clause 4.2(1)P* requires the corrosion protection to be adequate for its environment. Zinc coating to *clause 4.2(3)* is 'sufficient for internal floors in a non-aggressive environment'. This implies that it may not provide sufficient durability for use in a multi-storey car park or near the sea.

Clause 4.2(1)P
Clause 4.2(3)

CHAPTER 5

Structural analysis

Structural analysis may be performed at three levels: global analysis, member analysis, and local analysis. This chapter concerns global analysis to determine deformations and internal forces and moments in beams and framed structures. It corresponds to *Section 5*, which has the following clauses:

- Structural modelling for analysis   *Clause 5.1*
- Structural stability   *Clause 5.2*
- Imperfections   *Clause 5.3*
- Calculation of action effects   *Clause 5.4*
- Classification of cross-sections   *Clause 5.5*

Wherever possible, analyses for serviceability and ultimate limit states use the same methods. It is generally more convenient, therefore, to specify them together in a single section, rather than to include them in *Sections 6* and *7*. For composite slabs, though, all provisions, including those for global analysis, are given in *Section 9*.

The division of material between *Section 5* and *Section 6* (ultimate limit states) is not always obvious. Calculation of vertical shear is clearly 'analysis', but longitudinal shear is in *Section 6*. This is because its calculation for beams in buildings is dependent on the method used to determine the resistance to bending. However, for composite columns, methods of analysis and member imperfections are considered in *clause 6.7.3.4*. This separation of imperfections in frames from those in columns requires care, and receives detailed explanation after the comments on *clause 5.4*. The flow charts for global analysis (Fig. 5.1) include relevant provisions from *Section 6*.

5.1. Structural modelling for analysis

5.1.1. Structural modelling and basic assumptions
General provisions are given in EN 1990. The clause referred to says, in effect, that models shall be appropriate and based on established theory and practice and that the variables shall be relevant.

Composite members and joints are commonly used in conjunction with others of structural steel. *Clause 5.1.1(2)* makes clear that this is the type of construction envisaged in *Section 5*, which is aligned with and cross-refers to Section 5 of EN 1993-1-1 wherever possible. Where there are significant differences between these two sections, they are referred to here.

Clause 5.1.1(2)

5.1.2. Joint modelling
The three simplified joint models listed in *clause 5.1.2(2)* – simple, continuous and semi-continuous – are those given in EN 1993. The subject of joints in steelwork has its

Clause 5.1.2(2)

own Eurocode part, EN 1993-1-8.[24] For composite joints, its provisions are modified and supplemented by *Section 8* of EN 1994-1-1.

The first two joint models are those commonly used for beam-to-column joints in steel frames. For each joint in the 'simple' model, the location of the nominal pin relative to the centre-line of the column, the 'nominal eccentricity', has to be chosen. This determines the effective span of each beam and the bending moments in each column. Practice varies across Europe, and neither EN 1993-1-1 nor EN 1994-1-1 gives values for nominal eccentricities. Guidance may be given in a National Annex, or in other literature.

In reality, most joints in buildings are neither 'simple' (i.e. pinned) nor 'continuous'. The third model, 'semi-continuous', is appropriate for a wide range of joints with moment–rotation behaviours intermediate between 'simple' and 'continuous'. This model is rarely *Clause 5.1.2(3)* applicable to bridges, so the cross-reference to EN 1993-1-8 in *clause 5.1.2(3)* is 'for buildings'. The provisions of EN 1993-1-8 are for joints 'subjected to predominantly static loading' (its clause 1.1(1)). They are applicable to wind loading on buildings, but not to fatigue loading, which is covered in EN 1993-1-9 and in *clause 6.8*.

For composite beams, the need for continuity of slab reinforcement past the columns, to control cracking, causes joints to transmit moments. For the joint to 'have no effect on the analysis' (from the definition of a 'continuous' joint in clause 5.1.1(2) of EN 1993-1-8), so much reinforcement and stiffening of steelwork are needed that the design becomes uneconomic. Joints with some continuity are usually semi-continuous. Structural analysis then requires prior calculation of the properties of joints, except where they can be treated as 'simple' or 'continuous' on the basis of 'significant experience of previous satisfactory performance in similar cases' (clause 5.2.2.1(2) of EN 1993-1-8, referred to from *clause 8.2.3(1)*) or experimental evidence.

Clause 5.1.2(2) refers to clause 5.1.1 of EN 1993-1-8, which gives the terminology for the semi-continuous joint model. For elastic analysis, the joint is 'semi-rigid'. It has a rotational stiffness, and a design resistance which may be 'partial strength' or 'full strength', normally meaning less than or greater than the bending resistance of the connected beam. If the resistance of the joint is reached, then elastic–plastic or rigid plastic global analysis is required.

5.2. Structural stability

The following comments refer mainly to beam-and-column frames, and assume that the global analyses will be based on elastic theory. The exceptions, in *clauses 5.4.3, 5.4.4* and *5.4.5* are discussed later. All design methods must take account of errors in the initial positions of joints (global imperfections) and in the initial geometry of members (member imperfections); of the effects of cracking of concrete and of any semi-rigid joints; and of residual stresses in compression members.

The stage at which each of these is considered or allowed for will depend on the software being used, which leads to some complexity in *clauses 5.2* to *5.4*.

5.2.1. Effects of deformed geometry of the structure

In its clause 1.5.6, EN 1990 defines types of analysis. 'First-order' analysis is performed on the initial geometry of the structure. 'Second-order' analysis takes account of the deformations of the structure, which are a function of its loading. Clearly, second-order analysis may always be applied. With appropriate software increasingly available, second-order analysis is the most straightforward approach. The criteria for neglect of second-order effects *Clause 5.2.1(2)P* given in *clauses 5.2.1(2)P* and *5.2.1(3)* need not be considered. The analysis allowing for *Clause 5.2.1(3)* second-order effects will usually be iterative but normally the iteration will take place within the software. Methods for second-order analysis are described in textbooks such as that by Trahair *et al.*[27]

A disadvantage of second-order analysis is that, in general, the useful principle of superposition does not apply. *Clause 5.2.1(3)* provides a basis for the use of first-order analysis. The check is done for a particular load combination and arrangement. The provisions in this clause are similar to those for elastic analysis in the corresponding clause in EN 1993-1-1.

Clause 5.2.1(3)

In an elastic frame, second-order effects are dependent on the nearness of the design loads to the elastic critical load. This is the basis for *expression (5.1)*, in which α_{cr} is defined as '*the factor … to cause elastic instability*'. This may be taken as the load factor at which bifurcation of equilibrium occurs. For a conventional beam-and-column frame, it is assumed that the frame is perfect, and that only vertical loads are present, usually at their maximum design values. These are replaced by a set of loads which produces the same set of member axial forces without any bending. An eigenvalue analysis then gives the factor α_{cr}, applied to the whole of the loading, at which the total frame stiffness vanishes, and elastic instability occurs.

To sufficient accuracy, α_{cr} may also be determined by a second-order load–deflection analysis. The non-linear load–deflection response approaches asymptotically to the elastic critical value. Normally, though, it is pointless to use this method, as it is simpler to use the same software to account for the second-order effects due to the design loads. A more useful method for α_{cr} is given in *clause 5.2.2(1)*.

Unlike the corresponding clause in EN 1993-1-1, the check in *clause 5.2.1(3)* is not just for a sway mode. This is because *clause 5.2.1* is relevant not only to complete frames but also to the design of individual composite columns (see *clause 6.7.3.4*). Such members may be held in position against sway but still be subject to significant second-order effects due to bowing.

Clause 5.2.1(4)P is a reminder that the analysis needs to account for the reduction in stiffness arising from cracking and creep of concrete and from possible non-linear behaviour of the joints. Further remarks on how this should be done are made in the comments on *clauses 5.4.2.2, 5.4.2.3* and *8.2.2*, and the procedures are illustrated in Fig. 5.1(b)–(d). In general, such effects are dependent on the internal moments and forces, and iteration is therefore required. Manual intervention may be needed, to adjust stiffness values before repeating the analysis. It is expected, though, that advanced software will be written for EN 1994 to account automatically for these effects. The designer may of course make assumptions, although care is needed to ensure these are conservative. For example, assuming that joints have zero rotational stiffness (resulting in simply-supported composite beams) could lead to neglect of the reduction in beam stiffness due to cracking. The overall lateral stiffness would probably be a conservative value, but this is not certain. However, in a frame with stiff bracing it will be worth first calculating α_{cr}, assuming joints are pinned and beams are steel section only; it may well be found that this value of α_{cr} is sufficiently high for first-order global analysis to be used.

Clause 5.2.1(4)P

Using elastic analysis, it is not considered necessary to account for slip (see *clause 5.4.1.1(8)*), provided that the shear connection is in accordance with *clause 6.6*.

5.2.2. Methods of analysis for buildings

Clause 5.2.2(1) refers to clause 5.2.1(4) of EN 1993-1-1 for a simpler check, applicable to many structures for buildings. This requires calculation of sway deflections due to horizontal loads only, and first-order analysis can be used to determine these deflections. It is assumed that any significant second-order effects will arise only from interaction of column forces with sway deflection. It follows that the check will only be valid if axial compression in beams is not significant. Fig. 5.1(e) illustrates the procedure.

Clause 5.2.2(1)

Even where second-order effects are significant, *clause 5.2.2(2)* allows these to be determined by amplifying the results from a first-order analysis. No further information is given, but clause 5.2.2(5) of EN 1993-1-1 describes a method for frames, provided that the conditions in its clause 5.2.2(6) are satisfied.

Clause 5.2.2(2)

Clause 5.2.2(3)
Clause 5.2.2(4)
Clause 5.2.2(5)
Clause 5.2.2(6)
Clause 5.2.2(7)

Clauses 5.2.2(3) to *5.2.2(7)* concern the relationships between the analysis of the frame and the stability of individual members. A number of possibilities are presented. If relevant software is available, *clause 5.2.2(3)* provides a convenient route for composite columns, because column design to *clause 6.7* generally requires a second-order analysis. Usually, though, the global analysis will not account for all local effects, and *clause 5.2.2(4)* describes in general terms how the designer should then proceed. *Clause 5.2.2(5)* refers to the methods of EN 1994-1-1 for lateral–torsional buckling, which allow for member imperfections. This applies also to local and shear buckling in beams, so imperfections in beams can usually be omitted from global analyses.

In *clause 5.2.2(6)*, 'compression members' are referred to as well as columns, to include composite members used in bracing systems and trusses. Further comments on *clauses 5.2.2(3)* to *5.2.2(7)* are made in the sections of this guide dealing with *clauses 5.5, 6.2.2.3, 6.4* and *6.7*. Figure 5.1(a) illustrates how global and member analyses may be used, for a plane frame including composite columns.

5.3. Imperfections

5.3.1. Basis

Clause 5.3.1(1)P

Clause 5.3.1(1)P lists possible sources of imperfection. Subsequent clauses (and also *clause 5.2*) describe how these should be allowed for. This may be by inclusion in the global analyses or in methods of checking resistance, as explained above.

Clause 5.3.1(2)

Clause 5.3.1(2) requires imperfections to be in the most unfavourable direction and form. The most unfavourable geometric imperfection normally has the same shape as the lowest buckling mode. This can sometimes be difficult to find; but it can be assumed that this condition is satisfied by the Eurocode methods for checking resistance that include effects of member imperfections (see comments on *clause 5.2.2*).

5.3.2. Imperfections in buildings

Generally, an explicit treatment of geometric imperfections is required for composite frames. In both EN 1993-1-1 and EN 1994-1-1 the values are equivalent rather than measured values (*clause 5.3.2.1(1)*), because they allow for effects such as residual stresses, in addition to imperfections of shape. The codes define both global sway imperfections for frames and local bow imperfections of individual members (meaning a span of a beam or the length of a column between storeys).

Clause 5.3.2.1(1)

The usual aim in global analysis is to determine the action effects at the ends of members. If necessary, a member analysis is performed subsequently, as illustrated in Fig. 5.1(a); for example to determine the local moments in a column due to transverse loading. Normally the action effects at members' ends are affected by the global sway imperfections but not significantly by the local bow imperfections. In both EN 1993-1-1 and EN 1994-1-1 the effect of a bow imperfection on the end moments and forces may be neglected in global analysis if the design normal force N_{Ed} does not exceed 25% of the Euler buckling load for the pin-ended member (*clause 5.3.2.1(2)*).

Clause 5.3.2.1(2)
Clause 5.3.2.1(3)

Clause 5.3.2.1(3) is a reminder that an explicit treatment of bow imperfections is always required for checking individual composite columns, because the resistance formulae are for cross-sections only and do not allow for action effects caused by these imperfections.

Clause 5.3.2.1(4)

The reference to EN 1993-1-1 in *clause 5.3.2.1(4)* leads to two alternative methods of allowing for imperfections in steel columns. One method includes all imperfections in the global analysis. Like the method just described for composite columns, no individual stability check is then necessary.

The alternative approach is that familiar to most designers. Member imperfections are not accounted for in the global analysis. The stability of each member is then checked using end moments and forces from that analysis, with buckling formulae that take account of imperfections.

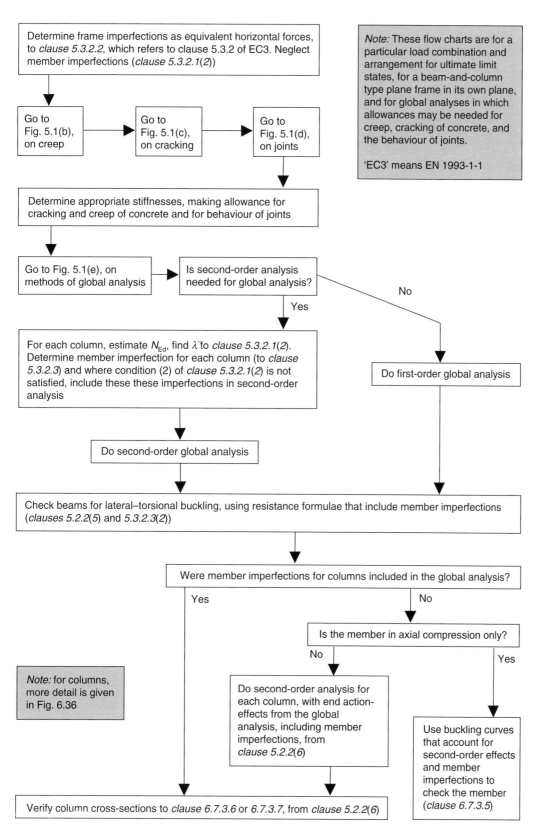

(a) Flow chart, global analysis of a plane frame with composite columns

Fig. 5.1. Global analysis of a plane frame

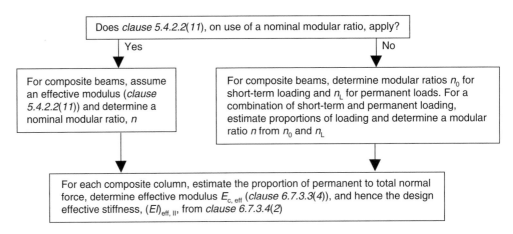

(b) Supplementary flow chart, creep

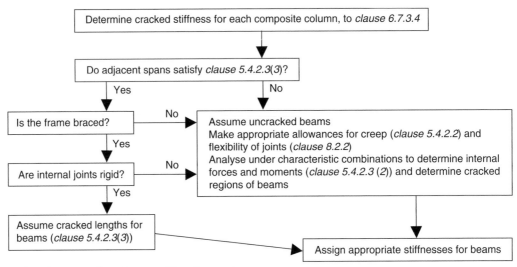

(c) Supplementary flow chart, cracking of concrete

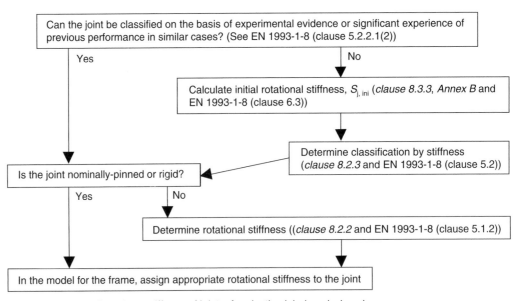

(d) Supplementary flow chart, stiffness of joints, for elastic global analysis only

Fig. 5.1. (Contd)

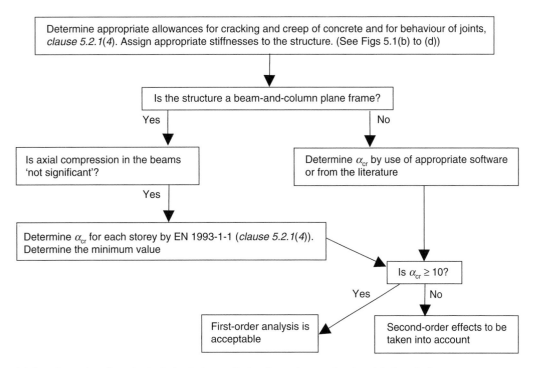

(e) Supplementary flow chart, choice between first-order and second-order global analysis

Fig. 5.1. (Contd)

Global imperfections

Clause 5.3.2.2(1) refers to clause 5.3.2 of EN 1993-1-1. This gives values for the global sway   *Clause 5.3.2.2(1)*
imperfections, describes how imperfections may be replaced by equivalent horizontal forces,
and permits these to be disregarded if the real horizontal forces (e.g. due to wind) are
significant relative to the design vertical load.

Member imperfections

Clause 5.3.2.3(1) refers to *Table 6.5*, which gives the amplitudes of the central bow of a   *Clause 5.3.2.3(1)*
member designed as straight. It makes little difference whether the curve is assumed to be a
half sine wave or a circular arc. These single-curvature shapes are assumed irrespective of
the shape of the bending-moment diagram for the member, but the designer has to decide on
which side of the member the bow is present.

   Clauses 5.3.2.3(2) and *5.3.2.3(3)* refer to member imperfections that need not be included   *Clause 5.3.2.3(2)*
in global analyses. If they are, only cross-section properties are required for checking   *Clause 5.3.2.3(3)*
resistances.

5.4. Calculation of action effects

5.4.1. Methods of global analysis

EN 1990 defines several types of analysis that may be appropriate for ultimate limit states.
For global analysis of buildings, EN 1994-1-1 gives four methods: linear elastic analysis (with
or without redistribution), non-linear analysis and rigid plastic analysis. *Clause 5.4.1.1* gives   *Clause 5.4.1.1*
guidance on matters common to more than one method.

   For reasons of economy, plastic (rectangular stress block) theory is preferred for checking
the resistance of cross-sections. In such cases, *clause 5.4.1.1(1)* allows the action effects to   *Clause 5.4.1.1(1)*

be determined by elastic analysis; for composite structures this method has the widest application.

Clause 5.4.1.1(2)   *Clause 5.4.1.1(2)* makes clear that for serviceability limit states, elastic analysis should be used. Linear elastic analysis is based on linear stress/strain laws, but for composite structures, cracking of concrete needs to be considered (*clause 5.4.2.3*). Other possible non-linear effects include the flexibility of semi-continuous joints (*Section 8*).

Clause 5.4.1.1(4)   Methods for satisfying the principle of *clause 5.4.1.1(4)* are given for local buckling in
Clause 5.4.1.1(5)   *clauses 5.4.1.1(5)* and *5.4.1.1(6)*, and for shear lag in concrete in *clause 5.4.1.2*. Reference is
Clause 5.4.1.1(6)   made to the classification of cross-sections. This is the established method of taking account of local buckling of steel elements in compression. It determines the available methods of global analysis and the basis for resistance to bending. The classification system is defined in *clause 5.5*.

There are several reasons[28,29] why the apparent incompatibility between the methods used for analysis and for resistance is accepted, as stated in *clause 5.4.1.1(1)*. There is no such incompatibility for Class 3 sections, as resistance is based on an elastic model. For Class 4 sections (those in which local buckling will occur before the attainment of yield), *clause 5.4.1.1(6)* refers to clause 2.2 of EN 1993-1-1, which gives a general reference to EN 1993-1-5 ('plated structural elements').[30] This defines those situations in which the effects of shear lag and local buckling in steel plating can be ignored in global analyses.

Clause 5.4.1.1(7)   *Clause 5.4.1.1(7)* reflects a general concern about slip, shared by EN 1993-1-1. For composite joints, *clause A.3* gives a method to account for deformation of the adjacent shear connectors.

Composite beams have to be provided with shear connection in accordance with *clause
Clause 5.4.1.1(8)   6.6*. *Clause 5.4.1.1(8)* therefore permits internal moments and forces to be determined assuming full interaction. For composite columns, *clause 6.7.3.4(2)* gives an effective flexural stiffness for use in global analysis.

Shear lag in concrete flanges, and effective width

Accurate values for effective width of an uncracked elastic flange can be determined by numerical analysis. They are influenced by many parameters and vary significantly along each span. They are increased both by inelasticity and by cracking of concrete. For the bending resistance of a beam, underestimates are conservative, so values in codes have often been based on elastic values.

Clause 5.4.1.2   The simplified values given in *clause 5.4.1.2* of EN 1994-1-1 are very similar to those used in BS 5950: Part 3.1:1990[31] and BS ENV 1994-1-1:1994. The values are generally lower than those in EN 1992-1-1 for reinforced concrete T-beams. To adopt those would often increase the number of shear connectors. Without evidence that the greater effective widths are any more accurate, the established values for composite beams have mainly been retained.

The effective width is based on the distance between points of contraflexure. In EN 1992-1-1, the sum of the distances for sagging and hogging regions equals the span of the beam. In reality, points of contraflexure are dependent on the load arrangement. EN 1994-1-1 therefore gives a larger effective width at an internal support, to reflect the critical load arrangement for this cross-section. In sagging regions, the assumed distances between points of contraflexure are the same in both codes.

Although there are significant differences between effective widths for supports and
Clause 5.4.1.2(4)   mid-span regions, it is possible to ignore this in elastic global analysis (*clause 5.4.1.2(4)*). This is because shear lag has limited influence on the results.

A small difference from earlier codes for buildings concerns the width of steel flange
Clause 5.4.1.2(5)   occupied by the shear connectors. *Clause 5.4.1.2(5)* allows this width to be included within the effective region. Alternatively, it may be ignored (*clause 5.4.1.2(9)*).

Clause 5.4.1.2(8)   *Clause 5.4.1.2(8)* is a reminder that *Fig. 5.1* is based on continuous beams. Although *clause 8.4.2.1(1)* refers to it, *clause 5.4.1.2* does not define the effective flange width adjacent to an external column. *Figure 5.1* may be used as a guide, or the width may be taken as the width occupied by slab reinforcement that is anchored to the column (see *Fig. 8.2*).

Example 5.1: effective width of concrete flange

The notation and method used are those of *clause 5.4.1.2*. A continuous beam of uniform section consists of two spans and a cantilever, as shown in Fig. 5.2. Values for b_{eff} are required for the mid-span regions AB and CD, for the support regions BC and DE, and for the support at A.

The calculation is shown in Table 5.1. The result for support A is found from *equations (5.4)* and *(5.5)*, as follows:

$$b_{eff} = 0.2 + [0.55 + (0.025 \times 6.8/0.4)] \times 0.4 +$$
$$[0.55 + (0.025 \times 6.8/0.85)] \times 0.85 = 1.23 \text{ m}$$

Global analysis may be based on stiffness calculated using the results for AB and CD, but the difference between them is so small that member ABCDE would be analysed as a beam of uniform section.

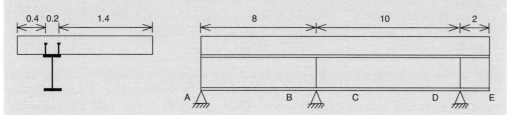

Fig. 5.2. Worked example: effective width

Table 5.1. Effective width of the concrete flange of a composite T-beam

	Region				
	AB	BC	CD	DE	Support A
L_e (from Fig. 5.2) (m)	6.80	4.5	7.0	4.0	6.80
$L_e/8$ (m)	0.85	0.562	0.875	0.50	–
b_{e1} (m)	0.40	0.4	0.4	0.4	0.40
b_{e2} (m)	0.85	0.562	0.875	0.50	0.85
b_{eff} (m)	1.45	1.162	1.475	1.10	1.23

5.4.2. Linear elastic analysis

The restrictions on the use of rigid plastic global analysis (plastic hinge analysis), in *clause 5.4.5*, are such that linear–elastic global analysis will often be used for composite frames.

Creep and shrinkage

There are some differences in *clause 5.4.2.2* from previous practice in the UK. The elastic modulus for concrete under short-term loading, E_{cm}, is a function of the grade and density of the concrete. For normal-weight concrete, it ranges from 30 kN/mm² for grade C20/25 to 39 kN/mm² for grade C60/75. With E_a for structural steel given as 210 kN/mm², the short-term modular ratio, given by $n_0 = E_a/E_{cm}$, thus ranges from 7 to 5.3.

Clause 5.4.2.2

Figure 5.1(b) illustrates the procedure to allow for creep in members of a composite frame. The proportion of loading that is permanent could be obtained by a preliminary global analysis, but in many cases this can be estimated by simpler calculations.

For composite beams in structures for buildings where first-order global analysis is acceptable (the majority), *clause 5.4.2.2(11)* allows the modular ratio to be taken as $2n_0$ for both short-term and long-term loading – an important simplification, not given in BS 5950. The only exceptions are:

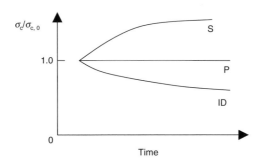

Fig. 5.3. Time-dependent compressive stress in concrete, for three types of loading

- structures where second-order global analysis is required by *clause 5.2*
- structures for buildings mainly intended for storage
- structures prestressed by 'controlled imposed deformations' – this would apply, for example, to the bending of steel beams by jacking before concrete is cast around one of the flanges.

Where the conditions of *clause 5.4.2.2(11)* do not apply, the modular ratio for use in analyses for the effects of long-term loading, n_L, depends on the type of loading and the creep coefficient φ_t. This coefficient depends on both the age of the concrete on first loading, t_0, and on the age at the time considered in the analysis, which is normally taken as 'infinity'.

The use of this method is excluded for members with both flanges composite; but as these occur mainly in bridges, no alternative is given in Part 1.1.

Clause 5.4.2.2(3)   Although *clause 5.4.2.2(4)* gives the age of loading by effects of shrinkage as 1 day, **clause 5.4.2.2(3)** allows one mean value of t_0 to be assumed. If, for example, unpropped construction is used for floor slabs, this might be taken as the age at which they could be subjected to non-trivial imposed loads. These are likely to be construction loads.

It makes quite a difference whether this age is assumed to be (for example) 2 weeks or 2 months. From *clause 5.4.2.2(2)*, the values for normal-weight concrete are found from clause 3.1.4 of EN 1992-1-1. Suppose that normal cement is used for grade C25/30 concrete, that the building will be centrally heated, so 'inside conditions' apply, and that composite floor slabs with a mean concrete thickness of 100 mm are used. Only one side of the slabs is exposed to drying, so the notional size is 200 mm. The increase in t_0 from 14 to 60 days reduces the creep coefficient from 3.0 to about 2.1.

The effect of type of loading is introduced by the symbol ψ_L in the equation

$$n_L = n_0(1 + \psi_L \varphi_t) \tag{5.6}$$

The reason for taking account of it is illustrated in Fig. 5.3. This shows three schematic curves of the change of compressive stress in concrete with time. The top one, labelled S, is typical of stress caused by the increase of shrinkage with time. Concrete is more susceptible to creep when young, so there is less creep than for the more uniform stress caused by permanent loads (line P). The effects of imposed deformations can be significantly reduced by creep when the concrete is young, so the curve is of type ID. The creep multiplier ψ_L has the values 0.55, 1.1 and 1.5, respectively, for these three types of loading. The value for permanent loading on reinforced concrete is 1.0. It is increased to 1.1 for composite members because the steel component does not creep. Stress in concrete is reduced by creep less than it would be in a reinforced member, so there is more creep.

These application rules are based mainly on extensive theoretical work on composite beams of many sizes and proportions,[32] and find application more in design of composite bridges, than in buildings.

Clause 5.4.2.2(6)   The '*time-dependent secondary effects due to creep*' referred to in **clause 5.4.2.2(6)** are most unlikely to be found in buildings. Their calculation is quite complex, and is explained, with an example, in Johnson and Hanswille.[33]

For creep in columns, *clause 5.4.2.2(9)* refers to *clause 6.7.3.4(2)*, which in turn refers to an effective modulus for concrete given in *clause 6.7.3.3(4)*. If separate analyses are to be made for long-term and short-term effects, *clause 6.7.3.3(4)* can be used, assuming that the ratio of permanent to total load is 1.0 and 0, respectively.

Shrinkage of concrete

For the determination of shrinkage strain, reference should be made to the commentary on *clause 3.1*. The effects in columns are unimportant, except in very tall structures. In beams with the slab above the steel member, shrinkage causes sagging curvature. This is its *'primary effect'*, which is reduced almost to zero where the concrete slab is cracked through its thickness.

In continuous beams, the primary curvature is incompatible with the levels of the supports. It is counteracted by bending moments caused by changes in the support reactions, which increase at internal supports and reduce at end supports. The moments and the associated shear forces are the *'secondary effects'* of shrinkage.

Clause 5.4.2.2(7) allows both types of effect to be neglected at ultimate limit states in a beam with all cross-sections in Class 1 or 2, unless its resistance to bending is reduced by lateral–torsional buckling. This restriction can be significant. **Clause 5.4.2.2(8)** allows the option of neglecting primary curvature in cracked regions.[34] This complicates the determination of the secondary effects, because the extent of the cracked regions has to be found, and the beam then has a non-uniform section. It may be simpler not to take the option, even though the secondary hogging bending moments at internal supports are then higher. These moments, being a permanent effect, enter into all load combinations, and may influence the design of what is often a critical region. *Clause 5.4.2.2(7)*

Clause 5.4.2.2(8)

The long-term effects of shrinkage are significantly reduced by creep. In the example above, on creep of concrete, $\varphi_t = 3$ for $t_0 = 14$ days. For shrinkage, with $t_0 = 1$ day, clause 3.1.4 of EN 1992-1-1 gives $\varphi_t = 5$, and *equation (5.6)* gives the modular ratio as:

$$n = n_0(1 + 0.55 \times 5) = 3.7n_0$$

Where it is necessary to consider shrinkage effects within the first year or so after casting, a value for the relevant free shrinkage strain can be obtained from clause 3.1.4(6) of EN 1992-1-1.

The influence of shrinkage on serviceability verifications is dealt with in Chapter 7.

Effects of cracking of concrete

Clause 5.4.2.3 is applicable to both serviceability and ultimate limit states. Figure 5.1(c) illustrates the procedure. *Clause 5.4.2.3*

In conventional composite beams with the slab above the steel section, cracking of concrete reduces the flexural stiffness in hogging moment regions, but not in sagging regions. The change in relative stiffness needs to be taken into account in elastic global analysis. This is unlike analysis of reinforced concrete structures, where cracking occurs in both hogging and sagging bending, and uncracked cross-sections can be assumed throughout.

EN 1994-1-1 provides several different methods to allow for cracking in beams. This is because its scope is both 'general' and 'buildings'. **Clause 5.4.2.3(2)** provides a general method. This is followed in *clause 5.4.2.3(3)* by a simplified approach of limited application. For buildings, a further method is given separately in *clause 5.4.4*. *Clause 5.4.2.3(2)*
Clause 5.4.2.3(3)

In the general method, the first step is to determine the expected extent of cracking in beams. The envelope of moments and shears is calculated for characteristic combinations of actions, assuming uncracked sections and including long-term effects. The section is assumed to crack if the extreme-fibre tensile stress in concrete exceeds twice the mean value of the axial tensile strength given by EN 1992-1-1. The cracked stiffness is then adopted for such sections, and the structure re-analysed. This requires the beams with cracked regions to be treated as beams of non-uniform section.

Table 5.2. Combination factors for imposed load and temperature

Action	ψ_0	ψ_1	ψ_2
Imposed load, building in category B	0.7	0.5	0.3
Temperature (non-fire) in buildings	0.6	0.5	0

The 'uncracked' and 'cracked' flexural stiffnesses E_aI_1 and E_aI_2 are defined in *clause 1.5.2*. Steel reinforcement is normally neglected in the calculation of I_1.

The reasons why stiffness is not reduced to the 'cracked' value until an extreme-fibre stress of twice the mean tensile strength of the concrete is reached, are as follows:

- the concrete is likely to be stronger than specified
- reaching f_{ctm} at the surface may not cause the slab to crack right through, and even if it does, the effects of tension stiffening are significant at the stage of initial cracking
- until after yielding of the reinforcement, the stiffness of a cracked region is greater than E_aI_2, because of tension stiffening between the cracks
- the calculation uses an envelope of moments, for which regions of slab in tension are more extensive than they are for any particular loading.

Clause 5.4.2.3(3)
Clause 5.4.2.3(4)
Clause 5.4.2.3(5)

Clauses 5.4.2.3(3) to *5.4.2.3(5)* provide a non-iterative method, but one that is applicable only to some situations. These include conventional continuous composite beams, and beams in braced frames. The cracked regions could differ significantly from the assumed values in a frame that resists wind loading by bending. Where the conditions are not satisfied, the general method of *clause 5.4.2.3 (2)* should be used.

Cracking affects the stiffness of a frame, and therefore needs to be considered in the criteria for use of first-order analysis (*clauses 5.2.1(3)* and *5.2.2(1)*). For braced frames within the scope of *clause 5.4.2.3(3)*, the cracked regions in beams are of fixed extent, and the effective stiffness of the columns is given by *clause 6.7.3.4(2)*. The corresponding value of the elastic critical factor α_{cr} can therefore be determined prior to analysis under the design loads. It is then worth checking if second-order effects can be neglected.

For unbraced frames, the extent of the cracking can only be determined from analysis under the design loads. This analysis therefore needs to be carried out before the criteria can be checked. It is more straightforward to carry out a second-order analysis, without attempting to prove whether or not it is strictly necessary. Where second-order analysis is necessary, strictly the extent of cracking in beams should take account of the second-order effects. However, as this extent is based on the envelope of internal forces and moments for characteristic combinations, these effects may not be significant.

The 'encasement' in *clause 5.4.2.3(5)* is a reference to the partially encased beams defined in *clause 6.1.1(1)P*. Fully encased beams are outside the scope of EN 1994-1-1.

Temperature effects

Clause 5.4.2.5(2)

Clause 5.4.2.5(2) states that temperature effects, specified in EN 1991-1-5,[35] may normally be neglected in analyses for certain situations. Its scope is narrow because it applies to all composite structures, not buildings only. It provides a further incentive to select steel sections for beams that are not weakened by lateral–torsional buckling.

Study of the ψ factors of Annex A1 of EN 1990[36] for combinations of actions for buildings will show, for many projects, that temperature effects do not influence design. This is illustrated for the design action effects due to the combination of imposed load (Q) with temperature (T), for a building with floors in category B, office areas. Similar comments apply to other combinations of actions and types of building.

The combination factors recommended in clause A1.2.2(1) of EN 1990 are given in Table 5.2. It is permitted to modify these values in a National Annex. For ultimate limit states, the combinations to be considered, in the usual notation and with the recommended γ_F factors, are

$$1.35G_k + 1.5(Q_k + 0.6T_k) \quad \text{and} \quad 1.35G_k + 1.5(T_k + 0.7Q_k)$$

The second one, with T leading, governs only where $T_k > 0.75Q_k$. Normally, action effects due to temperature are much smaller than those due to imposed load, and additional action effects resulting from the inclusion of T in the first combination are not significant.

For serviceability limit states, much depends on the project. Note 2 to clause 3.4(1)P of EN 1990 states: 'Usually the serviceability requirements are agreed for each individual project'. Similarly, clause A1.4.2(2) of Annex A1 of EN 1990 states, for buildings: 'The serviceability criteria should be specified for each project and agreed with the client. Note: The serviceability criteria may be defined in the National Annex.'

There are three combinations of actions given in EN 1990 for serviceability limit states: characteristic, frequent and quasi-permanent. The first of these uses the same combination factors ψ_0 as for ultimate limit states, and the comments made above therefore apply. The quasi-permanent combination is normally used for long-term effects, and temperature is therefore not included.

For the frequent combination, the alternatives are:

$$G_k + 0.5Q_k \quad \text{and} \quad G_k + 0.5T_k + 0.3Q_k$$

The second one governs only where $T_k > 0.4Q_k$.

This example suggests that unless there are members for which temperature is the most severe action, as can occur in some industrial structures, the effects T are unlikely to influence verifications for buildings.

Prestressing by controlled imposed deformations

Clause 5.4.2.6(2) draws attention to the need to consider the effects of deviations of deformations and stiffnesses from their intended or expected values. If the deformations are controlled, *clause 5.4.2.6(2)* permits design values of internal forces and moments arising from this form of prestressing to be calculated from the characteristic or nominal value of the deformation, which will usually be the intended or measured value.

Clause 5.4.2.6(2)

The nature of the control required is not specified. It should take account of the sensitivity of the structure to any error in the deformation.

Prestressing by jacking of supports is rarely used in buildings, as the subsequent loss of prestress can be high.

5.4.3. Non-linear global analysis

Clause 5.4.3 adds little to the corresponding clauses in EN 1992-1-1 and EN 1993-1-1, to which it refers. These clauses give provisions, mainly principles, that apply to any method of global analysis that does not conform to *clause 5.4.2, 5.4.4* or *5.4.5*. They are relevant, for example, to the use of finite-element methods.

Clause 5.4.3

There is some inconsistency in the use of the term 'non-linear' in the Eurocodes. The notes to clauses 1.5.6.6 and 1.5.6.7 of EN 1990 make clear that all of the methods of global analysis defined in clauses 1.5.6.6 to 1.5.6.11 (which include 'plastic' methods) are 'non-linear' in Eurocode terminology. 'Non-linear' in these clauses refers to the deformation properties of the materials.

Moderate geometrical non-linearity, such as can occur in composite structures, is allowed for by using analyses defined as 'second-order'. The much larger deformations that can occur, for example, in some cable-stayed structures, need special treatment.

In clause 5.4 of EN 1993-1-1, global analyses are either 'elastic' or 'plastic', and 'plastic' includes several types of non-linear analysis. The choice between these alternative methods should take account of the properties of composite joints given in *Section 8* of EN 1994-1-1.

Clause 5.7 in EN 1992-1-1 referred to from *clause 5.4.3(1)* is 'Non-linear analysis', which adds little new information.

Clause 5.4.3(1)

In EN 1994-1-1, non-linear analysis, *clause 5.4.3*, and rigid plastic analysis, *clause 5.4.5*, are treated as separate types of global analysis, so that *clause 5.4.3* is not applicable where *clause*

5.4.5 is being followed. The term 'non-linear' is used also for a type of resistance, in *clause 6.2.1.4.*

5.4.4. Linear elastic analysis with limited redistribution for buildings

The concept of redistribution of moments calculated by linear-elastic theory is well established in the design of concrete and composite framed structures. It makes limited allowance for inelastic behaviour, and enables the size of a design envelope of bending moments (from all relevant arrangements of variable loads) to be reduced. In composite beams it is generally easier to provide resistance to bending in mid-span regions than at internal supports. The flexural stiffness at mid-span is higher, sometimes much higher, than at internal supports, so that 'uncracked' global analyses overestimate hogging bending moments in continuous beams. A flow chart for this clause is given in Fig. 5.4.

Clause 5.4.4(1)

Clause 5.4.4(1) refers to redistribution in 'continuous beams and frames', but composite columns are not mentioned. At a beam–column intersection in a frame, there are usually bending moments in the column, arising from interaction with the beam. Redistribution for the beam may be done by assuming it to be continuous over simple supports. If the hogging moments are reduced, the bending moments in the column should be left unaltered. If hogging moments are increased, those in the column should be increased in proportion.

The clause is applicable provided second-order effects are not significant. Inelastic behaviour results in loss of stiffness, but EN 1994-1-1 does not require this to be taken into account when determining whether the clause is applicable. Although there is considerable experience in using *expression (5.1)* as a criterion for rigid plastic global analysis of steel frames with full-strength joints, to allow for non-linear material properties, clause 5.2.1(3) of EN 1993-1-1 gives the more severe limit, $\alpha_{cr} \geq 15$. This limit is a nationally determined parameter. EN 1994-1-1 retains the limit $\alpha_{cr} \geq 10$, but account should be taken of cracking and creep of concrete and the behaviour of joints.

Clause 5.4.4(2)

One of the requirements of *clause 5.4.4(2)* is that redistribution should take account of 'all types of buckling'. Where the shear resistance of a web is reduced to below the plastic value $V_{pl, Rd}$ to allow for web buckling, and the cross-section is not in Class 4, it would be prudent either to design it for the vertical shear before redistribution, or to treat it as if in Class 4.

Although the provisions of *clause 5.4.4* appear similar to those of clause 5.2.3.1 of BS 5950-3-1, there are important differences. Some of these arise because the scope of the British standard is limited to conventional composite beams in normal building structures. The Eurocode provisions are not applicable where:

(1) second-order global analysis is required
(2) a serviceability or fatigue limit state is being verified
(3) the structure is an unbraced frame
(4) semi-rigid or partial-strength joints are used
(5) beams are partially encased, unless the rotation capacity is sufficient or encasement in compression is neglected
(6) the depth of a beam varies within a span
(7) a beam with steel of grade higher than S355 has cross-sections in Class 3 or 4
(8) the resistance of the beam is reduced to allow for lateral–torsional buckling.

The reasons for these exclusions are now briefly explained:

(1) redistribution arises from inelastic behaviour, which lessens the stiffness of the structure and threatens stability
(2) fatigue verification is based on elastic analysis
(3) the amounts of redistribution given in *Table 5.1* have been established considering beams subjected only to gravity loading
(4) the amounts of redistribution given in *Table 5.1* allow for inelastic behaviour in composite beams, but not for the moment–rotation characteristics of semi-rigid or partial-strength joints

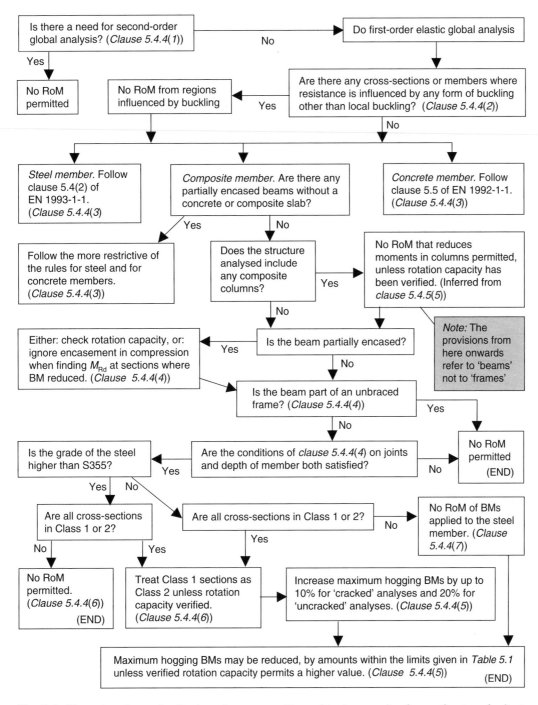

Fig. 5.4. Flow chart for redistribution of moments. Note: this chart applies for verifications for limit states other than fatigue, based on linear-elastic global analysis (RoM, redistribution of bending moments; BM, bending moment)

(5) crushing of the concrete encasement in compression may limit the rotation capacity needed to achieve redistribution; limits to redistribution for partially encased beams can be determined by using the rules for steel members or concrete members, whichever is the more restrictive (***clause 5.4.4(3)***)

Clause 5.4.4(3)

(6) the amounts of redistribution given in *Table 5.1* have been established only for beams of uniform section

(7) the greater strains associated with higher grade steels may increase the rotation needed to achieve redistribution

(8) lateral–torsional buckling may limit the rotation capacity available.

The last condition can be restrictive, as it may apply where $\overline{\lambda}_{LT} > 0.2$ (see *clause 6.4.2(4)*). However, for composite beams with rolled or equivalent welded steel sections, the value recommended in a note to clause 6.3.2.3(1) of EN 1993-1-1 is $\overline{\lambda}_{LT} > 0.4$.

The conditions above apply to the percentages given in *Table 5.1*, which applies only to beams. It should not be inferred that no redistribution is permitted in structures that fail to satisfy one or more of them. It would be necessary to show that any redistribution proposed satisfied *clause 5.4.4(2)*.

Under distributed loading, redistribution usually occurs from hogging to sagging regions of a beam (except of course at an end adjacent to a cantilever). The limits to this redistribution in *Table 5.1* are based on extensive experience in the use of earlier codes and on research. They have been checked by parametric studies, based on Eurocode 4, of beams in Class 2[28] and Class 3.[29]

The limits given in *Table 5.1* for 'uncracked' analyses are the same as in BS 5950,[31] but are more restrictive by 5% for 'cracked' analyses of beams in Class 1 or 2. This reflects the finding[37] that the difference caused by cracking, between moments calculated by elastic theory in such beams, is nearer 15% than 10%.

No provision is made in EN 1994-1-1 for a 'non-reinforced' subdivision of Class 1, for which redistribution up to 50% is allowed in BS 5950-3-1. The use of such sections is not prevented by EN 1994-1-1. The requirements for minimum reinforcement given in *clause 5.5.1(5)* are applicable only if the calculated resistance moment takes account of composite action. The resistance of a non-reinforced cross-section is that of the steel member alone.

The use of plastic resistance moments for action effects found by elastic global analysis (*clause 5.4.1.1(1)*) implies redistribution of moments, usually from internal supports to mid-span regions, additional to the degrees of redistribution permitted, but not required, by *clause 5.4.4(4)*.[38]

Clause 5.4.4(4)

Where there are heavy point loads, and in particular for adjacent spans of unequal length, there can be a need for redistribution from mid-span to supports. This is allowed, to a limited extent, by *clause 5.4.4(5)*.

Clause 5.4.4(5)

The effects of sequence of construction should be considered where unpropped construction is used and the composite member is in Class 3 or 4. As *Table 5.1* makes allowance for inelastic behaviour in a composite beam, *clause 5.4.4(7)* limits redistribution of moments to those arising after composite action is achieved. No such limitation applies to a cross-section in Class 1 or Class 2, as the moment resistance is determined by plastic analysis and is therefore independent of the loading sequence.

Clause 5.4.4(7)

The reference in *clause 5.4.4(3)(b)* to redistribution in steel members is to those that do not subsequently become composite.

5.4.5. Rigid plastic global analysis for buildings

Plastic hinge analysis, so well known in the UK, is referred to as 'rigid plastic' analysis because it is based on the assumption that the response of a member to bending moment is either rigid (no deformation) or plastic (rotation at constant bending moment). Other types of inelastic analysis defined in clause 1.5.6 of EN 1990 are covered in *clause 5.4.3*. Typical moment–curvature curves are shown in Fig. 5.5. No application rules are given for them because they require purpose-written computer programmes.

These other methods are potentially more accurate than rigid plastic analysis, but only if the stress–strain curves are realistic and account is taken of longitudinal slip, as required by *clause 5.4.3(2)P*.

Clause 5.4.5

Taking account of the cross-references in *clause 5.4.5*, the conditions under which use of rigid plastic global analysis is allowed extend over two pages, which need not be summarized here. Development of a collapse mechanism in a composite structure requires a greater

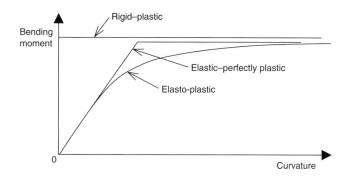

Fig. 5.5. Moment–curvature curves for various types of global analysis

degree of redistribution of elastic moments than in most steel structures, because beams are usually much stronger at mid-span than at supports. The purpose of the conditions is to ensure that this redistribution, and the large in-plane deformations associated with it, can occur without loss of resistance caused by buckling, fracture of steel, or crushing of concrete.

Rigid plastic analysis is applicable only if second-order effects are not significant. Comments on *clause 5.4.1.1* referred to the use of *expression (5.1)* when material behaviour is non-linear. Care needs to be taken if plastic hinges are expected to form in partial-strength joints.[39] These may be substantially weaker than the connected members and the plastic hinges may form at relatively low levels of load. It would be prudent to neglect the stiffness of such joints when determining α_{cr}.

Clause 5.4.5(1) requires cross-sections of 'steel members' to satisfy clause 5.6 of EN 1993-1-1. This applies during unpropped construction, but not to steel elements of composite members, except as provided in *clause 5.4.5(6)*. The provision on rotation capacity in clause 5.6(2) of EN 1993-1-1 is replaced by the conditions of *clause 5.4.5(4)* of EN 1994-1-1.

The rule on neutral axis depth in *clause 5.4.5(4)(g)* is discussed under *clause 6.2.1.2*.

Clause 5.4.5(1)

Clause 5.4.5(4)

5.5. Classification of cross-sections

Typical types of cross-section are shown in *Fig. 6.1*. The classification of cross-sections of composite beams is the established method of taking account in design of local buckling of steel elements in compression. It determines the available methods of global analysis and the basis for resistance to bending, in the same way as for steel members. Unlike the method in EN 1993-1-1, it does not apply to columns.

A flow diagram for the provisions of *clause 5.5* is given in Fig. 5.6. The clause numbers given are from EN 1994-1-1, unless noted otherwise.

Clause 5.5.1(1)P refers to EN 1993-1-1 for definitions of the four classes and the slendernesses that define the class boundaries. Classes 1 to 4 correspond respectively to the terms 'plastic', 'compact', ' semi-compact' and 'slender' that were formerly used in British codes. The limiting slendernesses are similar to those of BS 5950-3-1.[31] The numbers appear different because the two definitions of flange breadth are different, and the coefficient that takes account of yield strength, ε, is defined as $\sqrt{(235/f_y)}$ in the Eurocodes, and as $\sqrt{(275/f_y)}$ in BS 5950.

The scope of EN 1994-1-1 includes members where the cross-section of the steel component has no plane of symmetry parallel to the plane of its web (e.g. a channel section). Asymmetry of the concrete slab or its reinforcement is also acceptable.

The classifications are done separately for steel flanges in compression and steel webs, but the methods interact, as described below. The class of the cross-section is the less favourable of the classes so found (*clause 5.5.1(2)*), with three exceptions. One is where a web is assumed

Clause 5.5

Clause 5.5.1(1)P

Clause 5.5.1(2)

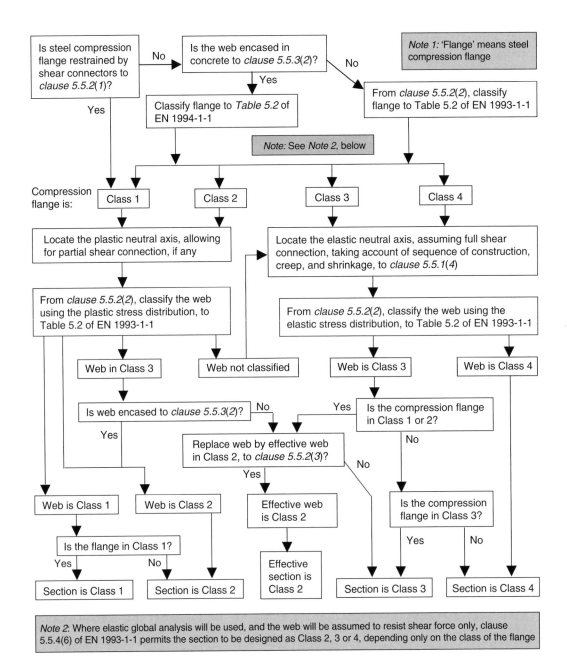

Fig. 5.6. Classification of a cross-section of a composite beam

to resist shear forces only (clause 5.5.2(12) of EN 1993-1-1). The others are the 'hole-in-web' option of *clause 5.5.2(3)* and the use of web encasement, both discussed later.

Reference is sometimes made to a beam in a certain class. This means that none of its cross-sections is in a less favourable class than the one stated, and may imply a certain distribution of bending moment. *Clause 5.5.1(2)* warns that the class of a composite section depends on the sign of the bending moment (sagging or hogging), as it does for a steel section that is not symmetrical about its neutral axis for bending.

Designers of structures for buildings normally select beams with steel sections such that the composite sections are in Class 1 or 2, for the following reasons:

- Rigid plastic global analysis is not excluded, provided that the sections at locations of plastic hinges are in Class 1.

- Bending resistances of beams can be found using plastic theory. For composite sections, this gives resistances from 20 to 40% above the elastic resistance, whereas the increase for steel sections is about 15%.
- The limits to redistribution of moments are more favourable than for Classes 3 and 4.
- Where composite floor slabs are used, it may be difficult to provide full shear connection. *Clause 6.6.1.1(14)* permits partial connection, but only where all beam cross-sections are in Class 1 or 2.

Simply-supported composite beams in buildings are almost always in Class 1 or 2, because the depth of web in compression (if any) is small, and the connection to the concrete slab prevents local buckling of the adjacent steel flange. *Clause 5.5.1(3)* refers to this, and *clause 5.5.2(1)* refers to the more useful *clause 6.6.5.5*, which limits the spacing of the shear connectors required.

Clause 5.5.1(3)

Since the class of a web depends on the level of the neutral axis, and this is different for elastic and plastic bending, it is not obvious which stress distribution should be used for a section near the boundary between Classes 2 and 3. *Clause 5.5.1(4)* provides the answer, the plastic distribution. This is because the use of the elastic distribution could place a section in Class 2, for which the bending resistance would be based on the plastic distribution, which in turn could place the section in Class 3.

Clause 5.5.1(4)

Clause 5.5.1(5), on the minimum area of reinforcement for a concrete flange, appears here, rather than in *Section 6*, because it gives a further condition for a cross-section to be placed in Class 1 or 2. The reason is that these sections must maintain their bending resistance, without fracture of the reinforcement, while subjected to higher rotation than those in Class 3 or 4. This is ensured by disallowing the use of bars in ductility Class A (the lowest), and by requiring a minimum cross-sectional area, which depends on the tensile force in the slab just before it cracks.[40] *Clause 5.5.1(6)*, on welded mesh, has the same objective.

Clause 5.5.1(5)

Clause 5.5.1(6)

Clause 5.5.1(7) draws attention to the use of unpropped construction, during which both the top flange and the web of a steel beam may be in a lower class until the member becomes composite.

Clause 5.5.1(7)

The hole-in-web method

This useful device first appeared in BS 5930-3-1.[31] It is now in clause 6.2.2.4 of EN 1993-1-1, which is referred to from *clause 5.5.2(3)*.

Clause 5.5.2(3)

In beams subjected to hogging bending, it often happens that the bottom flange is in Class 1 or 2, and the web is in Class 3. The initial effect of local buckling of the web would be a small reduction in the bending resistance of the section. The assumption that a defined depth of web, the 'hole', is not effective in bending enables the reduced section to be upgraded from Class 3 to Class 2, with the advantages for design that are listed above. The method is analogous to the use of effective areas for Class 4 sections, to allow for local buckling.

There is a limitation to its scope that is not evident from the wording in EN 1993-1-1:

> The proportion of the web in compression should be replaced by a part of $20\varepsilon t_w$ adjacent to the compression flange, with another part of $20\varepsilon t_w$ adjacent to the plastic neutral axis of the effective cross-section.

It follows that for a design yield strength f_{yd} the compressive force in the web is limited to $40\varepsilon t_w f_{yd}$. For a composite beam in hogging bending, the tensile force in the longitudinal reinforcement in the slab can exceed this value, especially where f_{yd} is reduced to allow for vertical shear. The method is then not applicable, because the second 'part of $20\varepsilon t_w$' is not adjacent to the plastic neutral axis, which lies within the top flange. The method, and this limitation, are illustrated in Examples 6.1 and 6.2.

Partially encased cross-sections

Partially encased sections are defined in *clause 6.1.1(1)P*. Those illustrated there also have concrete flanges. The web encasement improves the resistance of both the web and the other

Clause 5.5.3(1)   flange to local buckling. A concrete flange is not essential, as shown in ***clause 5.5.3(1)***, which gives the increased slenderness ratios for compression flanges in Classes 2 and 3. The limit for Class 1 is unaltered.

     The rest of *clause 5.5.3* specifies the encasement that enables a Class 3 web to be treated as Class 2, without loss of cross-section. Conditions under which the encasement contributes to the bending and shear resistance of the member are given in *Section 6,* where relevant comments will be found.

CHAPTER 6

Ultimate limit states

This chapter corresponds to *Section 6* of EN 1994-1-1, which has the following clauses:

Clauses 6.1 to *6.7* define resistances of cross-sections to static loading, for comparison with action effects determined by the methods of *Section 5*. The ultimate limit state considered is STR, defined in clause 6.4.1(1) of EN 1990 as:

> Internal failure or excessive deformation of the structure or structural members, ... where the strength of constructional materials of the structure governs.

For lateral–torsional buckling of beams and for columns, the resistance is influenced by the properties of the whole member, and there is an implicit assumption that the member is of uniform cross-section, apart from variations arising from cracking of concrete and from detailing.

The self-contained *clause 6.8*, 'Fatigue', covers steel, concrete and reinforcement by cross-reference to Eurocodes 2 and 3, and deals mainly with shear connection in beams.

Most of the provisions of *Section 6* are applicable to both buildings and bridges, but a number of clauses are headed 'for buildings', and are replaced by other clauses in EN 1994-2. Some of these differences arise from the different treatments of shear connection in the two codes, which are compared in comments on ***clause 6.1.1***.

Clause 6.1.1

6.1. Beams

6.1.1. Beams for buildings

Figure 6.1 shows typical examples of beams for buildings within the scope of EN 1994-1-1. The details include web encasement, and profiled sheeting with spans at right angles to the span of the beam, and continuous or discontinuous over the beam. The top right-hand diagram represents a longitudinal haunch. Not shown (and not excluded) is the common situation in which profiled sheeting spans are parallel to the span of the beam. A re-entrant trough is shown in the bottom right-hand diagram. Sheeting with trapezoidal troughs is also within the scope of the code.

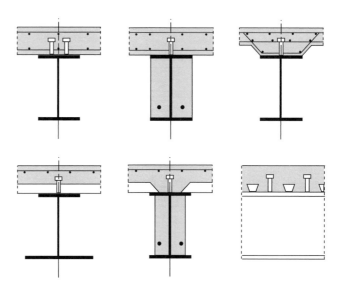

Fig. 6.1. Typical cross-sections of composite beams

The steel cross-section may be a rolled I- or H-section or may be a doubly-symmetrical or mono-symmetrical plate girder. Other possible types include any of those shown in sheet 1 of Table 5.2 of EN 1993-1-1; for example, rectangular hollow sections. Channel and angle sections should not be used unless the shear connection is designed to provide torsional restraint. Stub girders are not within the scope of EN 1994-1-1. There is an extensive literature on their design.[41]

Shear connection

In buildings, composite cross-sections are usually in Class 1 or 2, and the bending resistance is determined by plastic theory. At the plastic moment of resistance, the longitudinal force in a concrete flange is easily found, so design of shear connection for buildings is often based on the change in this force between two cross-sections where the force is known. This led to the

Clause 6.1.1(4)P   concepts of critical cross-sections (*clause 6.1.1(4)P* to *clause 6.1.1(6)*) and critical lengths (*clause 6.1.1(6)*). These concepts are not used in bridge design. Cross-sections in Class 3 or 4 are common in bridges, and elastic methods are used. Longitudinal shear flows are therefore found from the well-known result from elastic theory, $v_{\mathrm{L}} = VA\bar{y}/I$.

Points of contraflexure are not critical cross-sections, partly because their location is different for each arrangement of variable load. A critical length in a continuous beam may therefore include both a sagging and a hogging region. Where connectors are uniformly spaced over this length, the number in the hogging region may not correspond to the force that has to be transferred from the longitudinal slab reinforcement. This does not matter, provided that the reinforcing bars are long enough to be anchored beyond the relevant connectors. The need for consistency between the spacing of connectors and curtailment of reinforcement is treated in *clause 6.6.1.3(2)P*.

A sudden change in the cross-section of a member changes the longitudinal force in the concrete flange, even where the vertical shear is zero. In theory, shear connection to provide

Clause 6.1.1(5)   this change is needed. *Clause 6.1.1(5)* gives a criterion for deciding whether the change is sudden enough to be allowed for, and will normally show that changes in reinforcement can be ignored. Where the clause is applied, the new critical section has different forces in the flange on each side of it. It may not be clear which one to use.

One method is to use the result that gives the greater change of force over the critical length being considered. An alternative is to locate critical cross-sections on both sides of the change point, not more than about two beam depths apart. The shear connection in the short critical length between these two sections, based on the longitudinal forces at those sections, needs to take account of the change of section.

The application of *clause 6.1.1(5)* is clearer for a beam that is composite for only part of its length. The end of the composite region is then a critical section.

A tapering member has a gradually changing cross-section. This can occur from variation in the thickness or effective width of the concrete flange, as well as from non-uniformity in the steel section. Where elastic theory is used, the equation $v_{L, Ed} = V_{Ed} A\bar{y}/I$ should be replaced by

$$v_{L, Ed} = V_{Ed} A\bar{y}/I + M_{Ed} \frac{d(A\bar{y}/I)}{dx} \tag{D6.1}$$

where x is the coordinate along the member. For buildings, where resistances may be based on plastic theory, *clause 6.1.1(6)* enables the effect to be allowed for by using additional critical sections. It is applicable, for example, where the steel beam is haunched. The treatment of vertical shear then requires care, as part of it is resisted by the sloping steel flange.

Clause 6.1.1(6)

Provisions for composite floor slabs, using profiled steel sheeting, are given only for buildings. The space within the troughs available for the shear connection is often insufficient for the connectors needed to develop the ultimate compressive force in the concrete flange, and the resistance moment corresponding to that force is often more than is required, because of other constraints on design. This has led to the use of partial shear connection, which is defined in *clause 6.1.1(7)*. It is applicable only where the critical cross-sections are in Class 1 or 2. Thus, in buildings, bending resistances are often limited to what is needed, i.e. to M_{Ed}, with shear connection based on bending resistances; see *clause 6.6.2.2*.

Clause 6.1.1(7)

Where bending resistances of cross-sections are based on an elastic model and limiting stresses, longitudinal shear flows can be found from $v_{L, Ed} = V_{Ed} A\bar{y}/I$. They are related to action effects, not to resistances. Shear connection designed in this way, which is usual in bridges, is 'partial' according to the definition in *clause 6.1.1(7)P*, because increasing it would increase the bending resistances in the vicinity – though not in a way that is easily calculated, because inelastic behaviour and partial interaction are involved.

For these reasons, the concept 'partial shear connection' is confusing in bridge design and not relevant. Clauses in EN 1994-1-1 that refer to it are therefore labelled 'for buildings'.

Effective cross-section of a beam with a composite slab
Where the span of a composite slab is at right angles to that of the beam, as in the lower half of Fig. 6.1, the effective area of concrete does not include that within the ribs. Where the spans are parallel ($\theta = 0$), the effective area includes the area within the depth of the ribs, but usually this is neglected. For ribs that run at an angle θ to the beam, the effective area of concrete within an effective width of flange may be taken as the full area above the ribs plus $\cos^2 \theta$ times the area of concrete within the ribs. Where $\theta > 60°$, $\cos^2 \theta$ should be taken as zero.

Service ducts in slabs can cause a significant loss of effective cross-section.

6.1.2. Effective width for verification of cross-sections
The variation of effective width along a span, as given by *clause 5.4.1.2*, is too complex for verification of cross-sections in beams for buildings. The simplification in *clause 6.1.2(2)* often enables checks on the bending resistance of continuous beams to be limited to the supports and the mid-span regions. This paragraph should not be confused with *clause 5.4.1.2(4)*, which applies to global analysis.

Clause 6.1.2(2)

6.2. Resistances of cross-sections of beams
This clause is for beams without partial or full encasement in concrete. Most of it is applicable to both buildings and bridges. Partial encasement is treated for buildings only, in *clause 6.3*. Full encasement is outside the scope of EN 1994.

No guidance is given in EN 1994-1-1, or in EN 1993, on the treatment of large holes in steel webs, but specialized literature is available.[42,43] Bolt holes in steelwork should be treated in accordance with EN 1993-1-1, particularly clauses 6.2.2 to 6.2.6.

6.2.1. Bending resistance

In *clause 6.2.1.1*, three different approaches are given, based on rigid plastic theory, non-linear theory and elastic analysis. The 'non-linear theory' is that given in *clause 6.2.1.4*. This is not a reference to non-linear global analysis.

Clause 6.2.1.1(3)   The assumption that composite cross-sections remain plane is always permitted by *clause 6.2.1.1(3)*, where elastic and non-linear theory are used, because the conditions set will be satisfied if the design is in accordance with EN 1994. The implication is that longitudinal slip is negligible.

There is no requirement for slip to be determined. This would be difficult because the stiffness of shear connectors is not known accurately, especially where the slab is cracked. Wherever slip may not be negligible, the design methods of EN 1994-1-1 are intended to allow for its effects.

For beams with curvature in plan sufficiently sharp for torsional moments not to be
Clause 6.2.1.1(5)   negligible, *clause 6.2.1.1(5)* gives no guidance on how to allow for the effects of curvature. In analysis from first principles, checks for beams in buildings can be made by assuming that the changing direction of the longitudinal force in a flange (and a web, if significant) creates a transverse load on that flange, which is then designed as a horizontal beam to resist that load. A steel bottom flange may require horizontal restraint at points within the span of the beam, and the shear connection should be designed for both longitudinal and transverse forces.

Clause   'Full interaction' in *clause 6.2.1.2(1)(a)* means that no account need be taken of slip or
6.2.1.2(1)(a)   separation at the steel–concrete interface.

Reinforcement in compression

Clause   It is usual to neglect slab reinforcement in compression (*clause 6.2.1.2(1)(c)*). If it is included,
6.2.1.2(1)(c)   and the concrete cover is little greater than the bar diameter, consideration should be given to possible buckling of the bars. Guidance is given in clause 9.6.3(1) of EN 1992-1-1 on reinforcement in concrete walls. The meaning is that the reinforcement in compression should not be the layer nearest to the free surface of the slab.

Small concrete flanges

Where the concrete slab is in compression, the method of *clause 6.2.1.2* is based on the assumption that the whole effective areas of steel and concrete can reach their design strengths before the concrete begins to crush. This may not be so if the concrete flange is small compared with the steel section. This lowers the plastic neutral axis, and so increases the maximum compressive strain at the top of the slab, for a given tensile strain in the steel bottom flange.

A detailed study of the problem has been reported.[44] Laboratory tests on beams show that strain hardening of steel usually occurs before crushing of concrete. The effect of this, and the low probability that the strength of both the steel and the concrete will be only at the design level, led to the conclusion that premature crushing can be neglected unless the grade
Clause 6.2.1.2(2)   of the structural steel is higher than S355. *Clause 6.2.1.2(2)* specifies a reduction in $M_{pl,Rd}$ where the steel grade is S420 or S460 and the depth of the plastic neutral axis is high. This problem also affects the rotation capacity of plastic hinges. Extensive research[45,46] led to the upper limit to neutral-axis depth given in *clause 5.4.5(4)(g)*.

For composite columns, the risk of premature crushing led to a reduction in the factor α_M, given in *clause 6.7.3.6(1)*, for S420 and S460 steels.

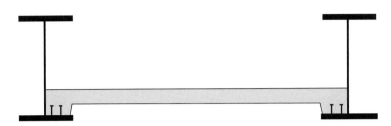

Fig. 6.2. Example of a composite beam with the slab in tension at mid-span

Ductility of reinforcement

Reinforcement with insufficient ductility to satisfy *clause 5.5.1(5)*, and welded mesh, should not be included within the effective section of beams in Class 1 or 2 (*clause 6.2.1.2(3)*). This is because laboratory tests on hogging moment regions have shown[19] that some reinforcing bars, and most welded meshes, fracture before the moment–rotation curve for a typical double-cantilever specimen reaches a plateau. The problem with welded mesh is explained in comments on *clause 3.2(1)*.

Clause 6.2.1.2(3)

Profiled steel sheeting

The contribution of profiled steel sheeting in compression to the plastic moment of resistance of a beam is ignored (*clause 6.2.1.2(4)*) because at large strains its resistance can be much reduced by local buckling. Profiled sheeting with troughs that are not parallel to the span of a beam is ineffective in tension. This is because deformation could arise from change in shape of the profile rather than strain resulting from stress. Where the troughs are parallel, resistance to tension may still be difficult to achieve. For advantage to be taken of *clause 6.2.1.2(5)*, the sheeting needs to be continuous, and interaction with other components of the cross-section has to be achieved.

Clause 6.2.1.2(4)

Clause 6.2.1.2(5)

Beams with partial shear connection in buildings

The background to the use of partial shear connection is explained in comments on *clause 6.1.1*. It is permitted only for the compressive force in the concrete slab (*clause 6.2.1.3(1)*). Where the slab is in tension the shear connection must be sufficient to 'ensure yielding' (*clause 6.2.1.3(2)*) of the reinforcement within the effective section. Full shear connection is required in hogging regions of composite beams for several reasons:

Clause 6.2.1.3(1)

Clause 6.2.1.3(2)

- the bending moment may be larger than predicted because the concrete has not cracked or, if it has, because of tension stiffening
- the yield strength of the reinforcement exceeds f_{sd} ($= f_{sk}/\gamma_S$)
- tests show that at high curvatures, strain hardening occurs in the reinforcement
- the design rules for lateral–torsional buckling do not allow for the effects of partial interaction.

It could be inferred from the definition of full shear connection in *clause 6.1.1(7)* that where the bending resistance is reduced below $M_{pl, Rd}$ by the effects of lateral buckling, shear connection is required only for the reduced resistance. *Clause 6.2.1.3(2)* makes it clear that the inference is incorrect. Thus, *clause 6.2.1.2* on the plastic resistance moment $M_{pl, Rd}$ applies, amongst other cases, to all beams in Class 1 or 2 with tensile force in the slab.

The words 'hogging bending' in *clause 6.2.1.3* imply that the concrete slab is above the steel beam. This is an assumption implicit in much of the drafting of the provisions 'for buildings'. In the 'general' clauses, phrases such as 'regions where the slab is in tension' are used instead, because in bridges this can occur in regions of sagging curvature (Fig. 6.2).

The provisions referred to in *clause 6.2.1.3(1)* include *clause 6.6.1.1(14)*, which begins 'If all cross-sections are in Class 1 or Class 2 ...'. This means all sections within the span considered. In practice, the use of an effective web in Class 2 (*clause 5.5.2(3)*) ensures that few Class 3 sections need be excluded.

Ductile connectors

Clause 6.2.1.3(3) **Clause 6.2.1.3(3)** refers to 'ductile connectors'. The basic condition for the use of partial shear connection is that the bending resistance must not fall below the design value until after the curvature has reached the minimum value relied upon in the method of global analysis used. Use of redistribution of moments, for example, relies upon curvatures beyond the elastic range.

In other words:

$$\text{slip required (i.e. relied on in design)} \leq \text{slip available} \tag{D6.2}$$

It has been shown by extensive numerical analyses, checked against test results,[47,48] that the slip required increases with the span of the beam and, of course, as the number of shear connectors is reduced. The latter parameter is represented by the ratio of the number of connectors provided within a critical length, n, to the number n_f required for 'full shear connection' (defined in *clause 6.1.1(7)P*), i.e. the number that will transmit the force $N_{c,f}$ to the slab (see *Fig. 6.2*). A reduced number, n, will transmit a reduced force, N_c. Thus, for connectors of a given shear strength, the 'degree of shear connection' is

$$\eta = N_c/N_{c,f} = n/n_f \tag{D6.3}$$

The application rules for general use are based on an available slip of 6 mm. Condition (D6.2) was then applied by defining combinations of η and span length such that the slip required did not exceed 6 mm.

Headed studs regarded as ductile are defined in *clause 6.6.1.2*, where a flow chart (see Fig. 6.11) and further comments are given. For partial shear connection with non-ductile connectors, reference should be made to comments on *clause 6.2.1.4*.

Calculation models

The calculation model given in *clause 6.2.1.3(3)* can be explained as follows. For a given cross-section, the force $N_{c,f}$ can be found using *clause 6.2.1.2*. For $\eta < 1$, the concrete stress block has a reduced depth, and a neutral axis at its lower edge. For longitudinal equilibrium, part of the steel beam must also be in compression, so it too has a neutral axis. The model assumes no separation of the slab from the beam, so their curvatures must be the same. The strain distribution is thus as shown in Fig. 6.3, which is for the situation shown in *Fig. 6.4* in EN 1994-1-1. At the interface between steel and concrete there is *slip strain*, i.e. rate of change of longitudinal slip. Neither the slip at this point nor the slip strain need be calculated in practice.

Clause 6.2.1.3(4) **Clauses 6.2.1.3(4)** and **6.2.1.3(5)** give two relationships between resistance moment M_{Rd}
Clause 6.2.1.3(5) and degree of shear connection. Calculations using the method above give curve AHC in the upper part of Fig. 6.4(a), in which $M_{pl,a,Rd}$ is the plastic resistance of the steel section. The line AC is a simpler and more conservative approximation to it. Their use is now illustrated. The lower half of Fig. 6.4(a) shows the limits to the use of partial shear connection given in *clause 6.6.1.2*.

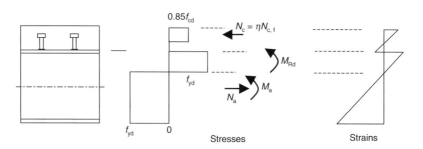

Fig. 6.3. Plastic stress and strain distributions under sagging bending for partial shear connection

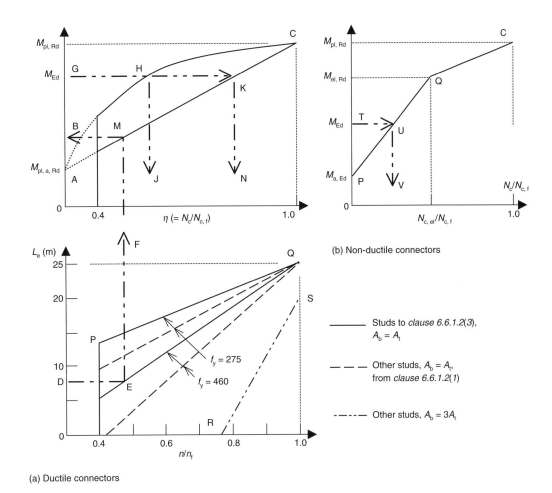

(b) Non-ductile connectors

(a) Ductile connectors

Fig. 6.4. Design methods for partial shear connection

Outline of a typical design procedure

The example is a simply-supported beam of span L, with a Class 1 section at mid-span. With full shear connection the resistance is $M_{pl,\,Rd}$. The steel section has flanges of equal area, and the loading is uniformly distributed. Stud connectors are to be used.

(1) Find the minimum shear connection, $(n/n_f)_{min}$, for which the connectors are ductile, from *clause 6.6.1.2* (e.g. route DEF in Fig. 6.4(a)), and the corresponding resistance to bending (route FMB).

(2) If that resistance exceeds the design moment M_{Ed}, this degree of shear connection is sufficient. Calculate the number of connectors for full shear connection, and then, from $(n/n_f)_{min}$, the number required.

(3) If the resistance, point B, is much higher than M_{Ed}, it may be possible to reduce the number of connectors by using the method for non-ductile connectors, as explained in Example 6.4 below.

(4) If the resistance, point B, is below M_{Ed}, as shown in Fig. 6.4(a), the interpolation method can be used (route GKN) to give the value of n/n_f required. Alternatively, point H can be determined, as shown below, and hence point J. The higher of the values of η given by points J and F is the minimum degree of shear connection, and, hence, n can be found.

(5) The spacing of the n connectors is now considered, along the length L_{cr} between the two relevant critical cross-sections (here, mid-span and a support). If the conditions of *clause 6.6.1.3(3)* are satisfied, as they are here if $M_{pl,\,Rd} \le 2.5M_{a,\,pl,\,Rd}$, the spacing may be

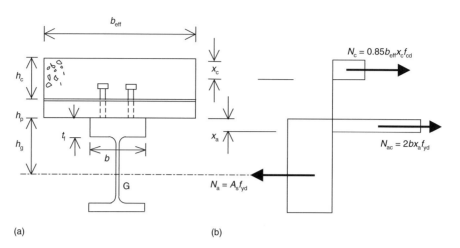

Fig. 6.5. Theory for force N_c. (a) Cross-section. (b) Longitudinal stresses

uniform. Otherwise, an intermediate critical section must be chosen, *clause 6.6.1.3(4)*, or the spacing must be related to the elastic distribution of longitudinal shear, *clause 6.6.1.3(5)*.

Determination of n for a given M_{Ed} by the equilibrium method

The number of connectors needed to develop the moment M_{Ed} is $n = N_c/P_{Rd}$, where P_{Rd} is the design resistance of a connector and N_c is the force referred to in *clause 6.2.1.3(3)*, for a moment M_{Ed}. Its calculation is tedious, but can be simplified a little, as shown here.

Figure 6.5 shows a cross-section of a beam in sagging bending, where the compressive force in the concrete slab is N_c, less than $N_{c,f}$ (equation (D6.3)), being limited by the strength of the shear connection. Following *clause 6.2.1.3(3)*, the plastic stress blocks are as shown in Fig. 6.5. The neutral axis in the steel is at a depth x_a below the interface. It is convenient to retain the known force N_a acting at the centre of area G of the steel section, and to take the compressive strength over depth x_a as $2f_{yd}$. This is because the stress in that area is to be changed from yield in tension to yield in compression, providing a compressive force N_{ac} in the steel. We need to find out whether or not $x_a > t_f$.

In most beams with full shear connection, $N_{c,f} = N_a$, because the plastic neutral axis lies within the slab. It is required that $N_c/N_{c,f} \geq 0.4$, from Fig. 6.4(a), so

$$N_c \geq 0.4N_{c,f} \geq 0.4N_a \tag{a}$$

From equilibrium,

$$N_c + N_{ac} = N_a \tag{b}$$

so, from expression (a),

$$N_{ac} \leq 0.6N_a \tag{c}$$

When the neutral axis is at the underside of the steel top flange, of area A_{top},

$$N_{ac}/N_a = 2A_{top}/A_a \tag{d}$$

For most rolled I-sections, $A_{top} \geq 0.3A_a$, so when $x_a = t_f$, from equation (d),

$$N_{ac} \geq 0.6N_a \tag{e}$$

From expressions (c) and (e), $x_a < t_f$ when the preceding assumptions are valid. They usually are, so only the case $x_a < t_f$ is considered. Force N_{ac} is then as shown in Fig. 6.5, and acts at a depth $h_c + h_p + 0.5x_a$ below the top of the slab. For rolled sections, $x_a \ll h_c + h_p$, so this depth can be taken as $h_c + h_p$. Taking moments about the top of the slab,

$$M_{Ed} = N_a(h_g + h_p + h_c) - \tfrac{1}{2}x_c N_c - N_{ac}(h_c + h_p) \tag{D6.4}$$

Substitution for N_{ac} from equation (b) and use of the expression for N_c in Fig. 6.5 gives

$$M_{Ed} = N_a h_g + 0.85 b_{eff} x_c f_{cd}(h_c + h_p - \tfrac{1}{2}x_c)$$

This can be solved for x_c, which gives N_c, and then n from $n = N_c/P_{Rd}$, since P_{Rd} is known for given connectors.

In practice, it may be simpler to calculate N_a, choose a convenient value for n, find N_c and then x_c, calculate N_{ac} from equation (b), and see whether or not equation (D6.4) gives a value that exceeds M_{Ed}. If it does not, n is increased and the process repeated.

There is much interaction between *clause 6.2.1.3* and *clauses 6.6.1.2* and *6.6.1.3*. The use of partial shear connection is illustrated in Example 6.7, which follows the comments on *clause 6.6*, in Examples 6.8 and 6.9, which are based on the same data, and in Fig. 6.11.

Non-ductile connectors

These are connectors that do not satisfy the requirements for ductile connectors given in *clauses 6.6.1.1* and *6.6.1.2*. Plastic behaviour of the shear connection can no longer be assumed. Non-linear or elastic theory should now be used to determine resistance to bending. Provisions are given in *clause 6.2.1.4* and *clause 6.2.1.5*.

Clause 6.2.1.4

The effect of slip at the steel–concrete interface is to increase curvature, and usually to reduce longitudinal shear, for a given distribution of bending moment along a span. Where connectors are not 'ductile', slip must be kept small, so it is rational to neglect slip when calculating longitudinal shear. This is why *clause 6.2.1.4(2)* says that cross-sections should be assumed to remain plane.

Clause 6.2.1.4(2)

Non-linear resistance to bending

There are two approaches, described in *clause 6.2.1.4*. With both, the calculations should be done at the critical sections for the design bending moments. The first approach, given in *clause 6.2.1.4(1)* to *6.2.1.4(5)*, enables the resistance of a section to be determined iteratively from the stress–strain relationships of the materials. A strain distribution is assumed for the cross-section, and the resulting stresses determined. Usually, the assumed strain distribution will have to be revised, to ensure that the stresses correspond to zero axial force on the section. Once this condition is satisfied, the bending moment is calculated from the stress distribution. This may show that the design bending moment does not exceed the resistance, in which case the calculation for bending resistance may be terminated. Otherwise, a general increase in strain should be made and the calculations repeated. For concrete, EN 1992-1-1 gives ultimate strains for concrete and reinforcement which eventually limit the moment resistance.

Clause 6.2.1.4(1)
Clause 6.2.1.4(2)
Clause 6.2.1.4(3)
Clause 6.2.1.4(4)
Clause 6.2.1.4(5)

Clearly, in practice this procedure requires the use of software. For sections in Class 1 or 2, a simplified approach is given in *clause 6.2.1.4(6)*. This is based on three points on the curve relating longitudinal force in the slab, N_c, to design bending moment M_{Ed} that are easily determined. With reference to Fig. 6.4(b), which is based on *Fig. 6.6*, these points are:

Clause 6.2.1.4(6)

- P, where the composite member resists no moment, so $N_c = 0$
- Q, which is defined by the results of an elastic analysis of the section
- C, based on plastic analysis of the section.

Accurate calculation shows QC to be a convex-upwards curve, so the straight line QC is a conservative approximation. *Clause 6.2.1.4(6)* thus enables hand calculation to be used. For buildings, *clause 6.2.1.4(7)* refers to a simplified treatment of creep.

Clause 6.2.1.4(7)

Shear connection to clause 6.2.1.4

Computations based on the stress–strain curves referred to in *clause 6.2.1.4(3)* to *6.2.1.4(5)* lead to a complete moment-curvature curve for the cross-section, including a falling branch. The definition of partial shear connection in *clause 6.1.1(7)P* is unhelpful, because the number of connectors for full shear connection can be found only from the stress distribution corresponding to the maximum moment. This is why $N_{c,f}$ in Fig. 6.4(b) is based on plastic analysis to *clause 6.2.1.2*. This figure is approximately to scale for a typical composite section in sagging bending, for which

$$M_{pl,Rd}/M_{el,Rd} = 1.33$$

$$N_{c,el}/N_{c,f} = 0.6$$

The position of line PQ depends on the method of construction. It is here assumed that the beam was unpropped, and that at the critical section for sagging bending, the moment $M_{a,Ed}$ applied to the steel alone was $0.25M_{pl,Rd}$.

For a given design moment M_{Ed} (which must include $M_{a,Ed}$, as resistances of sections are found by plastic theory), the required ratio n/n_f is given by route TUV in Fig. 6.4(b).

No specific guidance is given for the spacing of shear connectors when moment resistance is determined by non-linear theory. The theory is based on plane cross-sections (*clause 6.2.1.4(2)*), so the spacing of connectors should ideally correspond to the variation of the force in the slab, N_c, along the member. Where non-ductile connectors are used, this should be done. For ductile connectors, *clause 6.6.1.3(3)*, which permits uniform spacing, may be assumed to apply.

Elastic resistance to bending

Clause 6.2.1.4(6) includes, almost incidentally, a definition of $M_{el,Rd}$ that may seem strange. It is a peculiarity of composite structures that when unpropped construction is used, the elastic resistance to bending depends on the proportion of the total load that is applied before the member becomes composite. Let $M_{a,Ed}$ and M_{Ed} be the design bending moments for the steel and composite sections, respectively, for a section in Class 3. Their total is typically less than the elastic resistance to bending, so to find $M_{el,Rd}$, one or both of them must be increased

Clause 6.2.1.5(2) until one or more of the limiting stresses in *clause 6.2.1.5(2)* is reached. To enable a unique result to be obtained, *clause 6.2.1.4(6)* says that M_{Ed} is to be increased, and $M_{a,Ed}$ left unchanged. This is because $M_{a,Ed}$ is mainly from permanent actions, which are less uncertain than the variable actions whose effects comprise most of M_{Ed}.

Unpropped construction normally proceeds by stages, which may have to be considered individually in bridge design. For simply-supported spans in buildings, it is usually sufficiently accurate to assume that the whole of the wet concrete is placed simultaneously on the bare steelwork.

The weight of formwork is, in reality, applied to the steel structure and removed from the composite structure. This process leaves self-equilibrated residual stresses in composite cross-sections. For composite beams in buildings, these can usually be ignored in calculations for the final situation.

Clause 6.2.1.5(5) One permanent action that influences M_{Ed} is shrinkage of concrete. *Clause 6.2.1.5(5)* enables the primary stresses to be neglected in cracked concrete, but the implication is that they should be included where the slab is in compression. This provision, which affects $M_{el,Rd}$, should not be confused with *clause 5.4.2.2(8)*, which concerns global analysis to determine the secondary effects of shrinkage in statically-indeterminate structures. (Secondary effects are defined in *clause 2.3.3*.)

These complications explain why, for ultimate limit states in buildings, design methods based on elastic behaviour are best avoided, as far as possible.

Example 6.1: resistance moment in hogging bending, with effective web

A typical cross-section near an internal support of a continuous composite beam is shown in Fig. 6.6(a). The plastic and elastic methods of calculation for the hogging moment of resistance are illustrated by preparing a graph that shows changes in this resistance as the effective area of longitudinal reinforcement in the slab, A_s, is increased from zero to

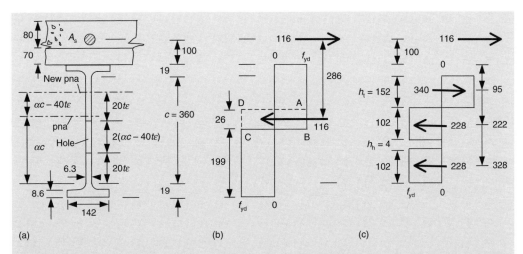

Fig. 6.6. Plastic resistance moment in hogging bending, for $A_s = 267$ mm^2 (units: mm and kN). (a) Cross-section of Class 3 beam with hole in web. (b) Stress blocks for $M_{pl, Rd}$ for Class 2 beam. (c) Stress blocks in web for $M_{pl, Rd}$ for Class 3 beam

1800 mm^2. The use of an effective web to *clause 5.5.2(3)*, discussed in Chapter 5, is also illustrated. The depth of the 'web', as used here, is the depth between flange fillets (or welds), defined as c in Table 5.2 of EN 1993-1-1, not the clear depth between the flanges. Also from EN 1993-1-1, αc is the depth of the web in compression, for a section in Class 1 or 2, and ε is the correction factor for yield strength of the steel.

The definition of the hole-in-web model, given in Fig. 6.3 of EN 1993-1-1, omits the depth of the hole and the location of the new plastic neutral axis (pna). They were given in ENV 1994-1-1,[49] and are shown in Fig. 6.6(a). The depth of the hole, $2(\alpha c - 40t\varepsilon)$, includes a small approximation, which is now explained.

In principle, the 'hole' should have zero depth when α, c, t and ε are such that the web is on the boundary between Class 2 and Class 3. When $\alpha > 0.5$ (as is usual), and from Table 5.2 of EN 1993-1-1, this is when

$$\alpha c/t\varepsilon = 456\alpha/(13\alpha - 1)$$

As α increases from 0.5 to 1.0, the right-hand side of this equation reduces from 41.4 to 38. For $\alpha < 0.5$, it is 41.5. For simplicity, it is taken as 40 for all values of α, so that the depth of web in compression can be defined as $40t\varepsilon$, in blocks of depth $20t\varepsilon$ above and below the hole.

The original depth in compression, αc, is reduced to $40t\varepsilon$. For equilibrium, the depth in tension must be reduced by $\alpha c - 40t\varepsilon$, so the plastic neutral axis moves up by this amount, as shown in Fig. 6.6(a), and the depth of the hole is thus $2(\alpha c - 40t\varepsilon)$.

Other useful results for a symmetrical steel section are as follows. The depth of web in compression, $40t\varepsilon$, includes the depth needed to balance the tensile force in the reinforcement, which is

$$h_r = A_s f_{sd}/t f_{yd} \tag{D6.5}$$

The tension in the top flange, including web fillets, balances the compression in the bottom flange, so for longitudinal equilibrium the depth of web in tension is

$$h_t = 40t\varepsilon - h_r \tag{D6.6}$$

The total depth of the web is c, so the depth of the hole is

$$h_h = c - 40t\varepsilon - h_t = c - 80t\varepsilon + h_r \tag{D6.7}$$

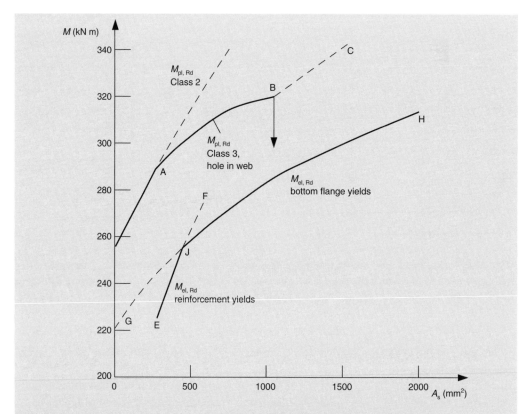

Fig. 6.7. Influence of longitudinal reinforcement on hogging moments of resistance

Data and results
Data for the calculations, in addition to the dimensions shown in Fig. 6.6, are:

- structural steel: $f_y = 355$ N/mm², $\gamma_M = 1.0$, so $f_{yd} = 355$ N/mm²
- reinforcement: $f_{sk} = 500$ N/mm², $\gamma_S = 1.15$, so $f_{sd} = 435$ N/mm²
- steel section: 406×140 UB39 with $A_a = 4940$ mm², $I_a = 124.5 \times 10^6$ mm⁴.

The upper limit chosen for A_s corresponds to a reinforcement ratio of 1.5%, which is quite high for a beam in a building, in a flange with $b_{eff} = 1.5$ m. If there were no profiled sheeting (which plays no part in these calculations) the ratio for the 150 mm slab would be 0.8%, and there would be two layers of bars. For simplicity, one layer of bars is assumed here, with propped construction.
The full results are shown in Fig. 6.7. Typical calculations only are given here.

Classification of the cross-section
Clause 5.5.1(1)P refers to EN 1993-1-1, where Table 5.2 applies. For $f_y = 355$ N/mm², it gives $\varepsilon = 0.81$.
For the bottom flange,

$$c = (142 - 6.3)/2 - 10.2 = 57.6 \text{ mm}$$

$$c/t\varepsilon = 57.6/(8.6 \times 0.81) = 8.3$$

This is less than 9, so the flange is in Class 1, irrespective of the area of slab reinforcement.
The web depth between fillets is $c = 360$ mm, so

$$c/t\varepsilon = 360/(6.3 \times 0.81) = 70.5$$

This is less than 72, so when $A_s = 0$, the web is in Class 1. Addition of reinforcement increases the depth of web in compression, so its class depends on A_s. Here, $\alpha > 0.5$, and from Table 5.2 in EN 1993-1-1 the limit for Class 2 is

$$c/t\varepsilon = 456/(13\alpha - 1)$$

For $c/t\varepsilon = 70.5$ this gives $\alpha = 0.574$. It will be shown that this corresponds to $A_s = 267$ mm^2, by calculating $M_{pl, Rd}$ by the methods for both a Class 2 and a Class 3 section.

$M_{pl, Rd}$ for Class 2 section with $A_s = 267$ mm^2

The stress blocks for the web are shown in Fig. 6.6(b).

(1) Find $M_{pl, a, Rd}$ for the steel section. For a rolled section, the plastic section modulus is usually found from tables. Here,

$$W_{pl} = 0.721 \times 10^6 \text{ mm}^3$$

so

$$M_{pl, a, Rd} = 0.721 \times 355 = 256 \text{ kN m}$$

(2) Find F_s, the force in the reinforcement at yield:

$$F_s = 267 \times 0.435 = 116 \text{ kN}$$

From equation (D6.5), the depth of web for this force is

$$h_r = 116/(6.3 \times 0.355) = 52 \text{ mm}$$

To balance the force F_s, the stress in a depth of web $h_r/2$ changes from $+f_{yd}$ to $-f_{yd}$. This is shown as ABCD in Fig. 6.6.

(3) The lever arm for the forces F_s is 286 mm, so taking moments,

$$M_{pl, Rd} = 256 + 116 \times 0.286 = \textbf{289 kN m}$$

$M_{pl, Rd}$ for Class 3 section with $A_s = 267$ mm^2

The hole-in-web method is now used. Steps 1 and 2 are as above.

(3) The contribution of the web is deducted from $M_{pl, a, Rd}$:

$$M_{pl, a, flanges} = 256 - 0.36^2 \times 6.3 \times 355/4 = 183.5 \text{ kN m}$$

(This value is not calculated directly because of the complex shape of each 'flange' which includes the web fillets, or, for a plate girder, a small depth of web.)

(4) From equation (D6.7), the depth of the hole is

$$h_h = 360 - 408 + 52 = 4 \text{ mm}$$

(5) From equation (D6.6), the depth of web in tension is

$$h_t = 204 - 52 = 152 \text{ mm}$$

and the force in it is

$$F_t = 152 \times 6.3 \times 0.355 = 340 \text{ kN}$$

(6) The stress blocks in the web are shown in Fig. 6.6(c). Taking moments about the bottom of the slab,

$$M_{pl, Rd} = 183.5 + 116 \times 0.1 - 340 \times 0.095 + 228(0.222 + 0.328) = \textbf{288 kN m}$$

This agrees with the result for the Class 2 member, point A in Fig. 6.7, because this section is at the class boundary. Hence, the depth of the hole is close to zero.

$M_{pl, Rd}$ for $A_s > 267$ mm^2

Similar calculations for higher values of A_s give curve AB in Fig. 6.7, with increasing depths of hole until, at $A_s = 1048$ mm^2, the new plastic neutral axis reaches the top of the web, $h_t = 0$, and the hole reaches its maximum depth. Further increase in A_s, ΔA_s say, causes changes of stress within the top flange only. Taking moments about the interface, it is evident that the plastic bending resistance is increased by

$$\Delta M_{pl, Rd} \approx \Delta A_s f_{yd} h_s$$

where h_s is the height of the reinforcement above the interface, 100 mm here. This is shown by line BC in Fig. 6.7.

The bending resistance given by this method no longer approaches that given by elastic theory (as it should, as the slenderness of the web in compression approaches the Class 3/4 boundary). Use of the method with the new plastic neutral axis in the top flange is excluded by Eurocode 3, as explained in comments on *clause 5.5.2(3)*. It is, in any case, not recommended because:

- the authors are not aware of any experimental validation for this situation (which is uncommon in practice)
- $M_{pl, Rd}$ is being calculated using a model where the compressive strain in the steel bottom flange is so high that the rotation capacity associated with a Class 2 section may not be available.

Equation (D6.6) shows that this restriction is equivalent to placing an upper limit of $40t\varepsilon$ on h_r. Any slab reinforcement that increases h_t above this value moves the section back into Class 3. This can also be a consequence of vertical shear, as illustrated in Example 6.2.

This point is relevant to the writing of software based on the code because software, once written, tends to be used blindly.

Elastic resistance to bending

For simplicity, $M_{el, Rd}$ has been calculated assuming propped construction. The stress in the reinforcement governs until A_s reaches 451 mm^2 (point J), after which $M_{el, Rd}$ is determined by yield of the bottom flange. This is shown by curves EF and GH in Fig. 6.7.

Web in Class 4

The hole-in-web method is available only for webs in Class 3, so in principle a check should be made that the web is not in Class 4, using the elastic stress distribution. A Class 4 web can occur in a plate girder, but is most unlikely in a rolled I- or H-section. In this example, the Class 3/4 boundary is reached at $A_s = 3720$ mm^2.

6.2.2. Resistance to vertical shear

Clause 6.2.2

Clause 6.2.2 is for beams without web encasement. The whole of the vertical shear is usually assumed to be resisted by the steel section, as in previous codes for composite beams. This enables the design rules of EN 1993-1-1, and EN 1993-1-5[30] where necessary, to be used. The assumption can be conservative where the slab is in compression. Even where it is in tension and cracked in flexure, consideration of equilibrium shows that the slab must make some contribution to shear resistance, except where the reinforcement has yielded. For solid slabs, the effect is significant where the depth of the steel beam is only twice that of the slab,[50] but diminishes as this ratio increases.

In composite plate girders with vertical stiffeners, the concrete slab can contribute to the anchorage of a tension field in the web,[51] but the shear connectors must then be designed for vertical forces (*clause 6.2.2.3(2)*). The simpler alternative is to follow Eurocode 3, ignoring both the interaction with the slab and vertical tension across the interface.

Clause 6.2.2.3(2)

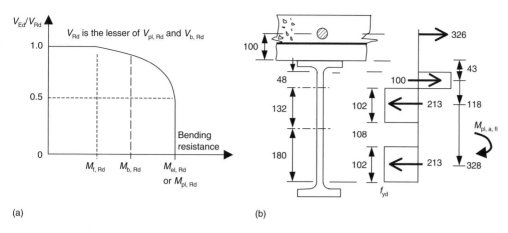

Fig. 6.8. Resistance to bending and vertical shear (dimensions in mm)

Bending and vertical shear

The methods of *clause 6.2.2.4* are summarized in Fig. 6.8. Shear stress does not significantly reduce bending resistance unless the shear is quite high. For this reason, the interaction may be neglected until the shear force exceeds half of the shear resistance (*clause 6.2.2.4(1)*). *Clause 6.2.2.4*

Both EN 1993-1-1 and EN 1994-1-1 use a parabolic interaction curve. In *clause 6.2.2.4(2)* the reduction factor for the design yield strength of the web is $(1 - \rho)$, where *Clause 6.2.2.4(1)* *Clause 6.2.2.4(2)*

$$\rho = [(2V_{Ed}/V_{Rd}) - 1]^2 \tag{6.5}$$

and V_{Rd} is the resistance in shear. For a design shear force equal to V_{Rd}, the bending resistance is that provided by the flanges alone, denoted $M_{f,Rd}$. This is calculated in Example 6.2.

The bending resistance at $V_{Ed} = 0$ may be the elastic or the plastic value, depending on the class of the cross-section. Where it is reduced to $M_{b,Rd}$ by lateral–torsional buckling, interaction between bending and shear does not begin until a higher shear force than $V_{Rd}/2$ is present, as shown in Fig. 6.8(a).

Where the shear resistance V_{Rd} is less than the plastic resistance to shear, $V_{pl,Rd}$, because of shear buckling, *clause 6.2.2.4(2)* replaces $V_{pl,Rd}$ by the shear buckling resistance $V_{b,Rd}$.

Where the design yield strength of the web is reduced to allow for vertical shear, the effect on a Class 3 section in hogging bending is to increase the depth of web in compression. If the change is small, the hole-in-web model can still be used, as shown in Example 6.2. For a higher shear force, the new plastic neutral axis may be within the top flange, and the hole-in-web method is inapplicable.

The section is then treated as Class 3 or 4, and *clause 6.2.2.4(3)* applies. It refers to EN 1993-1-5. For beams, the rule given there is essentially *Clause 6.2.2.4(3)*

$$M_{Ed}/M_{Rd} + (1 - M_{f,Rd}/M_{pl,Rd})(2V_{Ed}/V_{Rd} - 1)^2 \le 1 \tag{D6.8}$$

These symbols relate to the steel section only. For a composite section, longitudinal stresses are found by elastic theory. These lead to values of M_{Ed}, N_{Ed} and V_{Ed} acting on the steel section, which is then checked to EN 1993-1-5. It is fairly easy to check if a given combination of these action effects can be resisted – but calculation of bending resistance for a given vertical shear is difficult.

Example 6.2: resistance to bending and vertical shear

Vertical shear is more likely to reduce resistance to bending in a continuous beam than in a simply-supported one, and it is instructive to consider its influence on a beam with bending resistance found by the hole-in-web method. Where the web is not susceptible to shear buckling, the application of *clause 6.2.2.4* is straightforward. This example is therefore based on one of the few UB sections where web buckling can occur, if S355 steel is used. It is the section used in Example 6.1, 406 × 140 UB39, shown in Fig. 6.6, with longitudinal reinforcement of area $A_s = 750$ mm^2.

The bending resistance will be calculated when the design vertical shear is $V_{Ed} = 300$ kN. All other data are as in Example 6.1.

From EN 1993-1-1, resistance to shear buckling must be checked if $h_w/t_w > 72\varepsilon/\eta$, where η is a factor for which EN 1993-1-5 recommends the value 1.2. These clauses are usually applied to plate girders, for which h_w is the clear depth between the flanges. Ignoring the corner fillets of this rolled section, $h_w = 381$ mm, and for S355 steel, $\varepsilon = 0.81$, so

$$h_w \eta / t_w \varepsilon = 381 \times 1.2/(6.3 \times 0.81) = 90.5$$

The resistance of this unstiffened web to shear buckling is found using clauses 5.2 and 5.3 of EN 1993-1-5, assuming a web of area $h_w t_w$, that there is no contribution from the flanges, and that there are transverse stiffeners at the supports. The result is

$$V_{b, Rd} = 475 \text{ kN}$$

which is 85% of $V_{pl, Rd}$, as found by the method of EN 1993-1-1 for a rolled I-section. From *clause 6.2.2.4(2)*,

$$\rho = [(2V_{Ed}/V_{Rd}) - 1]^2 = (600/475 - 1)^2 = 0.068$$

The reduced yield strength of the web is $(1 - 0.068) \times 355 = 331$ N/mm^2. For hogging bending, the tensile force in the reinforcement is

$$F_s = 750 \times 0.5/1.15 = 326 \text{ kN} \tag{D6.9}$$

From plastic theory, the depth of web in compression that is above the neutral axis of the I-section is

$$326/(2 \times 0.331 \times 6.3) = 78 \text{ mm}$$

This places the cross-section in Class 3, so the hole-in-web method is applied. From Fig. 6.6(a), the depth of the compressive stress-blocks in the web is $20t\varepsilon$. The value for ε should be based on the full yield strength of the web, not on the reduced yield strength, so each block is 102 mm deep, as in Fig. 6.6(c). The use of the reduced yield strength would increase ε and so reduce the depth of the 'hole' in the web, which would be unconservative. However, the force in each stress block should be found using the reduced yield strength, and so is now

$$228 \times 331/355 = 213 \text{ kN}$$

The tensile force in the web is therefore

$$2 \times 213 - 326 = 100 \text{ kN}$$

and the longitudinal forces are as shown in Fig. 6.8(b).

From Example 6.1,

$$M_{pl, a, flanges} = 183.5 \text{ kN m}$$

Taking moments about the bottom of the slab,

$$\begin{aligned} M_{pl, Rd} &= 183.5 + 326 \times 0.1 + 213(0.118 + 0.328) - 100 \times 0.043 \\ &= 307 \text{ kN m} \end{aligned} \tag{D6.10}$$

For this cross-section in bending only, the method of Example 6.1, with $A_s = 750$ mm^2, gives

$$M_{pl, Rd} = 314 \text{ kN m}$$

The alternative to this method would be to use elastic theory. The result would then depend on the method of construction.

6.3. Resistance of cross-sections of beams for buildings with partial encasement

Encasement in concrete of the webs of steel beams is normally done before erection, casting one side at a time. This obviously increases the cost of fabrication, transport and erection, but when it satisfies *clause 5.5.3(2)* it has many advantages for design:

- it provides complete fire resistance for the web and, with longitudinal reinforcement, compensation for the weakness of the bottom flange in fire, in accordance with EN 1994-1-2[52]
- it enables a Class 3 web to be upgraded to Class 2, and the slenderness limit for a Class 2 compression flange to be increased by 40% (*clause 5.5.3*)
- it widens significantly the range of steel sections that are not susceptible to lateral–torsional buckling (*clause 6.4.3(1)(h)*)
- it increases resistance to vertical shear, to *clause 6.3.3(2)*
- it improves resistance to combined bending and shear, to *clause 6.3.4(2)*
- it improves resistance to buckling in shear, *clause 6.3.3(1)*.

6.3.1. Scope

To avoid shear buckling, ***clause 6.3.1(2)*** limits the slenderness of the encased web to $d/t_w \leq 124\varepsilon$. In practice, with encasement, steel sections in buildings are almost certain to be in Class 1 or 2. *Clause 6.3* is applicable only to these.

Clause 6.3.1(2)

6.3.2. Resistance to bending

The rules for resistance to bending, ***clause 6.3.2***, correspond to those for uncased sections of the same class, except that lateral–torsional buckling is not mentioned in ***clause 6.3.2(2)***. Encasement greatly improves resistance to lateral–torsional buckling. Example 6.3, the comments on *clause 6.4.2(7)*, and pp. 153–154 of Johnson and Molenstra,[44] are relevant. However, it is possible for a beam within the scope of *clause 6.3* to be susceptible; a web-encased IPE 450 section in S420 steel is an example. Continuous beams that do not satisfy *clause 6.4.3* should therefore be checked.

Clause 6.3.2
Clause 6.3.2(2)

Partial shear connection is permitted for a concrete flange, but not for web encasement. The resistance to longitudinal shear provided by studs within the encasement is found in the usual way, but no guidance is given on the contribution from bars that pass through holes in the web or stirrups welded to the web, in accordance with *clauses 5.5.3(2)* and *6.3.3(2)*. They are provided to ensure the integrity of the encased section.

The load–slip properties of different types of shear connection should be compatible (*clause 6.6.1.1(6)P*). It is known from research on 'Perfobond' shear connectors (longitudinal flange plates projecting into the slab, with holes through which bars pass) that these bars provide shear connection with good slip properties,[53,54] so a contribution from them could be used here; but welds to stirrups may be too brittle.

6.3.3–6.3.4. Resistance to vertical shear, and to bending and vertical shear

The rules in ***clause 6.3.3*** are based on the concept of superposition of resistances of composite and reinforced concrete members. This concept has been used in Japan for decades, in design of structures for earthquake resistance. The shear connection must be designed to ensure that the shear force is shared between the steel web and the concrete encasement. The references to EN 1992-1-1 are intended to ensure that the web encasement retains its shear resistance at a shear strain sufficient to cause yielding of the steel web.

Clause 6.3.3

Clause 6.3.3(1) shows that no account need be taken of web buckling in shear. Moment–shear interaction is treated in ***clause 6.3.4*** in a manner consistent with the rules for uncased sections.

Clause 6.3.3(1)
Clause 6.3.4

6.4. Lateral–torsional buckling of composite beams

6.4.1. General

Clause 6.4.1(1)

It is assumed in this section that in completed structures for buildings, the steel top flanges of all composite beams will be stabilized laterally by connection to a concrete or composite slab (*clause 6.4.1(1)*). The rules on maximum spacing of connectors in *clauses 6.6.5.5(1)* and *6.6.5.5(2)* relate to the classification of the top flange, and thus only to local buckling. For lateral–torsional buckling, the relevant rule, given in *clause 6.6.5.5(3)*, is less restrictive.

Clause 6.4.1(2)

Any steel top flange in compression that is not so stabilized should be checked for lateral buckling (*clause 6.4.1(2)*) using clause 6.3.2 of EN 1993-1-1. This applies particularly during unpropped construction. In a long span, it may be necessary to check a steel beam that is composite along only part of its length. The general method of *clause 6.4.2*, based on the use of a computed value of the elastic critical moment M_{cr}, is applicable, but no detailed guidance on the calculation of M_{cr} is given in either EN 1993-1-1 or EN 1994-1-1. Buckling of web-encased beams without a concrete flange has been studied.[55] However, for buildings, the construction phase is rarely critical in practice, because the loading is so much less than the design total load.

Steel bottom flanges are in compression only in cantilevers and continuous beams. The length in compression may include most of the span, when that span is lightly loaded and both adjacent spans are fully loaded. Bottom flanges in compression should always be restrained laterally at supports (*clause 6.4.3(1)(f)* is relevant). It should not be assumed that a point of contraflexure is equivalent to a lateral restraint.

In a composite beam, the concrete slab provides lateral restraint to the steel member, and also restrains its rotation about a longitudinal axis. Lateral buckling is always associated with distortion (change of shape) of the cross-section. Design methods for composite beams must take account of the bending of the web, Fig. 6.9(b). They differ in detail from the method of clause 6.3.2 of EN 1993-1-1, but the same imperfection factors and buckling curves are used, in the absence of any better-established alternatives.

Clause 6.4.1(3)

The reference in *clause 6.4.1(3)* to EN 1993-1-1 provides a general method for use where neither of the methods of EN 1994-1-1 are applicable (e.g. for a Class 4 beam).

6.4.2. Verification of lateral–torsional buckling of continuous composite beams with cross-sections in Class 1, 2 and 3 for buildings

This general method of design is written with distortional buckling of bottom flanges in mind. It would not apply, for example, to a mid-span cross-section of a beam with the slab at bottom-flange level (see Fig. 6.2). Although not stated, it is implied that the span concerned is of uniform composite section, excluding minor changes such as reinforcement details and effects of cracking of concrete. The use of this method for a two-span beam is illustrated in Example 6.7.

Clause 6.4.2(1)

Clause 6.4.2(2)
Clause 6.4.2(3)

The method is based closely on clause 6.3.2 of EN 1993-1-1. There is correspondence in the definitions of the reduction factor χ_{LT} (*clause 6.4.2(1)*) and the relative slenderness, $\bar{\lambda}_{LT}$ (*clause 6.4.2(4)*). The reduction factor is applied to the design resistance moment M_{Rd}, which is defined in *clauses 6.4.2(1)* to *6.4.2(3)*. Expressions for M_{Rd} include the design yield strength f_{yd}. The reference in these clauses to the use of γ_{M1} is provided because this is a check on instability. The recommended values for γ_{M0} and γ_{M1} are the same (1.0), but a National Annex could define different values.

The determination of M_{Rd} for a Class 3 section differs from that of $M_{el, Rd}$ in *clause 6.2.1.4(6)* only in that the limiting stress f_{cd} for concrete in compression need not be considered. It is necessary to take account of the method of construction.

The buckling resistance moment $M_{b, Rd}$ given by *equation (6.6)* must exceed the highest applied moment M_{Ed} within the unbraced length of compression flange considered.

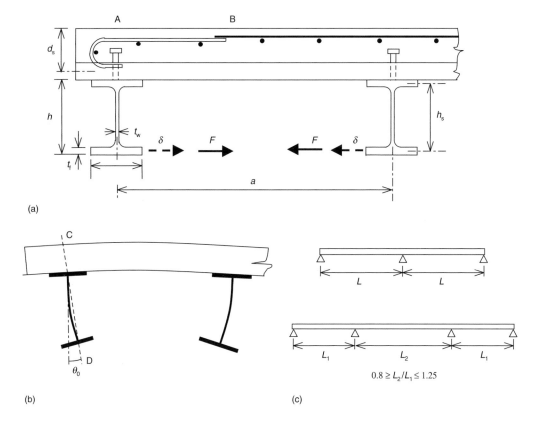

Fig. 6.9. U-frame action and distortional lateral buckling

Lateral buckling for a Class 3 cross-section with unpropped construction
The influence of method of construction on the verification of a Class 3 composite section for lateral buckling is as follows. From *equation (6.4)*

$$M_{Rd} = M_{el, Rd} = M_{a, Ed} + kM_{c, Ed} \qquad \text{(a)}$$

where the subscript c indicates the action effect on the composite member.
From *equation (6.6)* the verification is

$$M_{Ed} = M_{a, Ed} + M_{c, Ed} \le \chi_{LT} M_{el, Rd} \qquad \text{(b)}$$

which is

$$\chi_{LT} \ge (M_{a, Ed} + M_{c, Ed})/M_{el, Rd} = M_{Ed}/M_{el, Rd} \qquad \text{(c)}$$

The total hogging bending moment M_{Ed} may be almost independent of the method of construction. However, the stress limit that determines $M_{el, Rd}$ may be different for propped and unpropped construction. If it is bottom-flange compression in both cases, then $M_{el, Rd}$ is lower for unpropped construction, and the limit on χ_{LT} from equation (c) is more severe.

Elastic critical buckling moment
Clause 6.4.2(4) requires the determination of the elastic critical buckling moment, taking account of the relevant restraints, so their stiffnesses have to be calculated. The lateral restraint from the slab can usually be assumed to be rigid. Where the structure is such that a pair of steel beams and a concrete flange attached to them can be modelled as an inverted-U frame (*Fig. 6.11*), continuous along the span, the rotational restraining stiffness at top-flange level, k_s, can be found from **clauses 6.4.2(5)** to **6.4.2(7)**.

Clause 6.4.2(5) gives conditions that define this frame. Analysis is based on its stiffness per unit length, k_s, given by the ratio F/δ, where δ is the lateral displacement caused by a force F (Fig. 6.9(a)). The flexibility δ/F is the sum of flexibilities due to:

Clause 6.4.2(4)

Clause 6.4.2(5)
Clause 6.4.2(6)
Clause 6.4.2(7)

- bending of the slab, which may not be negligible: $1/k_1$ from *equation* (6.9)
- bending of the steel web, which predominates: $1/k_2$ from *equation* (6.10)
- flexibility of the shear connection.

It has been found[56] that this last flexibility can be neglected in design to EN 1994-1-1. This leads to *equation* (6.8) for stiffness k_s.

This 'continuous U-frame' concept has long been used in the design of steel bridges.[57] There is a similar 'discrete U-frame' concept, which would be relevant to composite beams if the steel sections had vertical web stiffeners. The shear connectors closest to those stiffeners would then have to transmit almost the whole of the bending moment *Fh* (Fig. 6.9(a)), where *F* is now a force on a discrete U-frame. The last of the three flexibilities listed above might then not be negligible, nor is it certain that the shear connection and the adjacent slab would be sufficiently strong.[58] Where stiffeners are present, the resistance of the connection above each stiffener to repeated transverse bending should be established, as there is a risk of local shear failure within the slab. There is at present no simple method of verification. The words 'may be unstiffened' in *clause 6.4.3(1)(f)* are misleading, as the resistance model is based on both theory and research on unstiffened webs. It should, in the authors' opinion, read '*should be unstiffened*'. The problem is avoided in bridge design by using transverse steel members, such as U- or H-frames (Fig. 6.10(a)).

The conditions in *clause 6.4.3(1)* referred to from *clause 6.4.2(5)* are commonly satisfied in buildings by the beams that support composite slabs; but where these are secondary beams, the method is not applicable to the primary beams because condition (*e*) is not satisfied. Bottom flanges of primary beams can sometimes be stabilized by bracing from the secondary beams.

The calculation of k_s is straightforward, apart from finding $(EI)_2$, the cracked flexural stiffness of a composite slab. An approximate method, used in Example 6.7, is derived in Appendix A.

Concrete-encased web

Clause 6.4.2(7)
Clause 6.4.2(9)

Clauses 6.4.2(7) and *6.4.2(9)* allow for the additional stiffness provided by web encasement. This is significant: for rolled steel sections, k_2 from *equation* (6.11) is from 10 to 40 times the value from *equation* (6.10), depending on the ratio of flange breadth to web thickness. Encasement will often remove any susceptibility to lateral–torsional buckling. The model used for *equation* (6.11) is explained in Appendix A.

Theory for the continuous inverted-U frame model

A formula for the elastic critical buckling moment for the U-frame model was given in Annex B of ENV 1994-1-1,[49] but was removed from EN 1994-1-1, as it was considered to be 'textbook material'. However, it is sufficiently unfamiliar to be worth giving here.

Subject to conditions discussed below, the elastic critical buckling moment at an internal support of a continuous beam is

$$M_{cr} = (k_c C_4/L)[(G_a I_{at} + k_s L^2/\pi^2)E_a I_{afz}]^{1/2} \tag{D6.11}$$

where: k_c is a property of the composite section, given below,
C_4 is a property of the distribution of bending moment within length L,
G_a is the shear modulus for steel ($G_a = E_a/[2(1 + \upsilon)] = 80.8 \text{ kN/mm}^2$),
I_{at} is the torsional moment of area of the steel section,
k_s is the rotational stiffness defined in *clause 6.4.2(6)*,
L is the length of the beam between points at which the bottom flange of the steel member is laterally restrained (typically, the span length), and
I_{afz} is the minor-axis second moment of area of the steel bottom flange.

Where the cross-section of the steel member is symmetrical about both axes, the factor k_c is given by

$$k_c = (h_s I_y/I_{ay})/[(h_s^2/4 + i_x^2)/e + h_s] \tag{D6.12}$$

with

$$e = AI_{ay}/[A_a z_c(A - A_a)] \tag{D6.13}$$

where: h_s is the distance between the centres of the flanges of the steel section,

I_y is the second moment of area for major-axis bending of the cracked composite section of area A,

I_{ay} is the corresponding second moment of area of the steel section,

$i_x^2 = (I_{ay} + I_{az})/A_a$, where I_{az} and A_a are properties of the steel section, and

z_c is the distance between the centroid of the steel beam and the mid-depth of the slab.

Four of the conditions for the use of these formulae are given in *paragraphs (c)* to *(f)* of *clause 6.4.3(1)*. Three further conditions were given in ENV 1994-1-1. These related to the resistance of the slab part of the U-frame to hogging transverse bending in the plane of the U-frame, to its flexural stiffness, and to the spacing of shear connectors. It is now considered that other requirements are such that these will, in practice, be satisfied. Further explanation is given in Appendix A.

The coefficient C_4 was given in a set of tables, determined by numerical analyses, in which its range is 6.2–47.6. These values are given in Appendix A (see Figs A.3 and A.4). The coefficient accounts for the increased resistance to lateral buckling where the bending moment is not uniform along the member. When checking lateral stability, the distribution of bending moments corresponding to C_4 must be used as the action effects, and not an equivalent uniform value. The calculation method is shown in Example 6.7.

Alternative theory for the elastic critical moment

There is an analogy between the differential equations for distortional lateral buckling, taking account of restraint to warping, and those for a compressed member on an elastic foundation. This has led[59] to an alternative expression for the elastic critical moment. Like equation (D6.11), its use requires computed values that depend on the bending-moment distribution and, for this method, also on the parameter

$$\eta_B^2 = k_s L^4/(E_a I_{\omega D})$$

where k_s, L and E_a are as above, and $I_{\omega D}$ is the sectorial moment of inertia of the steel member related to the centre of the restrained steel flange. Four graphs of these values are given in Hanswille,[59] and a more general set in Hanswille *et al.*[60]

Predictions of M_{cr} by this method and by equation (D6.11) were compared with results of finite-element analyses, for beams with IPE 500 and HEA 1000 rolled sections. This method was found to agree with the finite-element results for both internal and external spans. Equation (D6.11) was found to be satisfactory for internal spans, but to be less accurate generally for external spans, and unconservative by over 30% in some cases. This suggests that it needs further validation.

6.4.3. Simplified verification for buildings without direct calculation

As calculations for the U-frame model are quite extensive, a simplified method has been developed from it. *Clause 6.4.3(1)* defines continuous beams and cantilevers that may be designed without lateral bracing to the bottom flange, except at supports. Its *Table 6.1* gives limits to the steel grade and overall depth of the steel member, provided that it is an IPE or HE rolled section. The contribution from partial encasement is allowed for in *paragraph (h)* of this clause.

Clause 6.4.3(1)

These results are derived from equation (D6.11) for the elastic critical buckling moment, making assumptions that further reduce the scope of the method. Accounts of its origin are available in both English[61] and German.[62] It is outlined in Johnson and Fan,[56] and is similar to that used in the treatment of lateral–torsional buckling of haunched beams.[63]

The basis is that there shall be no reduction, due to lateral buckling, in the resistance of the beam to hogging bending. It is assumed that this is achieved when $\bar{\lambda}_{LT} \leq 0.4$. This value is given in a Note to clause 6.3.2.3 of EN 1993-1-1, which can be modified by a National Annex. Any National Annex that defines a lower limit should therefore also state if the method is permitted.

The slenderness $\bar{\lambda}_{LT}$ is a function of the variation of bending moment along the span. This was studied using various loadings on continuous beams of the types shown in Fig. 6.9(c), and on beams with cantilevers. The limitations in *paragraphs* (*a*) and (*b*) of *clause 6.4.3(1)* on spans and loading result from this work.

Simplified expression for $\bar{\lambda}_{LT}$, and use of British UB rolled sections
Table 6.1 applies only to IPE and HE rolled sections. Criteria for other rolled I- and H-sections are deduced in Appendix A. The basis for the method is as follows.

For uncased beams that satisfy the conditions that apply to equation (D6.11) for M_{cr}, have a double symmetrical steel section, and are not concrete encased, the slenderness ratio for a Class 1 or Class 2 cross-section may conservatively be taken as

$$\bar{\lambda}_{LT} = 5.0\left(1 + \frac{t_w h_s}{4 b_f t_f}\right)\left(\frac{h_s}{t_w}\right)^{0.75}\left(\frac{t_f}{b_f}\right)^{0.25}\left(\frac{f_y}{E_a C_4}\right)^{0.5} \tag{D6.14}$$

The derivation from equation (D6.11) is given in Appendix A. Most of the terms in equation (D6.14) define properties of the steel I-section; b_f is the breadth of the bottom flange, and other symbols are as in Fig. 6.9(a).

To check if a particular section qualifies for 'simplified verification', a section parameter F is calculated. From equation (D6.14), it is

$$F = \left(1 + \frac{t_w h_s}{4 b_f t_f}\right)\left(\frac{h_s}{t_w}\right)^{0.75}\left(\frac{t_f}{b_f}\right)^{0.25} \tag{D6.15}$$

Limiting values of F, F_{lim} say, are given in Appendix A (see Fig. A.5) for the nominal steel grades listed in Table 6.1. The horizontal 'S' line at or next above the plotted point F gives the highest grade of steel for which the method of *clause 6.3.3* can be used for that section.

Some examples are given in Table 6.1, with the values of F_{lim} in the column headings. Many of the heavier wide-flange sections in S275 steel qualify for verification without direct calculation, but few UB sections in S355 steel do so.

In ENV 1994-1-1, verification without direct calculation was permitted for hot-rolled sections of 'similar shape' to IPE and HE sections, that conformed to Table 6.1 and a geometrical condition similar to the limit on F. In EN 1994-1-1 this has been replaced by a reference to National Annexes.

Use of UB rolled sections with encased webs to clause 5.5.3(2)
It is shown in Appendix A (equation (DA.4)) that the effect of web encasement is to increase F_{lim} by at least 29%. All the sections shown in Table 6.1 now qualify for S275 steel, and all

Table 6.1. Qualification of some UB rolled steel sections for verification of lateral–torsional stability, in a composite beam, without direct calculation

Section	Right-hand side of expression (D6.15)	S275 steel, uncased (13.9)	S355 steel, uncased (12.3)	S275 steel, cased (18.0)	S355 steel, cased (15.8)
457 × 152 UB52	16.4	No	No	Yes	No
457 × 152 UB67	14.9	No	No	Yes	Yes
457 × 191 UB67	13.6	Yes	No	Yes	Yes
457 × 191 UB98	11.8	Yes	Yes	Yes	Yes
533 × 210 UB82	14.4	No	No	Yes	Yes
533 × 210 UB122	12.5	Yes	No	Yes	Yes
610 × 229 UB125	14.1	No	No	Yes	Yes
610 × 229 UB140	13.5	Yes	No	Yes	Yes
610 × 305 UB149	12.2	Yes	Yes	Yes	Yes
610 × 305 UB238	9.83	Yes	Yes	Yes	Yes

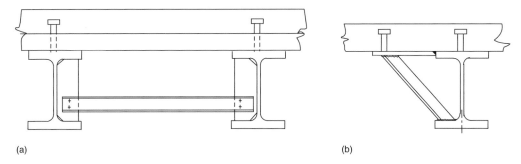

(a)   (b)

Fig. 6.10. Laterally restrained bottom flanges

except one do so for S355 steel. Web encasement is thus an effective option for improving the lateral stability of a rolled steel section in a continuous composite beam.

The method of *clause 6.4.2* should be used where the steel section does not qualify.

Use of intermediate lateral bracing

Where the buckling resistance moment $M_{b, Rd}$ as found by one of the preceding methods is significantly less than the design resistance moment M_{Rd} of the cross-sections concerned, it may be cost-effective to provide discrete lateral restraint to the steel bottom flange. Where the slab is composite, a steel cross-member may be needed (Fig. 6.10(a)), but for solid slabs, other solutions are possible (e.g. Fig. 6.10(b)).

Clause 6.3.2.1(2) of EN 1993-1-1 refers to 'beams with sufficient restraint to the compression flange', but does not define 'sufficient'. A Note to clause 6.3.2.4(3) of EN 1993-1-1 refers to Annex BB.3 in that EN standard for buckling of components of building structures 'with restraints'. Clause BB.3.2(1) gives the minimum 'stable length between lateral restraints', but this is intended to apply to lateral–torsional buckling, and may not be appropriate for distortional buckling. Further provisions for steel structures are given in EN 1993-2.[64]

There is no guidance in EN 1994-1-1 on the minimum strength or stiffness that a lateral restraint must have. There is guidance in Lawson and Rackham,[63] based on BS 5950: Part 1, clause 4.3.2.[65] This states that a discrete restraint should be designed for 2% of the *maximum* compressive force in the flange. It is suggested[63] that where discrete and continuous restraints act together, as in a composite beam, the design force can be reduced to 1% of the force in the flange. Provision of discrete bracing to make up a deficiency in continuous restraint is attractive in principle, but the relative stiffness of the two types of restraint must be such that they are effective in parallel.

Another proposal is to relate the restraining force to the total compression in the flange and the web at the cross-section where the bracing is provided, to take advantage of the steep moment gradient in a region of hogging bending.

In tests at the University of Warwick,[66] bracings that could resist 1% of the total compression, defined in this way, were found to be effective. The calculation of this compressive force involves an elastic analysis of the section, not otherwise needed, and the rule is unsafe near points of contraflexure. There is at present no simple design method better than the 2% rule quoted above, which can be over-conservative. An elastic analysis can be avoided by taking the stress in the flange as the yield stress.

The design methods based on equation (D6.11) for M_{cr} work well for complete spans, but become unsatisfactory (over-conservative) for short lengths of beam between lateral bracings. This is because the correct values of the factors C_4 are functions of the length between lateral restraints. For simplicity, only the minimum values of C_4 are given in the figures in Appendix B of this guide. They are applicable where the half-wavelength of a buckle is less than the length L in equation (D6.11). This is always so where L is a complete span, but where L is part of a span, the value given may be over-conservative. This is

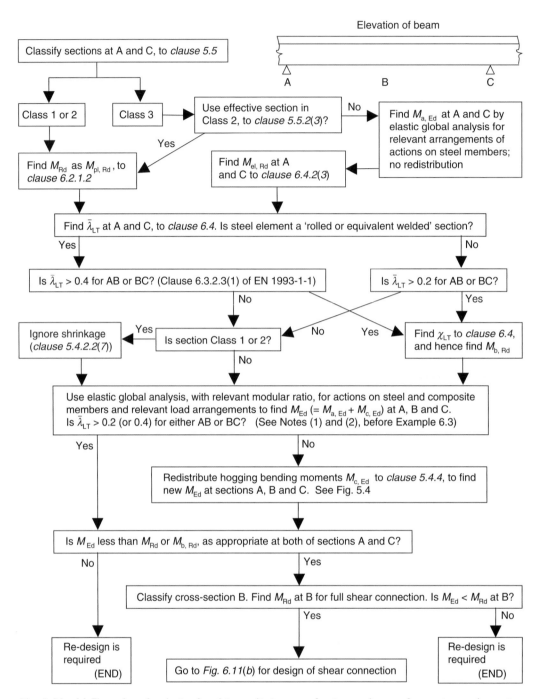

Fig. 6.11. (a) Flow chart for design for ultimate limit state of an internal span of a continuous beam in a building, with uniform steel section and no cross-sections in Class 4

illustrated at the end of Example 6.7, where the effect of providing lateral bracing is examined.

Flow charts for continuous beam
The flow charts in Fig. 6.11 cover some aspects of design of an internal span of a continuous composite beam. Their scope is limited to cross-sections in Class 1, 2 or 3, an uncased web, a uniform steel section, and no flexural interaction with supporting members. It is assumed that for lateral–torsional buckling, the simplified method of *clause 6.4.3* is not applicable. Figure 6.11(a) refers to the following notes:

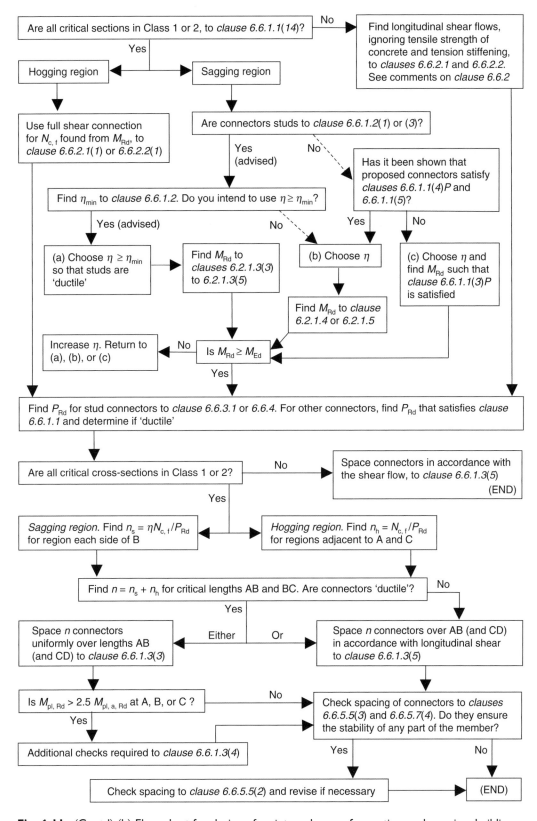

Fig. 6.11. (Contd) (b) Flow chart for design of an internal span of a continuous beam in a building – shear connection

(1) The elastic global analysis is simpler if the 'uncracked' model is used. The limits to redistribution of hogging moments include allowance for the effects of cracking, but redistribution is not permitted where allowance for lateral–torsional buckling is required (*clause 5.4.4(4)*). 'Cracked' analysis may then be preferred, as it gives lower hogging moments at internal supports.

(2) If fully propped construction is used, $M_{a, Ed}$ may be zero at all cross-sections.

Example 6.3: lateral–torsional buckling of two-span beam

The design method of *clause 6.4.2*, with application of the theory in Appendix A, is illustrated in Example 6.7, which will be found after the comments on *clause 6.6*. The length of the method is such that the 'simplified verification' of *clause 6.4.3* is used wherever possible.

Limitations of the simplified method are now illustrated, with reference to the two-span beam treated in Example 6.7. This uses an IPE 450 steel section in grade S355 steel, and is continuous over two 12 m spans. Details are shown in Figs 6.23–6.25.

Relevant results for hogging bending of the composite section at support B in Fig. 6.23(c) are as follows:

$$M_{pl, Rd} = 781 \text{ kN m} \qquad \overline{\lambda}_{LT} = 0.43 \qquad M_{b, Rd} = 687 \text{ kN m}$$

The design ultimate loads per unit length of beam, from Table 6.2, are

permanent: $7.80 + 1.62 = 9.42 \text{ kN/m}$

variable: 26.25 kN/m

The steel section fails the condition in *paragraph (g)* of *clause 6.4.3(1)*, which limits its depth to 400 mm. The beam satisfies all the other conditions except that in *paragraph (b)*, for its ratio of permanent to total load is only $9.42/35.67 = 0.26$, far below the specified minimum of 0.4.

The simplest way to satisfy *paragraph (g)* would be to encase the web in concrete, which increases the depth limit to 600 mm, and the permanent load to 11.9 kN/m.

The condition in *paragraph (b)* is quite severe. In this case, it is

$$11.9 \geq 0.4(11.9 + q_d)$$

whence

$$q_d \leq 17.8 \text{ kN/m}$$

This corresponds to a characteristic floor loading of

$$17.8/(1.5 \times 2.5) = 4.75 \text{ kN/m}^2$$

which is a big reduction from the 7 kN/m² specified, even though the required reduction in $\overline{\lambda}_{LT}$ (to ≤ 0.4) is less than 10%.

This result illustrates a common feature of 'simplified' methods. They have to cover so wide a variety of situations that they are over-conservative for some of them.

6.5. Transverse forces on webs

The local resistance of an unstiffened and unencased web to forces (typically, vertical forces) applied through a steel flange can be assumed to be the same in a composite member as in a

Clause 6.5

steel member, so *clause 6.5* consists mainly of references to EN 1993-1-5. The provisions of Section 8 of EN 1993-1-5 are not limited to rolled sections, so are applicable to webs where the neutral axis is not at mid-depth, as is usual in composite beams.

In buildings, local yielding or buckling of a web may occur where a composite beam is continuous over a steel beam that supports it. Rolled I-sections in Class 1 or 2 may not be susceptible, but a Class 3 web, treated as effective Class 2, should almost always be stiffened (*clause 6.5.1(3)*).

A plate girder launched over roller supports cannot be stiffened at every section, so the erection condition may be critical; but this situation is rare in buildings.

Flange-induced web buckling, *clause 6.5.2*, could occur where a large compression flange is restrained from buckling out of its plane by a weak or slender web. This is prevented by specifying a limit to the web slenderness, as a function of the ratio of flange area to web area. The slenderness limit is reduced if the flange is curved in elevation, to ensure that the web can resist the radial component of the force in the flange. This form of web buckling cannot occur with straight rolled steel I-sections, and needs to be checked only for plate girders of unusual proportions and for members sharply curved in elevation.

The effect of sharp curvature is illustrated by reference to an IPE 400 section of grade S355 steel, which has been cold curved about its major axis, before erection. Assuming that its plastic resistance moment is to be used, the minimum permitted radius of curvature given by clause 8(2) of EN 1993-1-5 is 2.1 m. Flange-induced buckling is clearly a rare problem for hot-rolled sections.

6.6. Shear connection

6.6.1. General

Basis of design

Clause 6.6 is applicable to shear connection in composite beams. *Clause 6.6.1.1(1)* refers also to 'other types of composite member'. Shear connection in composite columns is treated in *clause 6.7.4*, but reference is made to *clause 6.6.3.1* for the design resistance of headed stud connectors. Similarly, headed studs used for end anchorage in composite slabs are treated in *clause 9.7.4*, but some provisions in *clause 6.6* are also applicable.

Although the uncertain effects of bond are excluded by *clause 6.6.1.1(2)P*, friction is not excluded. Its essential difference from bond is that there must be compressive force across the relevant surfaces. This usually arises from wedging action. Provisions for shear connection by friction are given in *clauses 6.7.4.2(4)* (columns) and *9.1.2.1* (composite slabs).

'Inelastic redistribution of shear' (*clause 6.6.1.1(3)P*) is relied on in the many provisions that permit uniform spacing of connectors. *Clause 6.6.1.1(4)P* uses the term 'ductile' for connectors that have deformation capacity sufficient to assume ideal plastic behaviour of the shear connection. *Clause 6.6.1.1(5)* quantifies this as a characteristic slip capacity of 6 mm.[47] In practice, designers will not wish to calculate required and available slip capacities. *Clause 6.6.1.2(1)* enables such calculations to be avoided by limiting the extent of partial shear connection and by specifying the type and range of shear connectors.

The need for compatibility of load/slip properties, *clause 6.6.1.1(6)P*, is one reason why neither bond nor adhesives can be used to supplement the shear resistance of studs. The combined use of studs and block-and-hoop connectors has been discouraged for the same reason, though there is little doubt that effectively rigid projections into the concrete slab, such as bolt heads and ends of flange plates, contribute to shear connection.

'Separation', in *clause 6.6.1.1(7)P*, means separation sufficient for the curvatures of the two elements to be different at a cross-section, or for there to be a risk of local corrosion. None of the design methods in EN 1994-1-1 takes account of differences of curvature, which can arise from a very small separation. Even where most of the load is applied by or above the slab, as is usual, tests on beams with unheaded studs show separation, especially after inelastic behaviour begins. This arises from local variations in the flexural stiffnesses of the concrete and steel elements, and from the tendency of the slab to ride up on the weld collars. The standard heads of stud connectors have been found to be large enough to control separation, and the rule in *clause 6.6.1.1(8)* is intended to ensure that other types of connector, with anchoring devices if necessary, can do so.

Resistance to uplift is much influenced by the reinforcement near the bottom of the slab, so if the resistance of an anchor is to be checked by testing, reinforcement in accordance with *clause 6.6.6* should be provided in the test specimens. Anchors are inevitably subjected also to shear.

Clause 6.6.1.1(9) **Clause 6.6.1.1(9)** refers to 'direct tension'. Load from a travelling crane hanging from the steel member is an example. In bridges, it can be caused by the differential deflexions of adjacent beams under certain patterns of imposed load. Where it is present, its design magnitude must be determined.

Clause 6.6.1.1(10)P **Clause 6.6.1.1(10)P** is a principle that has led to many application rules. The shear forces are inevitably 'concentrated'. One research study[67] found that 70% of the shear on a stud was resisted by its weld collar, and that the local (triaxial) stress in the concrete was several times its cube strength. Transverse reinforcement performs a dual role. It acts as horizontal shear reinforcement for the concrete flanges, and controls and limits splitting. Its detailing is critical where connectors are close to a free surface of the slab.

Larger concentrated forces occur where precast slabs are used, and connectors are placed in groups in holes in the slabs. This influences the detailing of the reinforcement near these holes, and is referred to in Section 8 of EN 1994-2.

Clause 6.6.1.1(12) **Clause 6.6.1.1(12)** is intended to permit the use of other types of connector. ENV 1994-1-1 included provisions for many types of connector other than studs: block connectors, anchors, hoops, angles, and friction-grip bolts. They have all been omitted because of their limited use and to shorten the code.

Clause 6.6.1.1(13) **Clause 6.6.1.1(13)** says that connectors should resist *at least* the design shear force, meaning the action effect. Their design for Class 1 and 2 sections is based on the design bending resistances (see *clause 6.6.2*), and hence on a shear force that normally exceeds the action effect.

Clause 6.6.1.1(14)P The principle on partial shear connection, **clause 6.6.1.1(14)P**, leads to application rules in *clause 6.2.1.3*.

The flow chart in Fig. 6.11(b) is for a beam without web encasement, and may assist in following the comments on *clauses 6.2* and *6.6*.

Limitation on the use of partial shear connection in beams for buildings

As noted in comments on *clause 6.2.1.3*, the rules for partial shear connection are based on an available slip of 6 mm. Connectors defined as 'ductile' are those that had been shown to have (or were believed to have) a characteristic slip capacity (defined in *clause B.2.5(4)*) exceeding 6 mm.

Prediction of slip capacity is difficult. Push tests on stud connectors have been reported in scores of publications, but few tests were continued for slips exceeding 3 mm. Slip capacity depends on the degree of containment of the connector by the concrete and its reinforcement, and hence on the location of free surfaces (e.g. in haunches or edge beams) as well as on the shape, size and spacing of the connectors. The information has been summarized.[47,48] The conclusions led to the approval of certain stud connectors as 'ductile'

Clause 6.6.1.2(1) (*clause 6.6.1.2(1)*), and also friction-grip bolts, which were within the scope of ENV 1994-1-1.

These conclusions seem optimistic when compared with the results of some push tests using solid slabs, but connectors behave much better in beams reinforced as required by the Eurocode than in small push-test specimens, where splitting can cause premature failure. One might expect a lower available slip from studs in very strong concrete, but the 6 mm limit has been confirmed[68] by four push tests with cylinder strengths $f_{cm} \approx 86$ N/mm^2.

For certain types of profiled sheeting, available slips were found to be greater than 6 mm.[43,69] These results and other test data led to a relaxation of the limiting effective spans at which low degrees of shear connection can be used, as shown in the lower part of Fig.

Clause 6.6.1.2(3) 6.4(a). This applies only where the conditions in *paragraphs* (*a*)–(*e*) of **clause 6.6.1.2(3)** are satisfied, because these are the situations for which test data are available. There is no validated theoretical model that includes all the many relevant variables, so this relaxation is allowed only where the force N_c is determined by the more conservative of the two methods given in *clause 6.2.1.3*, the interpolation method.

Research continues on the influence on slip capacity of profile shape and the detailing of studs in troughs.

The limits to the use of partial shear connection in buildings are summarized in Fig. 6.4(a), where L_e is the effective span. The span limits given by the lines PQ to RS are from the provisions of *clause 6.6.1.2* for 'ductile' connectors. The design of a long-span beam with a low degree of shear connection is likely to be governed by the need to limit its deflection, unless it is propped during construction or is continuous.

For composite beams in sagging bending, the steel top flange must be wide enough to resist lateral buckling during erection, and for attachment of the connectors, but can often be smaller than the bottom flange. A smaller flange lowers the plastic neutral axis of the composite section, and increases the slip required by the model for partial-interaction design. This is why *clauses 6.6.1.2(1)* and *6.6.1.2(2)* give limits on the degree of shear connection that are less liberal than those for beams with equal steel flanges.

Spacing of shear connectors in beams for buildings

Clause 6.6.1.3(1)P extends *clause 6.6.1.1(2)P* a little, by referring to 'spacing' of connectors and an 'appropriate distribution' of longitudinal shear. The interpretation of 'appropriate' can depend on the method of analysis used and the ductility of the connectors. *Clause 6.6.1.3(1)P*

The principle may be assumed to be satisfied where connectors are spaced 'elastically' to *clause 6.6.1.3(5)*, which has general applicability. The more convenient use of uniform spacing requires the connectors to satisfy *clause 6.6.1.3(3)*, which implies (but does not require) the use of plastic resistance moments. The connectors must be 'ductile', as defined in *clauses 6.6.1.1(4)P* and *6.6.1.1(5)*. This is normally achieved by satisfying *clause 6.6.1.2*. *Clauses 6.6.1.1(3)P* to *6.6.1.1(5)* provide an alternative, which enables research-based evidence to be used, but its use is not appropriate for routine design.

In practice, it is possible to space connectors uniformly in most beams for buildings, so for continuous beams *clause 6.6.1.3(2)P* requires the tension reinforcement to be curtailed to suit the spacing of the shear connectors. *Clause 6.6.1.3(2)P*

Clause 6.6.1.3(4) could apply to a simply-supported or a continuous beam with a large concrete slab and a relatively small steel top flange. Connectors spaced uniformly along a critical length might then have insufficient available slip. Use of an additional critical section would lead to a more suitable distribution. *Clause 6.6.1.3(4)*

Example 6.4: arrangement of shear connectors

As an example of the use of these rules, a simply-supported beam of span 10 m is considered. It has distributed loading, equal steel flanges, a uniform cross-section in Class 2, S355 steel, and stud connectors. At mid-span, M_{Ed} is much less than $M_{pl, Rd}$. The cross-section is such that the required resistance to bending can be provided using 40% of full shear connection ($n/n_f = 0.4$).

Clause 6.6.1.2(1) gives $n/n_f \geq 0.55$. However, if the slab is composite, and the other conditions of *clause 6.6.1.2(3)* are satisfied, $n/n_f = 0.4$ may be used.

Suppose now that the span of the beam is 12 m. The preceding limits to n/n_f are increased to 0.61 and 0.48, respectively. One can either design using these limits, or go to *clause 6.6.1.3(5)*, which refers to 'longitudinal shear calculated by elastic theory'. This presumably means using $v_L = V_{Ed}A\bar{y}/I$, where V_{Ed} is the vertical shear on the composite section. This gives a triangular distribution of longitudinal shear, or separate distributions, to be superimposed, if creep is allowed for by using several modular ratios. The force in the slab at mid-span now depends on the proportion of M_{Ed} that is applied to the composite member, and on the proportions of the cross-section. Connectors corresponding to this force are then spaced accordingly, possibly with extra ones near mid-span to satisfy the rule of *clause 6.6.5.5(3)* on maximum spacing of studs.

Strictly, the envelope of vertical shear should be used for V_{Ed}, which gives non-zero shear at mid-span. For distributed loading this increases the shear connection needed by only 2%, but the envelope should certainly be used for more complex variable loading.

For continuous beams where M_{Ed} at mid-span is much less than $M_{pl, Rd}$, the method is more complex, as partial shear connection is permitted only where the slab is in compression. The envelope of design vertical shear from the global analysis should be used. For simplicity, longitudinal shear can be found using properties of the uncracked cross-section throughout, because this gives an overestimate in cracked regions. Examples 6.7 and 6.8 (see below) are relevant.

It does not help, in the present example, to define additional critical sections within the 6 m shear span of the beam, because the limits of *clause 6.6.1.2* are given in terms of effective span, not critical length.

6.6.2. Longitudinal shear force in beams for buildings

Clause 6.6.2.1
Clause 6.6.2.2

Clauses 6.6.2.1 and *6.6.2.2* say, in effect, that the design longitudinal shear force should be consistent with the bending *resistances* of the cross-sections at the ends of the critical length considered, not with the design vertical shear forces (the action effects). This is done for two reasons:

- simplicity – for the design bending moments often lie between the elastic and plastic resistances, and calculation of longitudinal shear becomes complex
- robustness – for otherwise longitudinal shear failure, which may be more brittle than flexural failure, could occur first.

Beam with Class 3 sections at supports and a Class 1 or 2 section at mid-span
Clause 6.6.2.1 applies because non-linear or elastic theory will have been 'applied to cross-sections'. The longitudinal forces in the slab at the Class 3 sections are then calculated by elastic theory, based on the bending moments in the composite section. At mid-span, it is not clear whether *clause 6.6.2.2* applies, because its heading does not say 'resistance of *all* cross-sections'. The simpler and recommended method is to assume that it does apply, and to calculate the longitudinal force at mid-span based on M_{Rd} at that section, as that is consistent with the model used for bending. The total shear flow between a support and mid-span is the sum of the longitudinal forces at those points. The alternative would be to find the longitudinal force at mid-span by elastic theory for the moments applied to the composite section, even though the bending stresses could exceed the specified limits.

Clause 6.6.2.2(3)

This absence of 'all' from the heading is also relevant to the use of *clause 6.6.2.2(3)*, on the use of partial shear connection. The design for a beam with Class 3 sections at internal supports limits the curvature of those regions, so the ultimate-load curvature at mid-span will be too low for the full-interaction bending resistance to be reached. The use of partial shear connection is then appropriate, with M_{Rd} less than $M_{pl, Rd}$.

6.6.3. Headed stud connectors in solid slabs and concrete encasement
Resistance to longitudinal shear
In BS 5950-3-1[31] and in earlier UK codes, the characteristic shear resistances of studs are given in a table, applicable only when the stud material has particular properties. There was no theoretical model for the shear resistance.

The Eurocodes must be applicable to a wider range of products, so design equations are essential. Those given in *clause 6.6.3.1(1)* are based on the model that a stud with a shank diameter d and an ultimate strength f_u, set in concrete with a characteristic strength f_{ck} and a mean secant modulus E_{cm}, fails either in the steel alone or in the concrete alone.

The concrete failure is found in tests to be influenced by both the stiffness and the strength of the concrete.

Clause 6.6.3.1(1)

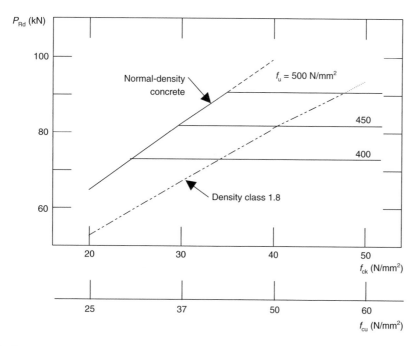

Fig. 6.12. Design shear resistances of 19 mm studs with $h/d \geq 4$ in solid slabs

This led to *equations (6.18)–(6.21)*, in which the numerical constants and partial safety factor γ_V have been deduced from analyses of test data. In situations where the resistances from *equations (6.18)* and *(6.19)* are similar, tests show that interaction occurs between the two assumed modes of failure. An equation based on analyses of test data, but not on a defined model,[70]

$$P_{Rd} = k(\pi d^2/4)f_u(E_{cm}/E_a)^{0.4}(f_{ck}/f_u)^{0.35} \tag{D6.16}$$

gives a curve with a shape that approximates better both to test data and to values tabulated in BS 5950.

In the statistical analyses done for EN 1994-1-1[71,72] both of these methods were studied. Equation (D6.16) gave results with slightly less scatter, but the equations of *clause 6.6.3.1(1)* were preferred because of their clear basis and experience of their use in some countries. Here, and elsewhere in *Section 6*, coefficients from such analyses were modified slightly, to enable a single partial factor, denoted γ_V ('V' for shear), 1.25, to be recommended for all types of shear connection. This value has been used in draft Eurocodes for over 20 years.

It was concluded from this study[72] that the coefficient in *equation (6.19)* should be 0.26. This result was based on push tests, where the mean number of studs per specimen was only six, and where lateral restraint from the narrow test slabs was usually less stiff than in the concrete flange of a composite beam. Strength of studs in many beams is also increased by the presence of hogging transverse bending of the slab. For these reasons the coefficient was increased from 0.26 to 0.29, a value that is supported by a subsequent calibration study[15] based on beams with partial shear connection.

Design resistances of 19 mm stud connectors in solid slabs, given by *clause 6.6.3.1*, are shown in Fig. 6.12. It is assumed that the penalty for short studs, *equation (6.20)*, does not apply. For any given values of f_u and f_{ck}, the figure shows which failure mode governs. It can be used for this purpose for studs of other diameters, provided that $h/d \geq 4$.

The 'overall nominal height' of a stud, used in *equations (6.20)* and *(6.21)*, is about 5 mm greater than the 'length after welding', a term which is also in use.

Weld collars

Clause 6.6.3.1(2) ***Clause 6.6.3.1*(2)** on weld collars refers to EN 13918,[26] which gives 'guide values' for the height and diameter of collars, with the note that these may vary in through-deck stud welding. It is known that for studs with normal weld collars, a high proportion of the shear is transmitted through the collar.[67] It should not be assumed that the shear resistances of *clause 6.6.3.1* are applicable to studs without collars (e.g. where friction welding by high-speed spinning is used). A normal collar should be fused to the shank of the stud. Typical collars in the test specimens from which the design formulae were deduced had a diameter not less than $1.25d$ and a minimum height not less than $0.15d$, where d is the diameter of the shank.

The collars of studs welded through profiled sheeting can be of different shape from those for studs welded direct to steel flanges, and the shear strength may also depend on the effective diameter of the weld between the sheeting and the flange, about which little is known. The resistances of *clause 6.6.3.1* are applicable where the welding is in accordance with EN ISO 14555,[73] as is required.

Studs with a diameter exceeding 20 mm are rarely used in buildings, as welding through sheeting becomes more difficult, and more powerful welding plant is required.

Splitting of the slab

Clause 6.6.3.1(3) ***Clause 6.6.3.1*(3)** refers to 'splitting forces in the direction of the slab thickness'. These occur where the axis of a stud lies in a plane parallel to that of the concrete slab; for example, if studs are welded to the web of a steel T-section that projects into a concrete flange. These are referred to as 'lying studs' in published research[74] on the local reinforcement needed to prevent or control splitting. There is an informative annex on this subject in EN 1994-2.[11] A similar problem occurs in composite L-beams with studs close to a free edge of the slab. This is addressed in *clause 6.6.5.3(2)*.

Tension in studs

Pressure under the head of a stud connector and friction on the shank normally causes the stud weld to be subjected to vertical tension before shear failure is reached. This is why *clause 6.6.1.1(8)* requires shear connectors to have a resistance to tension that is at least 10% of the
Clause 6.6.3.2(2) shear resistance. ***Clause 6.6.3.2*(2)** therefore permits tensile forces that are less than this to be neglected.

Resistance of studs to higher tensile forces has been found to depend on so many variables, especially the layout of local reinforcement, that no simple design rules could be given. It is usually possible to find other ways of resisting the vertical tension that occurs, e.g. where a travelling crane is supported from the steel element of a composite beam.

6.6.4. Design resistance of headed studs used with profiled steel sheeting in buildings

The load–slip behaviour of a stud connector in a trough (of sheeting) or rib (of concrete; both terms are used) (Fig. 6.13) is more complex than in a solid slab. It is influenced by

- the direction of the ribs relative to the span of the beam
- their mean breadth b_0 and depth h_p
- the diameter d and height h_{sc} of the stud
- the number n_r of the studs in one trough, and their spacing
- whether or not a stud is central within a trough, and, if not, by its eccentricity and the direction of the shear.

The interactions between these parameters have been explored by testing, with sheeting continuous across the beam. It is clear that the most significant are the ratios h_{sc}/h_p and b_0/h_p and, for ribs transverse to the supporting beams, n_r and the eccentricity, if any. In EN 1994-1-1, as in earlier codes, reduction factors k (≤ 1.0) are given, for application to the design resistances of studs in solid slabs. They are based entirely on testing and experience.

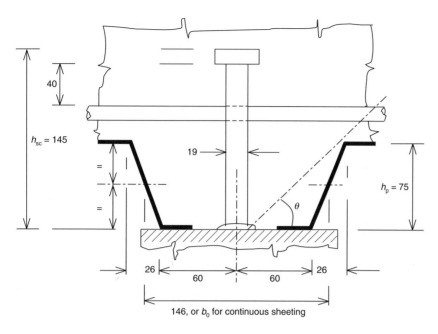

Fig. 6.13. Details of a haunch, with parallel sheeting (dimensions in mm)

Sheeting with ribs parallel to the supporting beams (**clause 6.6.4.1**)

Clause 6.6.4.1

There are two situations. The sheeting may be continuous across the beams – its side walls then provide lateral restraint to the concrete around the studs – or it may be discontinuous, as shown in Fig. 6.13, providing a haunch with a breadth that usually exceeds the breadth b_0 of a trough. Edge fixings provided for erection may not provide much lateral restraint. The detailing rules for studs in unsheeted haunches, *clause 6.6.5.4*, then provide a guide to good practice, and may be more conservative than the rules of *clause 6.6.4.1*. Alternatively, the sheeting may be anchored to the beam. As practice varies, the means to achieve appropriate anchorage is a matter for the National Annex.

A haunch that just complies with *clause 6.6.5.4* is shown, to scale, in Fig. 6.13. The rules specify:

- the angle θ ($\leq 45°$)
- the concrete side cover to the connector (≥ 50 mm)
- the depth of the transverse reinforcement below the underside of the head (≥ 40 mm).

The application of *clause 6.6.4.1(2)* to this haunch is now considered. The reduction factor is

$$k_\ell = 0.6(b_0/h_p)[(h_{sc}/h_p) - 1] \leq 1 \tag{6.22}$$

where h_{sc} may not be taken as greater than $h_p + 75$ mm. The equation is from Grant *et al.*,[75] dating from 1977 because there is little recent research on ribs parallel to the beam.[76] Here, it gives

$$k_\ell = 0.6(146/75)[(145/75) - 1] = 1.09$$

so there is no reduction. There would be, $k_\ell = 0.78$, if the height of the stud were reduced to, say, 125 mm. In an unsheeted haunch it would then be necessary to provide transverse reinforcement at a lower level than in Fig. 6.13, which might be impracticable. Reasonable consistence is thus shown between *clauses 6.6.4.1* and *6.6.5.4*.

There is no penalty for off-centre studs in either of these clauses, or for more than one at a cross-section. The rules of *clause 6.6.4.1* for continuous or anchored sheeting, and of *clause 6.6.5.4*, for discontinuous un-anchored sheeting, should ensure good detailing.

Where sheeting is continuous across a beam and through-deck stud welding is used, there may be shear transfer from the sheeting to the beam. No guidance is given on this complex situation, which may be ignored in design.

Sheeting with ribs transverse to the supporting beams (**clause 6.6.4.2**)

In the preceding paragraphs, the likely mode of failure was loss of restraint to the base of the stud due to bursting (lateral expansion) of the haunch. A rib transverse to the beam, shown in Fig. 6.14 with typical dimensions, is more highly stressed, as it has to transfer much of the shear from the base of the stud to the continuous slab above. Three modes of failure are shown in Fig. 6.15(a)–(c):

(a) failure surface above a stud that is too short ('concrete pullout')
(b) haunch too slender, with plastic hinges in the stud
(c) eccentricity on the 'weak' side of the centre, which reduces the effective breadth of the haunch,[69] and causes 'rib punching' failure.[77]

In BS 5950-3-1,[31] the reduction formula from Grant *et al.*[75] is given. It is, essentially,

$$k_t = 0.85(b_0/h_p)[(h_{sc}/h_p) - 1]/n_r^{0.5} \le k_{t, max} \tag{D6.17}$$

with $k_{t, max}$ falling from 1 to 0.6 as n_r, the number of studs in a rib, increases from 1 to 3. Where a single stud is placed on the weak side of the centre of a rib, the breadth b_0 is taken as $2e$ (Fig. 6.15(c)).

In a study of this subject[61] it was concluded that equation (D6.17) was inconsistent and could be unsafe. A new formula by Lawson[78] gave better predictions, and was recommended.

For the Eurocode, a review of Mottram and Johnson[69] and Lawson,[78] and their application to a wider range of profiles than is used in the UK, found that more test data were needed. It was initially decided[72] to reduce the factor 0.85 in equation (D6.17) to 0.7, to eliminate situations where it had been found to be unsafe, with the conditions: n_r not to be taken as greater than 2 in computations, $b_0 \ge h_p$, and $h_p \le 85$ mm, with $k_{t, max}$ as before. Where there is one stud per rib, Fig. 6.16 shows that:

- where $h_{sc} \ge 2h_p$ and $t > 1$ mm, the reduction factor is usually 1.0
- where $h_{sc} \le 1.5h_p$ and/or $t \le 1$ mm, reductions in resistance can be large.

Most of the test data had been from sheeting exceeding 1.0 mm in thickness, with through-deck welding of studs up to 20 mm in diameter. Later work led to the reductions in $k_{t, max}$ for other situations, given in *Table 6.2*, for thinner sheeting and studs welded through

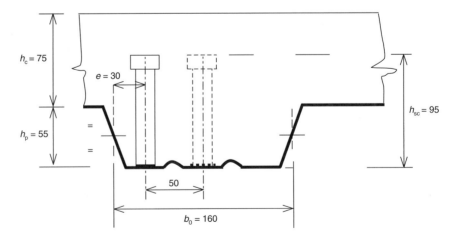

Fig. 6.14. Details of a haunch and positions of stud connectors, for trapezoidal sheeting transverse to the supporting beams (dimensions in mm)

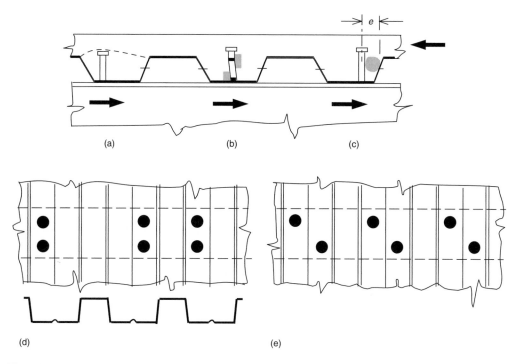

Fig. 6.15. Failure modes and placing of studs, for troughs of profiled sheeting. The alternate favourable and unfavourable placing of pairs of studs is shown in (d), and the diagonal placing of pairs of studs in (e)

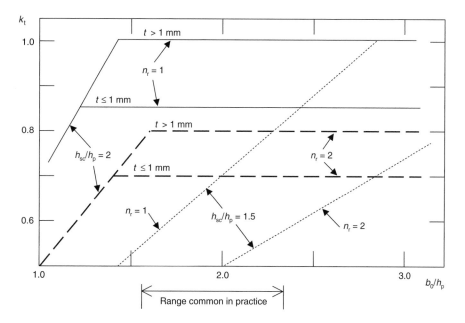

Fig. 6.16. Reduction factor k_t for studs with $d \leq 20$ mm and through-deck welding

holes. Research also found that the use of a reduction factor for the strength of studs in a solid slab is not appropriate where strong studs are placed in a relatively weak rib, so further limitations of scope were added:

- stud diameter not to exceed the limits given in *Table 6.2*
- ultimate strength of studs in sheeting not to be taken as greater than 450 N/mm^2.

Some trapezoidal sheetings have a small rib projecting above the main top surface; for example, as shown in Fig. 9.4. It is clear from *clause 6.6.4.1(1)* that in *equation (6.22)*, h_p is the depth including the rib. The words 'overall depth' are not repeated in *clause 6.6.4.2*, but should be assumed to apply, unless there is extensive test evidence that *equation (6.23)* gives safe predictions of k_t when h_p is taken as the depth excluding the rib.

Crowding studs into a rib reduces ductility[69] as well as strength. Ductility is needed most in long spans where, fortunately, longitudinal shears are usually low (in buildings) in relation to the width of steel top flange available for the placing of studs. This is relevant because the failures sketched in Fig. 6.15 are in reality three-dimensional, and resistances depend in a complex way on the arrangement of pairs of studs within a rib.

Where sheeting has a small stiffening rib that prevents studs from being placed centrally within each trough, and only one stud per trough is required, application of the rule given in *clause 6.6.5.8(3)* is straightforward. Comments on that clause are given later.

It is not clear from EN 1994-1-1 how two studs per trough should then be arranged. If there were no central rib, then two studs in line, spaced $\geq 5d$ apart (*clause 6.6.5.7(4)*) would be permitted. Small stiffening ribs, as shown in Fig. 6.14, should have little effect on shear resistance, so two-in-line is an acceptable layout. If the troughs are too narrow to permit this, then two studs side-by-side spaced $\geq 4d$ apart (*clause 6.6.5.7(4)*) fall within the scope of *clause 6.6.5.8(3)*, and can be arranged as shown in plan in Fig. 6.15(d). There is limited evidence from tests[76] that the diagonal layout of Fig. 6.15(e), to which the code does not refer, may be weaker than two studs in line.

Example 6.5: reduction factors for transverse sheeting

The sheeting is as shown in Fig. 6.14, with an assumed thickness $t = 0.9$ mm, including zinc coating. The overall depth is 55 mm. For one stud in the central location (shown by dashed lines in Fig. 6.14), $b_0 = 160$ mm, $h_{sc} = 95$ mm, and $n_r = 1$. *Equation (6.23)* and *Table 6.2* give

$$k_t = (0.7 \times 160/55)(95/55 - 1) = 1.48 \text{ (but} \leq \mathbf{0.85})$$

For two studs per trough, placed centrally and side by side,

$$k_t = 1.48/1.41 = 1.05 \text{ (but} \leq \mathbf{0.7})$$

Further calculations of reduction factors are included in Example 6.7.

Biaxial loading of shear connectors

Clause 6.6.4.3

The biaxial horizontal loading referred to in *clause 6.6.4.3* occurs where stud connectors are used to provide end anchorage for composite slabs, as shown in *Fig. 9.1(c)*. *Clause 9.7.4(3)* gives the design anchorage resistance as the lesser of that given by *clause 6.6* and $P_{pb,Rd}$, the bearing resistance of the sheet, from *equation (9.10)*. Even where 16 mm studs are used in lightweight concrete, the bearing resistance (typically about 14 kN) will be the lower of the two.

These studs resist horizontal shear from both the slab and the beam. The interaction equation of *clause 6.6.4.3(1)* is based on vectorial addition of the two shear forces.

6.6.5. Detailing of the shear connection and influence of execution

It is rarely possible to prove the general validity of application rules for detailing, because they apply to so great a variety of situations. They are based partly on previous practice. An adverse experience causes the relevant rule to be made more restrictive. In research, existing rules are often violated when test specimens are designed, in the hope that extensive good experience may enable existing rules to be relaxed.

Rules are often expressed in the form of limiting dimensions, even though most behaviour (excluding corrosion) is more influenced by ratios of dimensions than by a single value. Minimum dimensions that would be appropriate for an unusually large structural member

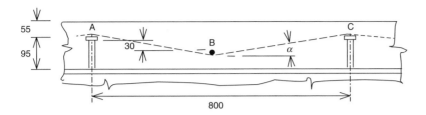

Fig. 6.17. Level of bottom transverse reinforcement (dimensions in mm)

could exceed those given in the code. Similarly, code maxima may be too large for use in a small member. Designers are unwise to follow detailing rules blindly, because no set of rules can be comprehensive.

Resistance to separation

The object of **clause 6.6.5.1(1)** on resistance to separation is to ensure that failure surfaces in the concrete cannot pass above the connectors and below the reinforcement, intersecting neither. Tests have found that these surfaces may not be plane; the problem is three-dimensional. A longitudinal section through a possible failure surface ABC is shown in Fig. 6.17. The studs are at the maximum spacing allowed by *clause 6.6.5.5(3)*.

    Clause 6.6.5.1 defines only the highest level for the bottom reinforcement. Ideally, its longitudinal location relative to the studs should also be defined, because the objective is to prevent failure surfaces where the angle α (Fig. 6.17) is small. It is impracticable to specify a minimum angle α, or to link detailing rules for reinforcement with those for connectors.

    The angle α obviously depends on the spacing of the bottom bars, assumed to be 800 mm in Fig. 6.17. What is the maximum permitted value for this spacing? The answer is quite complex.

    Clause 6.6.6.3(1) refers to clause 9.2.2(5) in EN 1992-1-1, where a Note recommends a minimum reinforcement ratio. For $f_{ck} = 30$ N/mm^2 and $f_{sk} = 500$ N/mm^2 this gives 0.088%, or 131 mm^2/m for this 150 mm slab. However, if the slab is continuous across the beam, most of this could be in the top of the slab.

    The minimum bottom reinforcement depends on whether the slab is continuous or not. If it is simply-supported on the beam, the bottom bars are 'principal reinforcement' to clause 9.3.1.1(3) of EN 1992-1-1, where a Note gives their maximum spacing as 400 mm for this example, and 450 mm for 'secondary' reinforcement. The rules of *clause 6.6.5.3(2)* on splitting may also apply.

    If the slab is continuous over the beam, there may be no need for bottom flexural reinforcement to EN 1992-1-1. Let us assume that there is a single row of 19 mm studs with a design resistance, 91 kN per stud, which is possible in concrete of class C50/60 (Fig. 6.12). The bottom transverse reinforcement will then be determined by the rules of *clause 6.6.6.1* for shear surfaces of type b–b or c–c. These show that 12 mm bars at 750 mm spacing are sufficient. There appears to be no rule that requires closer spacing, but it would be prudent to treat these bars as 'secondary flexural' bars to EN 1992-1-1, not least because it increases the angle α. Using its maximum spacing, 450 mm, 10 mm bars are sufficient.

Cover to connectors

Shear connectors must project significantly above profiled steel sheeting, because of the term $(h_{sc}/h_p - 1)$ in *equations (6.22)* and *(6.23)* and the rule in *clause 6.6.5.8(1)* for projection of 2d above 'the top of the steel deck'. The interpretation of this for profiles with a small additional top rib is not clear. If 2d is measured from this rib, and the rules of EN 1992-1-1 for cover are applied to the top of the connector, the resulting minimum thickness of a composite slab may govern its thickness. However, these slabs are normally used only in dry environments, where the concessions on minimum cover given in **clause 6.6.5.2** are appropriate.

Clause 6.6.5.1(1)

Clause 6.6.5.2

77

Loading of shear connection during execution

As almost all relevant provisions on execution appear in standards for either steel or
Clause 6.6.5.2(4)   concrete structures, there is no section on execution in EN 1994-1-1. This is why *clause
6.6.5.2(4)* appears here.

The method of construction of composite beams and slabs (i.e. whether propped or
unpropped), and also the sequence of concreting, affects stresses calculated by elastic
theory, and the magnitude of deflections. It is significant, therefore, in verifications of
resistance of cross-sections in Class 3 or 4, and in serviceability checks.

Where propped construction is used, it is usual to retain the props until the concrete has
achieved a compressive strength of at least 75% of its design value. If this is not done,
verifications at removal of props should be based on a reduced compressive strength.

Clause 6.6.5.2(4) gives a lower limit for this reduction in concrete strength. It also relates
to the staged casting of a concrete flange for an unpropped composite beam, setting, in
effect, a minimum time interval between successive stages of casting.

Local reinforcement in the slab

Where shear connectors are close to a longitudinal edge of a concrete flange, use of U-bars is
Clause 6.6.5.3(1)   almost the only way of providing the full anchorage required by *clause 6.6.5.3(1)*. The
Clause 6.6.5.3(2)   splitting referred to in *clause 6.6.5.3(2)* is a common mode of failure in push-test specimens
with narrow slabs (e.g. 300 mm, which has long been the standard width in British codes). It
was also found, in full-scale tests, to be the normal failure mode for composite L-beams
constructed with precast slabs.[79] Detailing rules are given in *clause 6.6.5.3(2)* for slabs where
the edge distance e in Fig. 6.18 is less than 300 mm. The required area of bottom transverse
reinforcement, A_b, per unit length of beam, should be found using *clause 6.6.6*. In the
unhaunched slab shown in Fig. 6.18, failure surface b–b will be critical (unless the slab is very
thick) because the shear on surface a–a is low in an L-beam with an asymmetrical concrete
flange.

To ensure that the reinforcement is fully anchored to the left of the line a–a, it is
recommended that U-bars be used. These can be in a horizontal plane or, where top
reinforcement is needed, in a vertical plane.

No rules are given for the effectiveness as transverse reinforcement of profiled sheeting
transverse to the supporting beams, with ribs that extend to a cantilever edge of the slab. The
length needed to develop the full tensile resistance of the sheeting will be known from the
design procedure for the composite slab. It is always greater than the minimum edge
distance of $6d$, and usually greater than 300 mm. Where it exceeds the length e available,
bottom transverse reinforcement will be needed. The situation can be improved by placing
all the connectors near the inner edge of the steel flange. Sheeting with ribs parallel to the
free edge should not be assumed to resist longitudinal splitting of the slab.

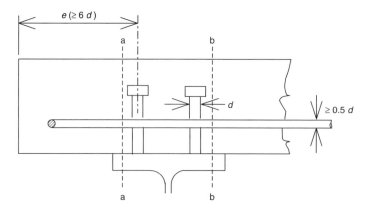

Fig. 6.18. Longitudinal shear reinforcement in an L-beam

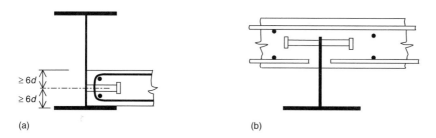

Fig. 6.19. Examples of details susceptible to longitudinal splitting

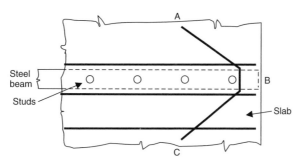

Transverse reinforcement not shown

Fig. 6.20. Reinforcement at the end of a cantilever

Lying studs

There is also a risk of splitting where the shank of a stud (a 'lying stud') is parallel and close to a free surface of the slab, as shown, for example, in Fig. 6.19. The U-bars should then be in a vertical plane. Research has found[74] that the '6d rule' for edge distance in *clause 6.6.5.3(2)* and the provision of hoops may not be sufficient to ensure that the design shear resistance of the stud is reached. The height of the stud and the longitudinal bars shown are also important.

The slip capacity may be less than 6 mm, so the shear connection may not be 'ductile'. The stud shown in Fig. 6.19(b) may be subjected to simultaneous axial tension and vertical and longitudinal shear, so details of this type should be avoided.

Lying studs are outside the scope of EN 1994-1-1. There is an informative annex in EN 1994-2.

Reinforcement at the end of a cantilever

At the end of a composite cantilever, the force on the concrete from the connectors acts towards the nearest edge of the slab. The effects of shrinkage and temperature can add further stresses[37] that tend to cause splitting in region B in Fig. 6.20, so reinforcement in this region needs careful detailing. *Clause 6.6.5.3(3)P* can be satisfied by providing 'herring-bone' bottom reinforcement (ABC in Fig. 6.20) sufficient to anchor the force from the connectors into the slab, and to ensure that the longitudinal bars provided to resist that force are anchored beyond their intersection with ABC.

The situation where a column is supported at point B is particularly critical. Incompatibility between the vertical stiffnesses of the steel beam and the slab can cause local shear failure of the slab, even where the steel beam alone is locally strong enough to carry the column.[80]

Clause 6.6.5.3(3)P

Haunches

The detailing rules of *clause 6.6.5.4* are based on limited test evidence, but are long-established.[81] In regions of high longitudinal shear, deep haunches should be used with caution because there may be little warning of failure.

Haunches formed by profiled sheeting are considered under *clause 6.6.4.1*.

Clause 6.6.5.4

Maximum spacing of connectors

Situations where the stability of a concrete slab is ensured by its connection to a steel beam are unlikely to occur in buildings. The converse situation, stabilization of the steel flange, is of interest only where the steel compression flange is not already in Class 1, so it rarely arises where rolled I-sections are used.

Where the steel beam is a plate girder, there is unlikely to be any need for a top flange in Class 1. Its proportions can usually be chosen such that it is in Class 2, unless a wide thin flange is needed to avoid lateral buckling during construction.

Clause 6.6.5.5(2)

Clause 6.6.5.5(2) is not restrictive in practice. As an example, a plate girder is considered, in steel with $f_y = 355$ N/mm^2, where the top flange has $t_f = 20$ mm, an overall breadth of 350 mm, and an outstand c of 165 mm. The ratio ε is 0.81 and the slenderness is

$$c/t_f \varepsilon = 165/(20 \times 0.81) = 10.2$$

so, from Table 5.2 of EN 1993-1-1, the flange is in Class 3. From *clause 6.6.5.5(2)*, it can be assumed to be in Class 1 if shear connectors are provided within 146 mm of each free edge, at a longitudinal spacing not exceeding 356 mm, for a solid slab.

The ratio 22 in this clause is based on the assumption that the steel flange cannot buckle towards the slab. Where there are transverse ribs (e.g. due to the use of profiled sheeting), the assumption may not be correct, so the ratio is reduced to 15. The maximum spacing in this example is then 243 mm.

The ratio 9 for edge distance, used in the formula $9t_f(235/f_y)^{0.5}$ is the same as in BS 5400: Part 5,[82] and the ratio 22 for longitudinal spacing is the same as the ratio for staggered rows given in BS 5400.

Clause 6.6.5.5(3)

The maximum longitudinal spacing in buildings, given in *clause 6.6.5.5(3)*, $6h_c$, ≤ 800 mm, is more liberal than the general rule of BS 5950-3-1,[31] though that code permits a conditional increase to $8h_c$. The rule of EN 1994-1-1 is based on behaviour observed in tests, particularly those where composite slabs have studs in alternate ribs only. Some uplift then occurs at intermediate ribs. Spacing at 800 mm would in some situations allow shear connection only in every third rib, and there was a requirement in ENV 1994-1-1 for anchorage, but not necessarily shear connection, to be provided in every rib. It is expected that this requirement will be included in the forthcoming EN 1090 for execution of steel structures.

Detailing, for stud connectors

Clause 6.6.5.6

The rules of *clause 6.6.5.6* are intended to prevent local overstress of a steel flange near a shear connector and to avoid problems with stud welding. Application rules for minimum

Clause 6.6.5.7

flange thickness are given in *clause 6.6.5.7*. Clauses *6.6.5.7(1)* and *6.6.5.7(2)* are concerned with resistance to uplift. Rules for resistance of studs, minimum cover and projection of studs above bottom reinforcement usually lead to the use of studs of height greater than $3d$.

Clause 6.6.5.7(3)

The limit 1.5 for the ratio d/t_f in *clause 6.6.5.7(3)* influences the design of shear connection for closed-top box girders in bridges. For buildings, the more liberal limit of *clause 6.6.5.7(5)* normally applies. It has appeared in several earlier codes.

Clause 6.6.5.7(4)

In *clause 6.6.5.7(4)*, the minimum lateral spacing of studs in 'solid slabs' has been reduced to $2.5d$, compared with the $4d$ of BS 5950-3-1. Although connection to precast slabs is outside the scope of EN 1994-1-1, this facilitates the use of large precast slabs supported on the edges of the steel flanges, with projecting U-bars that loop over pairs of studs. There is much experience, validated by tests,[83] of this form of construction, especially in multistorey car parks. Closely spaced pairs of studs must be well confined laterally. The term 'solid slabs' should therefore be understood to exclude haunches.

Further detailing rules for studs placed within troughs of profiled sheeting are given in

Clause 6.6.5.8

clause 6.6.5.8. The first two concern resistance to uplift and compaction of concrete around studs.

Clause 6.6.5.8(3) relates to a common situation: where a small stiffening rib in sheeting prevents the placing of studs centrally within a trough. It would be prudent to locate studs on the 'favourable' side (see Fig. 6.15(a)), which, for symmetrical loading on a simply-supported span, is the side nearest the nearer support. This was not given as an application rule because it is difficult to ensure that the 'favourable' side would be correctly chosen on site. Instead, alternate-side placing is recommended, with alternate studs on the 'unfavourable' side (see Fig. 6.15(c)). However, research has found[77] that the mean strength of pairs of studs placed on the two sides of a trough is about 5% less than if both were central, with a greater reduction for sheeting less than 1 mm thick. Sheeting profiles with troughs wide enough to have off-centre stiffening ribs are more suitable for composite slabs than those with central ribs. This clause does not refer to layouts that require two studs per trough. These are discussed in comments on *clause 6.6.4.2*

6.6.6. Longitudinal shear in concrete slabs

The subject of *clause 6.6.6* is the avoidance of local failure of a concrete flange near the shear connection, by the provision of appropriate reinforcement. These bars enhance the resistance of a thin concrete slab to in-plane shear in the same way that stirrups strengthen a concrete web in vertical shear. Transverse reinforcement is also needed to control and limit the longitudinal splitting of the slab that can be caused by local forces from individual connectors. In this respect, the detailing problem is more acute than in the flanges of concrete T-beams, where the shear from the web is applied more uniformly.

The principal change from earlier codes is that the equations for the required area of transverse reinforcement have been replaced by cross-reference to EN 1992-1-1. Its provisions are based on a truss analogy, as before, but a more general version of it, in which the angle between members of the truss can be chosen by the designer. It is an application of strut-and-tie modelling, which is widely used in EN 1992-1-1.

The definitions of shear surfaces in *clause 6.6.6.1(2)P* and the basic design method are as before. The method of presentation reflects the need to separate the 'general' provisions (*clauses 6.6.6.1 to 6.6.6.3*) from those restricted to 'buildings' (*clause 6.6.6.4*).

Clause 6.6.6.1(4) requires the design longitudinal shear to be 'consistent with' that used for the design of the shear connectors. This means that the distribution along the beam of resistance to in-plane shear in the slab should be the same as that assumed for the design of the shear connection. For example, uniform resistance to longitudinal shear flow (v_L) should be provided where the connectors are uniformly spaced, even if the vertical shear over the length considered is not constant. It does not mean, for example, that if, for reasons concerning detailing, $v_{L, Rd} = 1.3v_{L, Ed}$ for the connectors, the transverse reinforcement must provide the same degree of over-strength.

In applying *clause 6.6.6.1(5)*, it is sufficiently accurate to assume that longitudinal bending stress in the concrete flange is constant across its effective width, and zero outside it. The clause is relevant, for example, to finding the shear on the plane a–a in the haunched beam shown in *Fig. 6.15*, which, for a symmetrical flange, is less than half of the shear resisted by the connectors.

Resistance of a concrete flange to longitudinal shear

Clause 6.6.6.2(1) refers to clause 6.2.4 of EN 1992-1-1, which is written for a design longitudinal shear stress v_{Ed} acting on a cross-section of thickness h_f. The clause requires the area of transverse reinforcement A_{sf} at spacing s_f to satisfy

$$A_{sf}f_{yd}/s_f > v_{Ed}h_f/\cot\theta_f \qquad \text{(6.21 in EN 1992-1-1)}$$

and the longitudinal shear stress to satisfy

$$v_{Ed} < \nu f_{cd} \sin\theta_f \cos\theta_f \qquad \text{(6.22 in EN 1992-1-1)}$$

where $\nu = 0.6(1 - f_{ck}/250)$, with f_{ck} in units of newtons per square millimetre. (The Greek letter ν used here in EN 1992-1-1 should not be confused with the Roman letter v, which is used for shear stress.)

The angle θ_f between the diagonal strut and the axis of the beam is chosen (within limits) by the designer. The use of the method is illustrated in the following example.

Example 6.6: transverse reinforcement for longitudinal shear

Figure 6.21 shows a plan of an area ABCD of a concrete flange, assumed to be in longitudinal compression, with shear stress v_{Ed} and transverse reinforcing bars of area A_{sf} at spacing s_f. The shear force per transverse bar is

$$F_v = v_{Ed} h_f s_f$$

acting on side AB of the rectangle shown. It is transferred to side CD by a concrete strut AC at angle θ_f to AB, and with edges that pass through the mid-points of AB, etc., as shown, so that the width of the strut is $s_f \sin \theta_f$.

For equilibrium at A, the force in the strut is

$$F_c = F_v \sec \theta_f \qquad \text{(D6.18)}$$

For equilibrium at C, the force in the transverse bar BC is

$$F_t = F_c \sin \theta_f = F_v \tan \theta_f \qquad \text{(D6.19)}$$

For minimum area of transverse reinforcement, θ_f should be chosen to be as small as possible. For a flange in compression, the limits to θ_f given in clause 6.2.4(4) of EN 1992-1-1 are

$$45° \geq \theta_f \geq 26.5° \qquad \text{(D6.20)}$$

so the initial choice for θ_f is 26.5°. Then, from equation (D6.19),

$$F_t = 0.5 F_v \qquad \text{(D6.21)}$$

From equation (6.22) above,

$$v_{Ed} < 0.40 \nu f_{cd}$$

If this inequality is satisfied, then the value chosen for θ_f is satisfactory. However, let us assume that the concrete strut is over-stressed, because

$$v_{Ed} = 0.48 \nu f_{cd}$$

To satisfy *equation (6.22)*

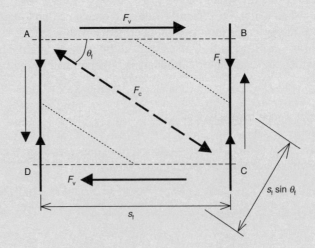

Fig. 6.21. Truss analogy for in-plane shear in a concrete flange

$$\sin \theta_f \cos \theta_f \geq 0.48$$

whence

$$\theta_f \geq 37°$$

The designer increases θ_f to 40°, which satisfies expression (D6.20). From equation (D6.19),

$$F_t = F_v \tan 40° = 0.84F_v$$

From equation (D6.21), the change in θ_f, made to limit the compressive stress in the concrete strut AC, increases the required area of transverse reinforcement by 68%.

The lengths of the sides of the triangle ABC in Fig. 6.21 are proportional to the forces F_v, F_t and F_c. For given F_v and s_f, increasing θ_f increases F_c, but for $\theta_f < 45°$ (the maximum value permitted), the increase in the width $s_f \sin \theta_f$ is greater, so the stress in the concrete is reduced.

Shear planes

Clause 6.6.6.1(3) refers to 'shear surfaces'. Those of types b–b, c–c, and d–d in *Fig. 6.15* are different from the type a–a surface because they resist almost the whole longitudinal shear, not (typically) about half of it. The relevant reinforcement intersects them twice, as shown by the factor 2 in the table in *Fig. 6.15*.

For a surface of type c–c in a beam with the steel section near one edge of the concrete flange, it is clearly wrong to assume that half of the shear crosses half of the surface c–c. However, in this situation the shear on the adjacent plane of type a–a will govern, so the method is not unsafe.

Minimum transverse reinforcement

Clause 6.6.6.3 on this subject is discussed under *clause 6.6.5.1* on resistance to separation.

Clause 6.6.6.3

Longitudinal shear in beams with composite slabs (**clause 6.6.6.4**)

Clause 6.6.6.4

Design rules are given for sheeting with troughs that run either transverse to the span of the steel beam, or parallel to it. Where they intersect a beam at some other angle, one can either use the more adverse of the two sets of rules, or combine them in an appropriate way. The rule for thickness of concrete in *clause 6.6.6.4(1)* is independent of the direction of the sheeting.

Clause 6.6.6.4(1)

In *clause 6.6.6.4(2)*, the 'type b–b' shear surface is as shown in *Fig. 6.16*, in which the labelling of the shear surfaces differs from that in *Fig. 6.15*.

Clause 6.6.6.4(2)

The contribution made by sheeting to resistance in longitudinal shear depends not only on its direction but also on whether the designer can determine the position of the ends of individual sheets, and whether these ends are attached to the steel beam by through-deck welding of stud connectors. If these decisions are made subsequently by the contractor, the designer may be unable to use transverse sheeting as reinforcement for shear in the plane of the slab. Its contribution to shear resistance is substantial where it is continuous across the beam (*clause 6.6.6.4(4)*) and is useful where through-deck welding is used (*clause 6.6.6.4(5)*). This is applied in Example 6.7.

Clause 6.6.6.4(4)
Clause 6.6.6.4(5)

Sheets attached only by fixings used for erection and those with their span parallel to that of the beam are ineffective as transverse reinforcement.

Through-deck welding of studs is also used to enhance the resistance of a composite slab to longitudinal shear. EN 1994-1-1 does not state whether both procedures can be used at once.

The question is discussed with reference to Fig. 6.22, which shows an exploded view of the base of a stud welded to a steel flange through a layer of sheeting, which spans towards the right-hand side of the diagram. The concrete in the mid-span region of the composite slab

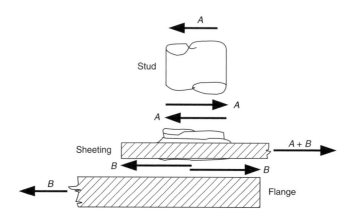

Fig. 6.22. A through-deck welded stud acting as an end anchorage for a composite slab, and also providing continuity for transverse reinforcement

applies the force A to the upper part of the stud, which enables it to anchor a tension A in the sheeting. The force B is due to the action of the steel top flange and the sheeting as equivalent transverse reinforcement.

It is clear from Fig. 6.22 that forces A and B are not additive for the stud, because A exists above the sheeting and B below it, but they are additive for the sheeting. The model in *clause 9.7.4(3)* for the calculation of resistance $P_{\mathrm{pb,\,Rd}}$ is not shear failure of the stud but bearing failure of the sheeting, which depends on the distance from the stud to the edge of the sheet.

This analysis shows that if the two procedures are used for the same stud, the available resistance $P_{\mathrm{pb,\,Rd}}$ should be split between them, in whatever ratio may be required.

Example 6.7: two-span beam with a composite slab – ultimate limit state

A floor structure for a department store consists of composite beams of uniform cross-section at 2.50 m spacing, fully continuous over two equal spans of 12.0 m. The floor consists of a composite slab of overall thickness 130 mm, spanning between the beams. The three supports for each beam may be treated as point supports, providing lateral and vertical restraint. A design is required for an internal beam, subjected to vertical loading only. The design service life is 50 years.

This particular concept is unlikely to be used in practice. The design will be found to be governed by resistance at the internal support, and only a small part of the bending resistance at mid-span can be used. However, it illustrates the use of many of the provisions of EN 1994-1-1, and is chosen for that reason. The design of the composite slab, the checking of the beam for serviceability limit states, and the influence of semi-continuous beam-to-column connections are the subjects of subsequent worked examples in this and later chapters of this guide.

It will be assumed initially that unpropped construction is used, and that the whole 24 m length of concrete flange is cast before significant composite action is developed in any of this length.

Loadings and materials
The characteristic imposed load, including partitions, is

$q_{\mathrm{k}} = 7.0 \text{ kN/m}^2 \qquad \gamma_{\mathrm{F}} = 1.50$

where γ_{F} is a partial safety factor. The floor finish adds

$g_{\mathrm{k1}} = 1.20 \text{ kN/m}^2 \qquad \gamma_{\mathrm{F}} = 1.35$

These are applied to the composite structure. For simplicity, the floor finish will be treated in global analyses as an imposed load, which is conservative.

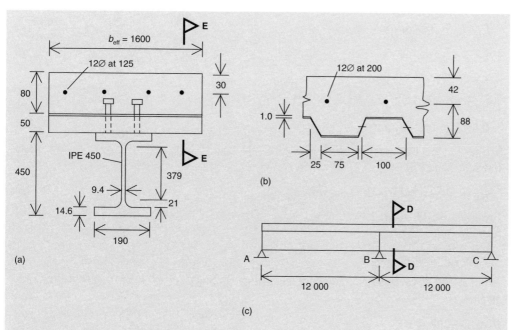

Fig. 6.23. Elevation and cross-sections of the two-span beam (dimensions in mm). (a) Section D–D. (b) Section E–E. (c) Elevation of beam

Table 6.2. Loadings per unit length of beam

	Load (kN/m)		
	Characteristic	Ultimate (minimum)	Ultimate (maximum)
Composite slab	5.02	6.78	6.78
Steel beam	0.76	1.02	1.02
Total, on steel beam	5.78	7.80	7.80
Floor finishes	1.20	1.62	1.62
Imposed load	17.50	0	26.25
Total, for composite beam	18.7	1.62	27.9
Total, for vertical shear	24.5	9.42	35.7

Preliminary studies have led to the choice of lightweight-aggregate concrete, of density class 1.8 and strength class LC25/28. For an oven-dry density not exceeding 1800 kg/m³, Table 11.1 in clause 11.3 of EN 1992-1-1 gives the design density of this reinforced concrete as 1950 kg/m³, which is now assumed to include the sheeting.

The chosen steel section is IPE 450, with the dimensions shown in Fig. 6.23. Its weight is $g_{k3} = 0.76$ kN/m, with $\gamma_F = 1.35$. Table 6.2 gives the loadings for a beam spacing of 2.5 m.

At this stage, the shape for the profiled sheeting is assumed to be as in Fig. 6.23. The mean thickness of the floor is 0.105 m, giving a characteristic load

$$g_{k2} = 0.105 \times 1.95 \times 9.81 = 2.01 \text{ kN/m}^2$$

with a partial safety factor $\gamma_F = 1.35$.

Properties of materials
Structural steel: grade S355, with $\gamma_M = 1.0$, so

$$f_y = f_{yd} = 355 \text{ N/mm}^2 \tag{D6.22}$$

and

$$\varepsilon = \sqrt{(235/255)} = 0.81$$

Concrete: $f_{ck} = 25 \text{ N/mm}^2$, $\gamma_C = 1.5$,

$$0.85f_{cd} = 14.2 \text{ N/mm}^2 \tag{D6.23}$$

From clause 11.3.1 of EN 1992-1-1, $\eta_1 = 0.4 + 0.6 \times 1800/2200 = 0.891$, so the mean tensile strength is

$$f_{lctm} = 0.891 \times 2.6 = 2.32 \text{ N/mm}^2 \tag{D6.24}$$

From clause 11.3.2 of EN 1992-1-1, $E_{lcm} = 31 \times (18/22)^2 = 20.7 \text{ kN/mm}^2$, so the short-term modular ratio is

$$n_0 = 210/20.7 = 10.1$$

From informative *Annex C*, and a 'dry' environment, the 'nominal total final free shrinkage strain' is

$$\varepsilon_{cs} = -500 \times 10^{-6}$$

Reinforcement: $f_{sk} = 500 \text{ N/mm}^2$, $\gamma_S = 1.15$,

$$f_{sd} = 435 \text{ N/mm}^2$$

Ductility: to be in Class B or C, from *clause 5.5.1(5)*.

Shear connectors: it is assumed that 19 mm studs will be used, welded through the steel sheeting, with ultimate tensile strength

$$f_u = 500 \text{ N/mm}^2$$

and $\gamma_V = 1.25$.

Durability

The floor finish is assumed to be such that the top of the slab is exposed to 'low air humidity'. From clause 4.2 of EN 1992-1-1, the exposure class is XC1. The minimum cover (clause 4.4.1) is then 15 mm for a service life of 50 years, plus a tolerance of between 5 and 10 mm that depends on the quality assurance system, and is here taken as 9 mm. At the internal support, the 12 mm longitudinal bars are placed above the transverse bars, with a top cover of 24 mm, as shown in Fig. 6.23.

Properties of the IPE 450 cross-section

From section tables:

Area:	$A_a = 9880 \text{ mm}^2$	fillet radius: $r = 21 \text{ mm}$
Second moments of area:	$10^{-6}I_{ay} = 337.4 \text{ mm}^4$	$10^{-6}I_{az} = 16.8 \text{ mm}^4$
Torsional moment of area:	$10^{-6}I_{at} = 0.659 \text{ mm}^4$	
Radii of gyration:	$i_y = 185 \text{ mm}$ $\quad i_z = 41.2 \text{ mm}$	$i_x = 190 \text{ mm}$
Section moduli:	$10^{-6}W_{ay} = 1.50 \text{ mm}^3$	$10^{-6}W_{az} = 0.176 \text{ mm}^3$
Plastic section modulus:	$10^{-6}W_{pl,a,y} = 1.702 \text{ mm}^3$	(D6.25)

The factor 10^{-6} is used to enable moments in kN m to be related to stresses in N/mm^2 without further adjustment, and because it gives numbers of convenient size.

Effective widths of concrete flange
In *Fig. 5.1* of *clause 5.4.1.2*, $L_1 = L_2 = 12.0$ m; L_e for $b_{eff,1} = 10.2$ m. Assume $b_0 = 0.1$ m; then

$$b_1 = b_2 = 2.5/2 - 0.05 = 1.20 \text{ m}$$

At mid-span,

$$b_{eff} = 0.1 + 2 \times 10.2/8 = 2.65 \text{ m (but} \leq \textbf{2.5 m)}$$

so $b_{ei} = 2.4/2 = 1.2$ m. At the internal support, L_e for $b_{eff,2} = 0.25 \times 24 = 6$ m;

$$b_{eff} = 0.1 + 2 \times 6/8 = \textbf{1.60 m}$$

At an end support, $b_{ei} = 1.20$ m;

$$\beta_i = 0.55 + 0.025 \times 10.2/1.20 = 0.762$$

$$b_{eff} = 0.1 + 2 \times 0.762 \times 1.2 = \textbf{1.83 m}$$

Classification of composite cross-section
The class of the web is quite sensitive to the area of longitudinal reinforcement in the slab at the internal support. It is (inconveniently) necessary to assume a value for this before the checks that govern it can be made. Large-diameter bars may not give sufficient control of crack widths, so the reinforcement is assumed to be **12 mm bars at 125 mm**, giving 13 bars within a 1.625 m width, so

$$A_s = \textbf{1470 mm}^2$$

The effective area of concrete slab is 1.6 m by 80 mm, so

$$A_s/A_c = \rho_s = \textbf{0.0113}$$

The requirement of *clause 5.5.1(5)* for minimum ρ_s will be checked during the design for crack-width control; see Example 7.1.
The force in these bars at yield is

$$F_{s,y} = 1470 \times 0.435 = 639 \text{ kN}$$

Assuming a Class 2 section, the stress distribution for $M_{pl,Rd}$ is needed. Starting from the stress distribution for $M_{pl,a,Rd}$, the depth of steel web that changes from tension to compression is

$$639/(9.4 \times 2 \times 0.355) = 96 \text{ mm}$$

For classification, *clause 5.5.1(1)P* refers to clause 5.5.2 of EN 1993-1-1. Its Table 5.2 defines the depth of web, c, as that bounded by the root radii. Here, $c = 379$ mm, of which the depth in compression is

$$379/2 + 96 = 285 \text{ mm}$$

whence

$$\alpha = 285/379 = 0.75$$

This exceeds $c/2$, so from Table 5.2, for Class 2,

$$c/t \leq 456 \, \varepsilon/(13\alpha - 1) = 42.2$$

The actual $c/t = 381/9.4 = 40.5$; so at the internal support, **the web is Class 2**. At mid-span, it is obviously in Class 1 or 2. For the compression flange, from Table 5.2,

$$c = (190 - 9.4)/23 - 21 = 69.3 \text{ mm}$$

Hence

$c/t\varepsilon = 69.3/(14.6 \times 0.81) = 5.86$

The limit for a Class 1 flange is 9.0; so **the bottom flange is Class 1**.
The member is Class 2 at the internal support and Class 1 or 2 at mid-span.

It follows from *clause 5.4.2.4(2)* that for global analyses for ultimate limit states, (provided that lateral–torsional buckling does not govern) the whole of the loading may be assumed to act on the composite member; and from *clause 6.2.1.1(1)P* that rigid-plastic theory may be used for resistances to bending at all cross-sections of the beam.

The use of partial shear connection (*clause 6.2.1.3(1)*) is limited to sagging regions, in accordance with *clause 6.6.2.2*, which is for '*beams in which plastic theory is used for resistance of cross-sections*' (i.e. sections in Class 1 or 2).

Design is thus much simpler when there are no beams with cross-sections in Class 3 or 4. This can usually be achieved in buildings, but rarely in multi-span bridges.

It is notable that if the steel top flange were in Class 3, its connection to the slab would not enable it to be upgraded, because the condition of *clause 6.6.5.5(2)* is that the spacing of shear connectors does not exceed $15t_f\varepsilon$, which is $15 \times 14.6 \times 0.81 = 177$ mm. This would be impracticable with the sheeting profile shown in Fig. 6.23.

Plastic resistance to bending (clause 6.2.1.2)
At the internal support, it has been found (above) that a 96 mm depth of the upper half of the web is in compression. The design plastic resistance to hogging bending is that of the steel section plus the effect of the reinforcing bars, shown in Fig. 6.24(a):

$$M_{\text{pl, a, Rd}} = 1.702 \times 0.355 = \textbf{604 kN m} \qquad \text{(hogging and sagging)}$$

$$M_{\text{pl, Rd}} = 604 + 639 \times 0.277 = \textbf{781 kN m} \qquad \text{(hogging)}$$

The characteristic plastic resistance is also needed. With $\gamma_S = 1$ for the reinforcement, its force at yield increases to $639 \times 1.15 = 735$ kN; the depth of web to change stress is 110 mm; and, by the method used for $M_{\text{pl, Rd}}$,

$$M_{\text{pl, Rk}} = \textbf{802 kN m} \qquad \text{(hogging)}$$

All of these resistances may need to be reduced to allow for lateral–torsional buckling or vertical shear.

For sagging bending at mid-span, reinforcement in compression is ignored, and the available area of concrete is 2.5 m wide and 80 mm thick. If it is all stressed to $0.85f_{\text{cd}}$, the compressive force is

$$F_c = 14.2 \times 2.5 \times 80 = 2840 \text{ kN} \qquad \text{(D6.26)}$$

If the whole steel section is at yield, the tensile force is

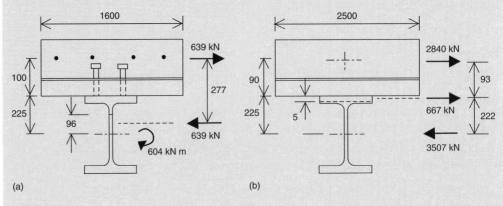

Fig. 6.24. Plastic moments of resistance in (a) hogging and (b) sagging bending (dimensions in mm)

Table 6.3. Elastic section properties of the composite cross-section

Cross-section	Modular ratio	b_{eff} (m)	Neutral axis (mm)	$10^{-6}I_y$ (mm^4)	$10^{-6}W_{c, top}$ (mm^3)
(1) Support, cracked, reinforced	–	1.6	42	467	–
(2) Support, uncracked	10.1	1.6	177	894	50.7
(3) Support, uncracked	20.2	1.6	123	718	62.5
(4) Mid-span, uncracked	10.1	2.5	210	996	69.5
(5) Mid-span, uncracked	20.2	2.5	158	828	84.7
(6) Mid-span, uncracked	28.7	2.5	130	741	94.5

$$F_a = 9880 \times 0.355 = 3507 \text{ kN}$$

Assuming full shear connection, with the plastic neutral axis in the steel top flange, the thickness of flange to change from tension to compression is

$$t_{f, c} = (3507 - 2840)/(2 \times 0.355 \times 190) = 5.0 \text{ mm}$$

The longitudinal forces are then as shown in Fig. 6.24(b), and

$$M_{pl, Rd} = 2840 \times 0.315 + 667 \times 0.222 = \mathbf{1043 \text{ kN m}} \quad \text{(sagging)} \quad \text{(D6.27)}$$

This resistance will be reduced later by the use of partial shear connection.

Plastic resistance to vertical shear
Clause 6.2.2.2 refers to clause 6.2.6 of EN 1993-1-1. This defines the shear area of a rolled I-section as

$$A_v = A - 2bt_f + (t_w + 2r)t_f = 9880 - 380 \times 14.6 + 51.4 \times 14.6 = 5082 \text{ mm}^2$$

and gives the design plastic shear resistance as

$$V_{pl, Rd} = A_v(f_y/\sqrt{3})/\gamma_{M0} = 5082 \times 0.355/\sqrt{3} = \mathbf{1042 \text{ kN}}$$

For shear buckling, *clause 6.2.2.3* refers to Section 5 of EN 1993-1-5. No buckling check is required, because h_w/t for the steel web, based on the depth between the flanges, is 45, below the limit of 48.6.

Flexural properties of elastic cross-sections
Several sets of elastic properties are needed, even where the steel beam is of uniform section, because of changes of modular ratio and effective width, and the use of 'cracked' and 'uncracked' sections. Here, slab reinforcement is ignored in the 'uncracked' analyses. The error is conservative (except for the shear connection) and usually very small. It is convenient to calculate all these properties at the outset (Table 6.3).

From *clause 5.4.2.2(11)*, creep may be allowed for by using a modular ratio $n = 2n_0 = 20.2$ for both short-term and long-term loadings. Results for $n = n_0$ are included in Table 6.3 for use in Chapter 7. Effects of shrinkage are unusually high in this example. For these, it helps to use the more accurate modular ratio 28.7, as explained later.

The calculation for the uncracked properties at the internal support, with $n = 10.1$, is now given, as an example. In 'steel' units, the width of the slab is $1.6/10.1 = 0.158$ m, so the composite section is as shown in Fig. 6.25. Its properties are:

Area:

$$A = 9880 + 158 \times 80 = 9880 + 12640 = \mathbf{22\,520 \text{ mm}^2}$$

Height of neutral axis above centre of steel section:

$$z_{na} = 12\,640 \times 315/22\,520 = 177 \text{ mm}$$

Second moment of area:

$$10^{-6}I_y = 337.4 + 9880 \times 0.177^2 + 12\,640 \times 0.138^2 = 894 \text{ mm}^4$$

Flexural stiffness:

$$10^{-6}E_a I_y = 210 \times 894 = 187\,700 \text{ kN mm}^2$$

Section modulus, top of slab, in concrete units:

$$10^{-6}W_{c,\,top} = 894 \times 10.1/178 = 50.7 \text{ mm}^3$$

Similar calculations were done for the other elastic section properties required. The results are given in Table 6.3.

Global analysis
The resistance to lateral–torsional buckling of the beam near the internal support, $M_{b,\,Rd}$, depends on the bending-moment distribution, so global analysis is done next.

Wherever possible, the rules for global analysis in *Section 5* apply to both ultimate and serviceability limit states. Where alternatives are permitted, both types of limit state should be considered before making a choice.

For this beam, there is no need to take account of the flexibility of joints (*clause 5.1.2*). First-order elastic theory may be used (*clauses 5.2.2(1)* and *5.4.1.1(1)*).

Clause 5.2.2(4) on imperfections is satisfied, because lateral–torsional buckling is the only type of instability that need be considered, and its resistance formulae take account of imperfections.

The simplest method of allowing for cracking, in *clause 5.4.2.3(3)*, is applicable here, and will be used. Cracking almost always occurs in continuous beams. In this example, calculations for uncracked sections, using the longer method of *clause 5.4.2.3(2)*, found that for the ultimate imposed loading on both spans, the tensile stress in the concrete at the internal support exceeded three times its tensile strength. This ignored shrinkage, which further increases the tension.

For this beam, *clause 5.4.2.3(3)* requires the use of cracked section properties over a length of 1.8 m each side of the internal support. For global analysis, *clause 5.4.1.2(4)* permits the use of the mid-span effective width for the whole span; but here b_{eff} for the cracked region is taken as 1.6 m, because resistances are based on this width and reinforcement outside it may be quite light.

The proposed use of $n = 20.2$ for the uncracked region merits discussion. Most of the permanent load is applied to the steel beam, which does not creep, but resistances are based on the whole of the load acting on the composite beam. Bending moment at the internal support governs. Creep increases this, and the long-term effects of shrinkage are so significant that the case $t \rightarrow \infty$ is more critical than $t \approx 0$.

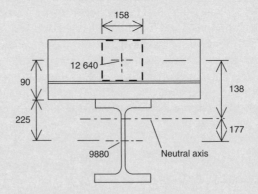

Fig. 6.25. Uncracked composite section at internal support, with $n_0 = 10.1$ (dimensions in mm)

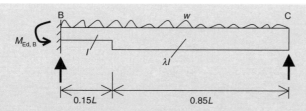

Fig. 6.26. Elastic propped cantilever with change of section at 0.15L

Table 6.4. Design ultimate bending moments at the fixed end of the propped cantilever

Loading	w (kN/m)	n	$10^{-6}I_y$ (mm⁴)	λ	$M_{Ed, B}$ (kN m)
Permanent	9.42	10.1	996	2.13	133
Permanent	9.42	20.2	828	1.77	142
Variable	26.25	10.1	996	2.13	370
Variable	26.25	20.2	828	1.77	394

For the quasi-permanent combination, the coefficient ψ_2 for variable load in a department store is given in clause A1.2.2(1) of EN 1990 as 0.6, and $0.6q_k$ is 40% of $1.5q_k$, so some creep of the composite member is likely.

In this example, $n = 2n_0 = 20.2$ will be used for all action effects except shrinkage, for which a more accurate value is determined, as follows.

Modular ratio for the effects of shrinkage
From *clause 5.4.2.2(4)*, the age of loading can be assumed to be 1 day. Creep coefficients for normal-weight concrete are given in Fig. 3.1 of EN 1992-1-1 in terms of h_0, the notional size of the cross-section. For a slab with both surfaces exposed, this equals the slab thickness; but the slab here has one sealed surface, and h_0 is twice its thickness. The mean thickness (see Fig. 6.23) is 105 mm, so $h_0 = 210$ mm.

For normally hardening cement and 'inside conditions', Fig. 3.1 of EN 1992-1-1 gives the creep coefficient $\varphi(\infty, t_0)$ as 5.0. For lightweight concrete, clause 11.3.3(1) of EN 1992-1-1 gives a correction factor, which in this case is $(18/22)^2$, giving $\varphi = 3.35$. The creep multiplier ψ_L in *clause 5.4.2.2(2)* takes account of the shape of the stress–time curve for the effect considered, and is 0.55 for shrinkage. The modular ratio for shrinkage effects is

$$n = n_0(1 + \psi_L\varphi_t) = 10.1(1 + 0.55 \times 3.35) = 28.7$$

Bending moments
Although, through cracking, the beam is of non-uniform section, calculation of bending moments algebraically is straightforward, because the two spans are equal. When both spans are fully loaded, only a propped cantilever need be considered (Fig. 6.26).

For distributed loading w per unit length, and ratio of flexural stiffnesses λ, as shown, an equation for the elastic bending moment M_{Ed} at B is derived in the first edition of Johnson and Buckby[37] (p. 375). It is

$$M_{Ed, B} = (wL^2/4)(0.110\lambda + 0.890)/(0.772\lambda + 1.228)$$

The results are given in Table 6.4.

Hence, the design bending moment for the internal support, excluding shrinkage effects, with $n = 20.2$, is

$$M_{Ed, B} = 394 + 142 = \textbf{536 kN m}$$

The vertical shear at the internal support is

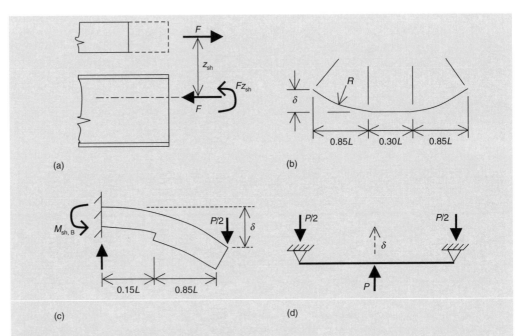

Fig. 6.27. Secondary effects of shrinkage

$$V_{\text{Ed, B}} = (9.42 + 26.25) \times 6 + 536/12 = \textbf{259 kN}$$

The plastic shear resistance of the IPE 450 section, $V_{\text{pl, Rd}}$, was found earlier to be 1042 kN. From *clause 6.2.2.4(1)*, bending resistance is not reduced by shear until $V_{\text{Ed}} > V_{\text{pl, Rd}}/2$, so there is no reduction here.

Redistribution of moments is not used because *clause 5.4.4(4)* does not permit it if allowance for lateral–torsional buckling is required.

Secondary effects of shrinkage
Shrinkage of the slab causes sagging curvature and shortening of the composite member, the 'primary effects'. In a continuous beam, the curvature causes bending moments and shear forces, the 'secondary effects'. In regions assumed to be cracked, both the curvature and the stresses from the primary effects are neglected (*clauses 5.4.2.2(8) and 6.2.1.5(5)*).

The important secondary effect in this beam, a hogging bending moment at the internal support, is now calculated. Shrinkage is a permanent action, and so is not reduced by a combination factor ψ_0.

The slab is imagined to be separated from the steel beam, Fig. 6.27(a). Its area A_c is that of the concrete above the sheeting. It shrinks. A force is applied to extend it to its original length. It is

$$F = A_c(E_a/n)|\varepsilon_{\text{cs}}| \tag{D6.28}$$

This acts at the centre of the slab, at a distance z_{sh} above the centroid of the composite section. The parts of the beam are reconnected. To restore equilibrium, an opposite force F and a sagging moment Fz_{sh} are applied to the composite section.

The radius of curvature of the uncracked part of the beam is

$$R = E_a\lambda I_y/Fz_{\text{sh}} \tag{D6.29}$$

If the centre support is removed, the deflection δ at that point is

$$\delta = (0.85L)^2/2R \tag{D6.30}$$

from the geometry of the circle (Fig. 6.27(b)).

It remains to calculate the force P, applied at that point, to reduce the deflection to zero, so that the centre support can be replaced (Fig. 6.27(d)). The secondary hogging bending moment at B is

$$M_{Ed, sh, B} = PL/2 \tag{D6.31}$$

and the vertical shear is $P/2$.

Using slope and deflection coefficients for a cantilever (Fig. 6.27(c)), P can be found from the result

$$\delta = (P/2)L^3(0.13\lambda + 0.20)/(E_a I_y \lambda) \tag{D6.32}$$

The calculation is as follows:

$$A_c = 2.5 \times 0.08 = 0.20 \text{ m}^2$$

$E_a = 210$ kN/mm², $n = 28.7$ and $\varepsilon_{cs} = -500 \times 10^{-6}$; so, from equation (D6.28), $F = 732$ kN. From Table 6.3,

$$\lambda I_y = 741 \times 10^6 \text{ mm}^4 \qquad z_{sh} = 225 - 40 = 185 \text{ mm}$$

so, from equation (D6.29), $R = 1149$ m, and, from equation (D6.30) with $L = 12$ m, $\delta = 45.3$ mm. From Table 6.3,

$$I_y = 467 \times 10^6 \text{ mm}^4$$

so

$$\lambda = 741/467 = 1.587$$

so, from equation (D6.32),

$$P/2 = 10.0 \text{ kN}$$

and

$$M_{Ed, sh, B} = 10 \times 12 = \textbf{120 kN m}$$

Should shrinkage be neglected at ultimate load?
This unusually high value, 120 kN m, results from the use of a material with high shrinkage and a continuous beam with two equal spans. It increases the ultimate design bending moment at B by 22%. *Clause 5.4.2.2(7)* permits this to be neglected if resistance is not influenced by lateral–torsional buckling.

The reasoning is that as the bending resistances of the sections are determined by plastic theory, the ultimate condition approaches a collapse mechanism, in which elastic deformations (e.g. those from shrinkage) become negligible in comparison with total deformations.

However, if the resistance at the internal support is governed by lateral–torsional buckling, and if the buckling moment (to be calculated) is far below the plastic moment, the inelastic behaviour may not be sufficient for the shrinkage effects to become negligible, before failure occurs at the internal support. Hence, the secondary shrinkage moment is not neglected at this stage, even though this beam happens to have a large reserve of strength at mid-span, and would not fail until the support section was far into the post-buckling phase.

Resistance to lateral–torsional buckling
The top flange of the steel beam is restrained in both position and direction by the composite slab. Lateral buckling of the bottom flange near the internal support is accompanied by bending of the web, so the problem here is *distortional* lateral buckling.

The provisions in EN 1994-1-1 headed 'lateral–torsional buckling' (*clause 6.4*), are in fact for distortional buckling. *Clause 6.4.1(3)* permits, as an alternative, use of the provisions in EN 1993-1-1 for steel beams. The method of *clause 6.4.2* is used here. The detailed comments on it, both in the main text and in Appendix A, should be referred to as required. The method requires the calculation of the elastic critical buckling moment at the internal support, M_{cr}, for which information is given in tables in ENV 1994-1-1 (reproduced as graphs in Appendix A (Figs A.3 and A.4)). The simple method of *clause 6.4.3* is not available, as the loading does not conform to *paragraph (b)* of *clause 6.4.3(1)*.

Buckling near an internal support is often most critical in a span with minimum load that is adjacent to a fully loaded span. In this beam it was found that although the buckling moment $M_{b, Rd}$ is increased when both spans are loaded (because the length of bottom flange in compression is reduced), the increase in the applied moment M_{Ed} is greater, so the both-spans-loaded case is more critical. This case is now considered, with $n = 20.2$ and all load assumed to act on the composite member.

From Table 6.4, the bending moments in the beam are as shown in Fig. 6.28. Shrinkage is considered separately. The 'simply-supported' moment M_0 is $35.7 \times 12^2/8 = 643$ kN m, so, from Fig. A.3 for C_4 (see Appendix A),

$$\psi = M_B/M_0 = 536/643 = 0.834 \qquad \text{and} \qquad C_4 = 28.3$$

The elastic critical buckling moment was given earlier as

$$M_{cr} = (k_c C_4/L)[(G_a I_{at} + k_s L^2/\pi^2)E_a I_{afz}]^{1/2} \tag{D6.11}$$

where k_c is a property of the composite section, given in Section 6.4.2, G_a is the shear modulus for steel,

$$G_a = E_a/[2(1 + \upsilon_a)] = 80.8 \text{ kN/mm}^2$$

I_{at} is the torsional moment of area of the steel section,

$$I_{at} = 0.659 \times 10^6 \text{ mm}^4$$

k_s is defined in *clause 6.4.2(6)*, and I_{afz} is the minor-axis second moment of area of the steel bottom flange,

$$10^{-6}I_{afz} = 1.90^3 \times 14.6/12 = 8.345 \text{ mm}^4$$

The stiffness k_s is now found. It depends on the lesser of the 'cracked' flexural stiffnesses of the composite slab at a support and at mid-span, $(EI)_2$. The value at the support governs. An approximation for this, derived in Appendix A, is

$$(EI)_2 = E_a[A_s A_e z^2/(A_s + A_e) + A_e h_p^2/12]$$

where A_e is the equivalent transformed area per unit width of concrete in compression,

$$A_e = b_0 h_p/nb_s$$

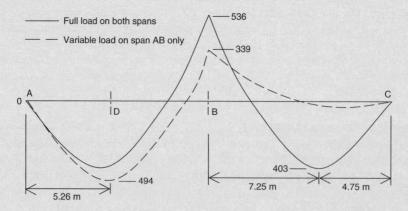

Fig. 6.28. Bending-moment distributions for ultimate limit state, excluding shrinkage

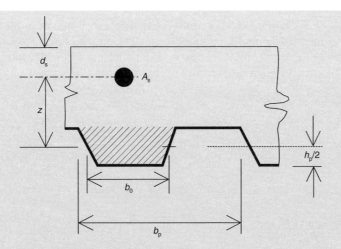

Fig. 6.29. Cross-section of the composite slab

where b_0 is the mean width of the troughs, b_s is the spacing of the troughs, h_p is the depth of the sheeting, A_s is the area of top reinforcement per unit width of slab and z is the 'lever arm', as shown in Fig. A.1 of Appendix A.

Calculation of $(EI)_2$ *for the composite slab, and* k_s
It is assumed that the transverse reinforcement above the steel beam will be below the longitudinal bars and not less than **12 mm bars at 200 mm**, giving $A_s = 565$ mm²/m and $d_s = 42$ mm, whence $z = 63$ mm (Fig. 6.29).

Assuming that buckling is caused by a short-term overload, n is taken as 10.1. From Fig. 6.23, $b_0/b_s = 0.5$; $h_p = 50$ mm; so $A_e = 2475$ mm²/m. Hence,

$$(EI)_2 = 210[0.565 \times 2.475 \times 63^2/3040 + 2.475 \times 50^2/12\,000] = 491 \text{ kN m}^2/\text{m}$$

From *clause 6.4.2(6)*, for unit width of a slab continuous across the steel beams at spacing a, and assuming that the conditions for using $\alpha = 4$ apply,

$$k_1 = 4(EI)_2/a = 4 \times 491/2.5 = 786 \text{ kN m/rad}$$

per metre width, and

$$k_2 = E_a t_w^3/[4h_s(1 - v_a^2)]$$

where h_s is the distance between the centres of the flanges of the IPE 450 section, 435 mm. Thus,

$$k_2 = 210 \times 9.4^3/(4 \times 435 \times 0.91) = 110 \text{ kN/rad}$$

and

$$k_s = k_1 k_2/(k_1 + k_2) = 786 \times 110/896 = 96.4 \text{ kN/rad}$$

Calculation of k_c
For a doubly symmetrical steel section, from equations (D6.12) and (D6.13),

$$k_c = (h_s I_y/I_{ay})/[(h_s^2/4 + i_x^2)/e + h_s]$$

with

$$e = AI_{ay}/[A_a z_c(A - A_a)]$$

In these expressions, the symbols are properties of the steel section, given earlier, except that A is the area of the cracked composite section,

$$A = A_a + A_s = 11\,350 \text{ mm}^2$$

and z_c is the distance between the centroid of the steel beam and mid-depth of the slab. Here, 'slab' means the 130 mm-deep composite slab, not the 80 mm depth of concrete that contributes to the composite section. It is the stiffness of the composite slab in the transverse direction that prevents rotation of the steel top flange; so

$$z_c = 225 + 130/2 = 290 \text{ mm}$$

Hence,

$$e = 11\,350 \times 337 \times 10^6/(9880 \times 290 \times 1470) = 909 \text{ mm}$$

and

$$k_c = (435 \times 467/337)/[(218^2 + 190^2)/909 + 435] = 1.15$$

Calculation of M_{cr} *and* $M_{b, Rd}$
From equation (D6.11) for M_{cr}:

$$M_{cr} = (1.15 \times 28.3/12)[(80.8 \times 0.659 + 96.4 \times 12^2/\pi^2) \times 210 \times 8.345]^{1/2} = \mathbf{4340 \text{ kN m}}$$

From *clause 6.4.2(4)*, the relative slenderness depends also on the characteristic resistance moment, calculated earlier. The slenderness is

$$\bar{\lambda}_{LT} = \sqrt{(M_{Rk}/M_{cr})} = (802/4340)^{1/2} = 0.430$$

For the reduction factor χ_{LT} for a rolled section, *clause 6.4.2(1)* refers to clause 6.3.2.3 of EN 1993-1-1, where buckling curve c is specified for this IPE section. This could be taken to mean the curve c plotted in Fig. 6.4 of EN 1993-1-1; but that curve is inconsistent with the equation for χ_{LT} in *clause 6.3.2.3*. This is understood to mean that the value of α_{LT} given for curve c in Table 6.3 of EN 1993-1-1 should be used in calculating χ_{LT}. Its value depends on the parameters $\bar{\lambda}_{LT,0}$ and β, which can be given in a National Annex. The recommended values, 0.4 and 0.75 respectively, are used here.
    The calculation is

$$\Phi_{LT} = 0.5[1 + \alpha_{LT}(\bar{\lambda}_{LT} - \bar{\lambda}_{LT,0}) + \beta\bar{\lambda}_{LT}^2] = 0.577$$

$$\chi_{LT} = \frac{1}{[\Phi_{LT} + \sqrt{(\Phi_{LT}^2 - \beta\bar{\lambda}_{LT}^2)}]} = 0.983$$

(The use of Fig. 6.4 gives the much lower result $\chi_{LT} = 0.88$.)
    The buckling resistance is

$$M_{b, Rd} = \chi_{LT}M_{pl, Rd} = 0.983 \times 781 = \mathbf{767 \text{ kN m}}$$

This is well above the design ultimate moment with shrinkage included, $M_{Ed} = 656$ kN m. The result is quite sensitive to the values specified for $\bar{\lambda}_{LT,0}$ and β.
    Clause 6.3.2.2 of EN 1993-1-1 includes a rule that if $M_{Ed}/M_{cr} \leq 0.16$, lateral–torsional buckling effects may be ignored. This applies here: $M_{Ed} = 0.153M_{cr}$. The rule appears to be linked to the use of $\bar{\lambda}_{LT,0} = 0.4$. It is not clear whether it applies if a National Annex specifies a lower value.
    The provision of bracing to the bottom flange is considered at the end of this example.

Design for sagging bending
The maximum sagging bending occurs in a span when the other span carries minimum load, and is reduced by creep, so $n = 10.1$ is assumed. Removal of variable load from one span halves the bending moment it causes at the internal support, so from Table 6.4 the bending moment at the internal support is

$$M_{Ed, B} = 133 + 370/2 = 318 \text{ kN m}$$

For the span with loading 35.67 kN/m, the end reaction is

$V_{Ed, A} = 35.67 \times 6 - 318/12 = 188$ kN

so the point of maximum moment is at a distance $188/35.67 = 5.26$ m from the support, and the maximum sagging moment is

$M_{Ed} = 188 \times 5.26/2 = $ **494 kN m**

This is so far below $M_{pl, Rd}$, 1043 kN m, that the least permitted degree of shear connection will be used. M_{Ed} is even below $M_{pl, a, Rd}$, which is 604 kN m.

From *clause 6.6.1.2(1)* the span length in sagging bending may be taken as $0.85L$, or 10.2 m here. From *equation (6.12)* with $f_y = 355$ N/mm^2, the minimum degree of shear connection is

$\eta = n/n_f = 1 - (0.75 - 0.03 \times 10.2) = 0.56$

Clause 6.6.1.2(3) permits a lower value, subject to some conditions. It was found that one of these – that there should be only one stud connector per rib of sheeting – could not be satisfied. The minimum number of connectors in each half of the sagging region is therefore $0.56n_f$, where n_f is the number for full shear connection. From Fig. 6.24(b), the compressive force in the slab is then not less than $2840 \times 0.56 = 1590$ kN. Recalculation of $M_{pl, Rd}$, by the method used before gives

$M_{pl, Rd} = $ **946 kN m**

which is almost twice the resistance required.

It does not follow that the design of this beam as non-composite would be satisfactory. Example 7.1 shows that its deflection would probably be excessive.

Design of the shear connection

The degree of shear connection used here enables the studs to be treated as 'ductile'. An alternative design, using non-ductile connectors, is given in Example 6.8.

From *clause 6.6.5.8(1)* the height of the 19 mm studs must be at least $50 + 2 \times 19 = 88$ mm. The standard height of 95 mm, after welding, satisfies this rule.

The design shear resistance per stud is governed by *equation (6.19)* of *clause 6.6.3.1(1)*:

$P_{Rd} = 0.29d^2(f_{ck}E_{cm})^{1/2}/\gamma_V = 0.29 \times 19^2(25 \times 20\ 700)^{1/2}/(1000 \times 1.25) = 60.25$ kN

This result is modified by a factor k_t given in *clause 6.6.4.2*. It depends on the height of the stud, h_{sc}, the dimensions of the trough in the sheeting (see Fig. 6.23), the thickness of the sheeting (assumed to be 1.0 mm) and the number of studs per trough, n_r.

For $n_r = 1$: $k_t = 0.7 \times 100/50 \times (95/50 - 1) = 1.26$, but ≤ 0.85

For $n_r = 2$: $k_t = 1.26/\sqrt{2} = 0.89$, but ≤ 0.70

Provided that the studs are not also required to anchor the profiled sheeting, the resistances are therefore

$P_{Rd, 1} = 0.85 \times 60.25 = $ **51.2 kN**   (D6.33)

$P_{Rd, 2} = 0.7 \times 60.25 = $ **42.2 kN**   (D6.34)

so that a trough with two studs provides the equivalent of $2 \times 42.2/51.2 = 1.65$ single studs.

From Fig. 6.28, the studs for maximum sagging bending have to be provided within a length of 5.26 m. The troughs are spaced at 0.2 m, so 26 are available. The design compressive force in the slab is 1590 kN, so the design shear flow is

$1590/5.2 = 306$ kN/m

The number of single studs required is

$n_s = 1590/51.2 = 31$

Hence, two studs per trough have to be used over part of the span.

For a shear span in a building, EN 1994-1-1 does not specify how non-uniform shear connection should be arranged. Slip is minimized when the density of the connection is related to the shear per unit length, so the regions with pairs of studs should be adjacent to the supports.

If the minimum number of troughs with two studs is n_{2s},

$$1.65n_{2s} + 26 - n_{2s} = 31$$

whence

$$n_{2s} \geq 7.8$$

For the cracked section in hogging bending, $A_s f_{sd} = 639$ kN, which requires 12.5 single studs. When the hogging moment is a maximum, the distance from an internal support to the cross-section of maximum sagging moment is 7.25 m (Fig. 6.28), so 36 troughs are available for a total of $31 + 12.5 = 43.5$ single studs.

If the minimum number of troughs with two studs is n_{2h},

$$1.65n_{2h} + 36 - n_{2h} = 43.5$$

whence

$$n_{2h} \geq 11.6$$

The design shear flow is

$$(1590 + 639)/7.2 = 310 \text{ kN/m}$$

The arrangement of studs shown in Fig. 6.30 provides the equivalent of 31.2 and 43.8 studs, within the lengths 5.2 and 7.2 m, respectively.

The maximum sagging and hogging bending moments are caused by different arrangements of imposed loading. This method of calculation takes account of this, with the result that two studs near mid-span are effective for both sagging and hogging resistance.

It is quicker to assume that the maximum sagging and hogging bending moments are caused by a single loading. The resulting increase in the total number of studs is negligible. The disadvantage is that it is not clear how many of the troughs with two studs per trough should be near each end of the span.

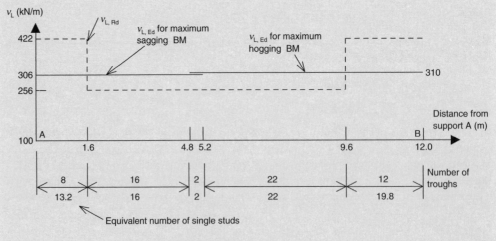

Fig. 6.30. Arrangement of stud connectors in one 12 m span

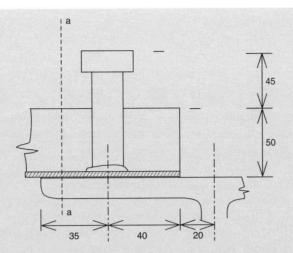

Fig. 6.31. Detail of a stud welded through discontinuous profiled sheeting (dimensions in mm)

Design of the transverse reinforcement

Clause 6.6.6.1(4) says that the design longitudinal shear for the concrete slab should be *'consistent with the design and spacing of the shear connectors'*. This is taken to mean that the resistance of the shear connection, rather than the design loading, determines the longitudinal shear. Its maximum occurs where there are two studs per trough, and is

$$v_{L, Ed} = 10 \times 42.2 = 422 \text{ kN/m}$$

From *clause 6.6.6.4(2)*, shear surfaces that pass closely around a stud need not be considered. The critical situation is thus where sheeting is not continuous across a beam. It is assumed to be anchored by a stud, as shown in Fig. 6.31. From symmetry, the critical shear plane, labelled a–a, is to be designed to resist 211 kN/m.

The shear resisted by the sheeting is given in *clause 6.6.6.4(5)*. For the design bearing resistance of the sheeting it refers to *clause 9.7.4*. For the detailing shown in Fig. 6.31, the end distance *a* is 40 mm. The diameter of the weld collar is taken as

$$1.1 \times 19 = 20.9 \text{ mm}$$

whence k_φ in *clause 9.7.4(3)* is

$$k_\varphi = 1 + 40/20.9 = 2.91$$

The thickness of the profiled sheeting is shown in Fig. 6.23 as 1.0 mm; but the composite slab has not yet been designed. Here, it is assumed to be at least 0.9 mm thick, with a yield strength of 350 N/mm² and $\gamma_M = 1.0$. From *equation (9.10)*,

$$P_{pb, Rd} = k_\varphi d_{d0} t f_{yp, d} = 2.91 \times 20.9 \times 0.9 \times 0.35 = 19.1 \text{ kN/stud}$$

From *clause 6.6.6.4(5)*, with a stud spacing of 200 mm, the shear resistance provided by the sheeting is

$$v_{L, pd, Rd} = 19.1/0.2 = 95 \text{ kN/m}$$

This must not exceed the yield strength of the sheeting, $A_p f_{yp, d}$, which for this sheeting is over 400 kN/m.

The design shear for the concrete slab, of thickness 80 mm, is

$$v_{L, Ed} = 211 - 95 = 116 \text{ kN/m}$$

Clause 6.6.6.2(1) refers to clause 6.2.4 of EN 1992-1-1, for shear between web and flanges of T-sections. The method is a truss analogy, with some choice provided for the angle θ_f between the concrete diagonals of the truss and the longitudinal direction. The reinforcement required increases with the angle θ_f. For simplicity, the minimum angle given in clause 6.2.4(4) of EN 1992-1-1 for a tension flange, 38.6°, will be used for the whole length of the span.

The area of transverse reinforcement per unit length is given by

$$A_{sf} > v_{L,Ed}/(f_{sd} \cot \theta_f) = 116/(0.435 \times 1.25) = 213 \text{ mm}^2/\text{m}$$

This is much less than the amount assumed in design for lateral buckling (565 mm²/m). It may also be affected by the need for crack control above the beam, which arises in the design of the composite slab.

Design of bracing to bottom flanges near the internal support
It is now shown that the values of factor C_4 given in Appendix A are not suitable for design based on M_{cr} where intermediate lateral bracing is provided.

From Fig. 6.28, with full loading on both spans, the distance of a point of contraflexure from support B is $12 - 2 \times 4.75 = 2.5$ m. Let us suppose that lateral bracing is to be provided at this point, so that L in equation (D6.11) is reduced from 12 to 2.5 m. Assuming that the bending-moment distribution over this 2.5 m length is linear, Fig. A.4 in Appendix A gives $C_4 = 11.1$. Substituting these values into equation (D.6.11), with other values unchanged, gives $M_{cr} = 2285$ kN m, which is much lower than the previous value, 4340 kN m.

For this situation, it is necessary to find M_{cr} from elastic critical analysis by computer.

Summary of Example 6.7
All important aspects of the design of this beam for persistent situations for ultimate limit states have now been considered. Serviceability checks are given in the worked example at the end of Chapter 7. The same beam with semi-continuous joints at support B is studied in Examples 8.1 and 10.1.

Example 6.8: partial shear connection with non-ductile connectors

The design bending-moment diagram for sagging bending in the preceding worked example is shown in Fig. 6.28. The shear connection for the length AD of span AB was designed for connectors that satisfied the definition of 'ductile' in *clause 6.6.1.2*. The result is shown in Fig. 6.30.

This work is now repeated, using the same data, except that the proposed connectors are not 'ductile', to illustrate the use of *clause 6.6.1.3(5)*. This requires the calculation of the shear flow $v_{L,Ed}$ by elastic theory. No 'inelastic redistribution of shear' is required, so *clause 6.6.1.1(3)P* on deformation capacity does not apply.

Calculation of the resistance moment M_{Rd} according to *clause 6.2.1.3(3)* is not permitted, so stresses are calculated by elastic theory and checked against the limits in *clause 6.2.1.5(2)*. From equations (D6.22) and (D6.23), these are

$$f_{cd} = f_{ck}/\gamma_C = 25/1.5 = 16.7 \text{ N/mm}^2 \tag{D6.35}$$

and

$$f_{yd} = f_{yk} = 355 \text{ N/mm}^2 \tag{D6.36}$$

In this continuous beam, creep reduces stiffness at mid-span more than at the internal support, where the concrete is cracked, so the sagging bending moment and longitudinal shear (for constant loading) reduce over time. The short-term modular ratio, 10.1, is therefore used. Taking account of the use of unpropped construction, it is found for the loads in Table 6.2 that the maximum sagging bending moment acting on the composite section, $M_{c,Ed}$, occurs at 5.4 m from support A (Fig. 6.28), and is

$$M_{c,Ed} = 404 \text{ kN m} \quad \text{with} \quad M_{a,Ed} = 110 \text{ kN m}$$

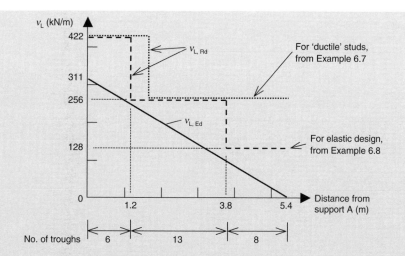

Fig. 6.32. Longitudinal shear and shear resistance for length AD of the beam in Fig. 6.28

Shrinkage of concrete in this beam reduces both the mid-span moments and the compressive stress in concrete. For simplicity and safety, its effects are ignored.

Using the elastic section properties from row 4 of Table 6.3, the stresses are found to be well below the limits given above. The mean stress in the 80 mm thickness of the concrete slab, with $b_{eff} = 2.5$ m, is 4.20 N/mm², giving the longitudinal force in the slab as

$$N_c = 4.2 \times 2.5 \times 80 = 840 \text{ kN}$$

From equation (D6.26), the force for full shear connection is

$$N_{c,f} = F_c = 2840 \text{ kN}$$

so the degree of shear connection needed is

$$\eta = N_c/N_{c,f} = 840/2840 = 0.30$$

The elastic shear flow diagram is triangular, so the shear flow at support A is

$$v_{L,Ed} = 2 \times 840/5.4 = 311 \text{ kN/m}$$

Stud connectors will be used, as before. They are not 'ductile' at this low degree of shear connection. Their resistances are given by equations (D6.33) and (D6.34). For the profiled sheeting used (Fig. 6.23(b)), there are five troughs per metre. One stud per trough ($v_{L,Rd} = 256$ kN/m) is not sufficient near support A. Two studs per trough provide 422 kN/m. Near mid-span, it is possible to use one stud every other trough, ($v_{L,Rd} = 128$ kN/m) as their spacing, 400 mm, is less than the limit set in *clause 6.6.5.5(3)*.

Details of a possible layout of studs are shown in Fig. 6.32. This also shows the resistance provided over this 5.4 m length from Fig. 6.30. That is higher because in the previous example, $\eta = 0.56$, not 0.30, and shear connection is provided for the whole load, not just that applied to the composite member.

This is not a typical result, because the design sagging moment here is unusually low, in relation to the plastic resistance to sagging bending. It may become more typical in design to the Eurocodes, because of the influence of lateral–torsional buckling on accounting for shrinkage and the restrictions on redistribution of moments.

Example 6.9: elastic resistance to bending, and influence of degree of shear connection and type of connector on bending resistance

This example makes use of the properties of materials and cross-sections found in Example 6.7 on the two-span beam, and of the results from Example 6.8 on non-ductile

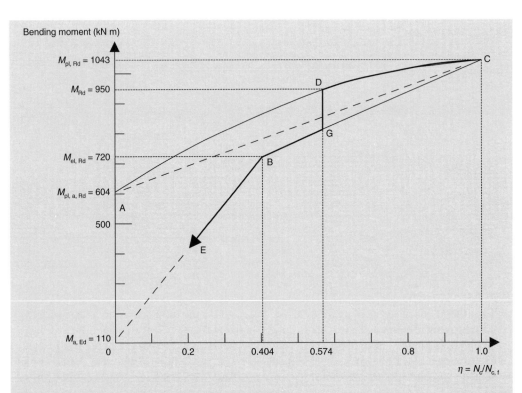

Fig. 6.33. Design methods for partial shear connection

connectors. The cross-section of maximum sagging bending moment, point D, was then found to be 5.4 m from support A in Fig. 6.28.

For simplicity, the beam is now assumed to be simply-supported and of span 10.8 m, so that this cross-section is at mid-span, with unpropped construction as before, so that the bending moment in the steel beam at this section is $M_{a,\,Ed} = 110$ kN m. Shrinkage effects are beneficial, and are neglected.

The purpose is to find the relationship between the degree of shear connection, η, and the bending resistance of the beam at mid-span, in accordance with *clauses 6.2.1.3–6.2.1.5, 6.6.1.2* and *6.6.1.3*. The result is shown in Fig. 6.33.

At low degrees of shear connection, only elastic design is permitted, so the elastic bending resistance $M_{el,\,Rd}$ is required, to *clause 6.2.1.4(6)*. It depends on the modular ratio. It is found that the limiting stress (equations (D6.35) and (D6.36)) is reached first in the steel bottom flange, and is increased by creep, so $n = 20.2$ is assumed.

For $M_{a,\,Ed} = 110$ kN m, the maximum stress in the steel beam is 73 N/mm², leaving $355 - 73 = 282$ N/mm² for loading on the composite beam. Using the elastic section properties from row 5 of Table 6.3, the steel reaches yield when the bending moment on the composite section is 610 kN m, so

$$M_{el,\,Rd} = 110 + 610 = \mathbf{720 \ kN \ m}$$

The compressive force in the concrete slab is then $N_{c,\,el} = 1148$ kN, so that

$$\eta = N_{c,\,el}/N_{c,\,f} = 1148/2840 = \mathbf{0.404}$$

Figure 6.33 is based on *Figs 6.5* and *6.6(b)* of EN 1994-1-1. The results above enable point B to be plotted.

When $M_{Ed} = 110$ kN m, $N_c = 0$. From *equation (6.2)* in *clause 6.2.1.4(6)*, line BE is drawn towards the point (0, 110) as shown. No lower limit to η is defined. It will in practice be determined by the detailing rules for the shear connection.

For full shear connection,

$M_{pl, Rd} = 1043$ **kN m**

from equation (D6.27). This fixes point C in Fig. 6.33, and line BC (from *equation (6.3)*) is drawn. Line EBC applies whether the connection is 'ductile' or not.

For this beam, with $f_y = 355$ N/mm^2 and equal steel flanges, *equation (6.12)* in *clause 6.6.1.2(1)* gives

$$\eta \geq 1 - (0.75 - 0.03 \times 10.8) = \mathbf{0.574}$$

Hence,

$$N_c \geq 0.574 \times 2840 = 1630 \text{ kN}$$

Using the method of *clause 6.2.1.3(3)* for ductile connectors, illustrated in Fig. 6.3, the plastic bending resistance is

$M_{Rd} = 950$ **kN m**

This gives point D in Fig. 6.33.

When $\eta = 0$, the plastic resistance is $M_{pl, a, Rd}$. From equation (D6.25) this is

$M_{pl, a, Rd} = 1.702 \times 355 = \mathbf{604}$ **kN m**

which is point A in Fig. 6.33.

Similar calculations for assumed degrees of shear connection give the curve ADC, which can, for simplicity, be replaced by the line AC (*clause 6.2.1.3(5)*). Both the curve and the line are valid only where η is high enough for the connection to be 'ductile'.

The design bending resistances for this example are therefore given by EBGDC in Fig. 6.33. Line BE gives the least shear connection that may be used when $M_{Ed} < M_{el, Rd}$, without restriction on the type of connector.

For higher values of M_{Ed}, the required degree of shear connection for non-ductile connectors is given by the line BC. The bonus for using ductile connectors (as defined in *clause 6.6.1.2*) is the area GDC, where the position of the line GD is determined by the span of the beam, and moves to the right as the span increases.

For the beam analysed here, with $M_{a, Ed} = 110$ kN m, a total bending moment $M_{Ed} = 1000$ kN m (for example) requires shear connection for about 2100 kN ($\eta \approx 0.74$) if headed studs to *clause 6.6.1.2* are used, but this increases to over 2600 kN for non-ductile connectors.

6.7. Composite columns and composite compression members

6.7.1. General

Scope

A composite column is defined in *clause 1.5.2.5* as '*a composite member subjected mainly to compression or to compression and bending*'. The title of *clause 6.7* includes 'compression members', to make clear that its scope is not limited to vertical members but includes, for example, composite members in triangulated or Vierendeel girders. These girders may also have composite tension members, for which provisions are given in EN 1994-2.

In this guide, references to 'columns' includes other composite compression members, unless noted otherwise, and for buildings, 'column' means a length of column between adjacent lateral restraints; typically, a storey height.

Design rules for columns sometimes refer to 'effective length'. That term is not generally used in *clause 6.7*. Instead, the 'relative slenderness' is defined, in *clause 6.7.3.3(2)*, in terms of N_{cr}, '*the elastic critical normal force for the relevant buckling mode*'.

This use of N_{cr} is explained in the comments on *clause 6.7.3.3*.

Clause 6.7.1(1)P refers to *Fig. 6.17*, in which all the sections shown have double symmetry; but *clause 6.7.1(6)* makes clear that the scope of the general method of *clause 6.7.2* includes members of non-symmetrical section.[84]

Clause 6.7.1(1)P

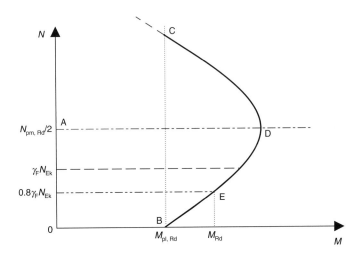

Fig. 6.34. Independent bending moment and normal force (not to scale)

The bending moment in a column depends on the assumed location of the line of action of the axial force, N. Where the cross-section has double symmetry, this is the intersection of the axes of symmetry. In other cases the choice, made in the modelling for global analysis, should be retained for the analysis of the cross-sections. A small degree of asymmetry (e.g. due to an embedded pipe) can be allowed for by ignoring in calculations concrete areas elsewhere, such that symmetry is restored.

No shear connectors are shown in the cross-sections in *Fig. 6.17*, because within a column length the longitudinal shear is normally much lower than in a beam, and sufficient interaction may be provided by bond or friction. Shear connectors should be provided for load introduction, following *clause 6.7.4*.

The minimum compression for a member to be regarded as a column, rather than a beam, is not stated. As shown in Example 6.11, the use of the cross-sections in *Fig. 6.17* as beams without shear connectors is usually prevented by the low design shear strengths due to bond and friction (*clause 6.7.4.3*).

Clause 6.7.1(2)P   The strengths of materials in *clause 6.7.1(2)P* are as for beams, except that class C60/75 and lightweight-aggregate concretes are excluded. For these, additional provisions (e.g. for creep, shrinkage, and strain capacity) would be required.[85,86]

Clause 6.7.1(3)   *Clause 6.7.1(3)* and *clause 5.1.1(2)* both concern the scope of EN 1994-1-1. They appear to exclude composite columns in high-rise buildings with a reinforced concrete core. For these 'mixed' structures, additional consideration in the global analysis of the effects of shrinkage, creep, and column shortening may be needed.

Clause 6.7.1(4)   The steel contribution ratio (*clause 6.7.1(4)*), is essentially the proportion of the squash load of the section that is provided by the structural steel member. If it is outside the limits given, the member should be treated as reinforced concrete or as structural steel, as appropriate.

Independent action effects
The interaction curve for the resistance of a column cross-section to combined axial force N and uniaxial bending M is shown in *Fig. 6.19*, and, as a polygon, in Fig. 6.38 of this guide. It
Clause 6.7.1(7)   has a region BD where an increase in N_{Ed} increases M_{Rd}. *Clause 6.7.1(7)* refers to a situation where at ultimate load the factored bending moment, $\gamma_F M_{Ek}$, could co-exist with an 'independent' axial force that was less than its design value, $\gamma_F N_{Ek}$. It says that verification should be based on the lower value, $0.8\gamma_F N_{Ek}$.

Discussion of this rule is illustrated in Fig. 6.34, which shows region BDC of the interaction curve in *Fig. 6.19*, which is symmetrical about the line AD. If

$$\gamma_F N_{Ek} < N_{pm,Rd}/2 \tag{D6.37}$$

then M_{Rd} should be found for an axial force of $0.8\gamma_F N_{Ek}$, as shown by point E. The reduction in M_{Rd} is usually small.

A simpler but more conservative rule is given in ENV 1994-1-1, with a clearer definition of 'independent actions': if M_{Rd} corresponding to $\gamma_F N_{Ek}$ is found to exceed $M_{pl,Rd}$, M_{Rd} should be taken as $M_{pl,Rd}$. It is applicable unless the bending moment M_{Ed} is due solely to the eccentricity of the force N_{Ed}. Its effect is to replace the curve BDC in Fig. 6.34 with the line BC.

Local buckling

The principle of *clause 6.7.1(8)P* is followed by its application rules. They ensure that the concrete (which will be reinforced in accordance with EN 1992-1-1) restrains the steel and prevents it from buckling even when yielded.

Clause 6.7.1(8)P

For partly encased sections, the encasement prevents local buckling of the steel web, and prevents rotation of the steel flange at its junction with the web, so that a higher b_f/t ratio may be used than for a bare steel section. *Table 6.3* gives the limit as 44ε, compared with about 22ε (from EN 1993-1-1) for a Class 2 flange. (In EN 1994, as in EN 1993, $\varepsilon = \sqrt{(235/f_y)}$, in units of newtons per square millimetre.)

For concrete-filled rectangular hollow steel sections (RHS), the limit of 52ε compares with about 41ε for a steel RHS. For a concrete-filled circular hollow section, the limiting d/t of $90\varepsilon^2$ compares with $70\varepsilon^2$ for Class 2 in EN 1993-1-1.

6.7.2. General method of design

Designers of composite columns will normally ensure that they fall within the scope of the simplified method of *clause 6.7.3*; but occasionally the need arises for a non-uniform or asymmetric member. The 'general method' of *clause 6.7.2* is provided both for this reason, and to enable advanced software-based methods to be used.

Clause 6.7.2

Clause 6.7.2 is more a set of principles than a design method. Development of software that satisfies these principles is a complex task. *Clause 6.7.2(3)P* refers to 'internal forces'. These are the action effects within the column length, found from those acting on its ends, determined by global analysis to *Section 5*. At present, such an analysis is likely to exclude member imperfections and second-order effects within members, but comprehensive software may become available.

Clause 6.7.2(3)P

Clause 6.7.2(3) also refers to 'elastic-plastic analysis'. This is defined in clause 1.5.6.10 of EN 1990 as 'structural analysis that uses stress/strain or moment/curvature relationships consisting of a linear elastic part followed by a plastic part with or without hardening.'

As the three materials in a composite section follow different non-linear relationships, direct analysis of cross-sections is not possible. One has first to assume the dimensions and materials of the member, and then determine the axial force N and bending moment M at a cross-section from assumed values of axial strain and curvature ϕ, using the relevant material properties. The M–N–ϕ relationship for each section can be found from many such calculations. This becomes even more complex where biaxial bending is present.[87]

Integration along the length of the column then leads to a non-linear member stiffness matrix that relates axial force and end moments to the axial change of length and end rotations.

6.7.3. Simplified method of design

Scope of the simplified method

The method has been calibrated by comparison with test results.[88] Its scope (*clause 6.7.3.1*) is limited mainly by the range of results available, which leads to the restriction $\bar{\lambda} \leq 2$ in *clause 6.7.3.1(1)*. For most columns, the method requires second-order analysis in which explicit account is taken of imperfections. The use of strut curves is limited to axially loaded members.

Clause 6.7.3.1
Clause 6.7.3.1(1)

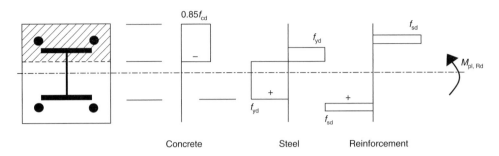

Fig. 6.35. Stress distributions for resistance in bending (tension positive)

The restriction on unconnected steel sections in *clause 6.7.3.1(1)* is to prevent loss of stiffness due to slip, which would invalidate the formulae for EI of the column cross-section.

Clause 6.7.3.1(2) The limits to concrete cover in *clause 6.7.3.1(2)* arise from concern over strain softening of concrete invalidating the interaction diagram (*Fig. 6.19*), and from the limited test data for columns with thicker covers. These provisions normally ensure that for each axis of bending, the flexural stiffness of the steel section makes a significant contribution to the total stiffness. Greater cover can be used by ignoring in calculation the concrete that exceeds the stated limits.

Clause 6.7.3.1(3) The limit of 6% in *clause 6.7.3.1(3)* on the reinforcement used in calculation is more liberal than the 4% (except at laps) recommended in EN 1992-1-1. This limit and that on maximum slenderness are unlikely to be restrictive in practice.

Clause 6.7.3.1(4) *Clause 6.7.3.1(4)* is intended to prevent the use of sections susceptible to lateral–torsional buckling. The reference to $h_c < b_c$ arises because h_c is defined as the overall depth in the direction normal to the major axis of the steel section (*Fig. 6.17*). The term 'major axis' can be misleading, because some column sections have $I_z > I_y$, even though $I_{a,y} > I_{a,z}$.

Resistance of cross-sections

Calculations for composite sections, with three materials, are potentially more complex than for reinforced concrete, so simplifications to some provisions of EN 1992-1-1 are made in EN 1994-1-1. Reference to the partial safety factors for the materials is avoided by specifying resistances in terms of design values for strength, rather than characteristic values; for

Clause 6.7.3.2(1) example in *equation (6.30)* for plastic resistance to compression in *clause 6.7.3.2(1)*. This resistance, $N_{pl,Rd}$, is the ultimate axial load that a short column can sustain, assuming that the structural steel and reinforcement are yielding and the concrete is crushing.

For concrete-encased sections, the crushing stress is taken as 85% of the design cylinder strength, as explained in the comments on *clause 3.1*. For concrete-filled sections, the concrete component develops a higher strength because of the confinement from the steel section, and the 15% reduction is not made; see also the comments on *clause 6.7.3.2(6)*.

Resistance to combined compression and bending

The bending resistance of a column cross-section, $M_{pl,Rd}$, is calculated as for a composite

Clause 6.7.3.2(2) beam in Class 1 or 2 (*clause 6.7.3.2(2)*). Points on the interaction curve shown in *Figs 6.18* and *6.19* represent limiting combinations of compressive axial load N and moment M which correspond to the plastic resistance of the cross-section.

The resistance is found using rectangular stress blocks. For simplicity, that for the concrete extends to the neutral axis, as shown in Fig. 6.35 for resistance to bending (point B in *Fig. 6.19* and Fig. 6.38). As explained in the comments on *clause 3.1(1)*, this simplification is unconservative in comparison with stress/strain curves for concrete and the rules of EN 1992-1-1. To compensate for this, the plastic resistance moment for the column section is reduced by a factor α_M in *clause 6.7.3.6(1)*.

As axial compression increases, the neutral axis moves; for example, towards the lower edge of the section shown in Fig. 6.35, and then outside the section. The interaction curve is therefore determined by moving the neutral axis in increments across the section, and finding pairs of values of M and N from the corresponding stress blocks. This requires a computer program, unless the simplification given in *clause 6.7.3.2(5)* is used. Simplified expressions for the coordinates of points B, C and D on the interaction curve in Fig. 6.34 are given in Appendix C. Further comment is given in Examples 6.10 and C.1.

Influence of transverse shear

Clauses 6.7.3.2(3) and *6.7.3.2(4)*, on the influence of transverse shear on the interaction curve, are generally the same as *clause 6.2.2.4* on moment–shear interaction in beams. One assumes first that the shear V_{Ed} acts on the structural steel section alone. If it is less than $0.5V_{pl, a, Rd}$, it has no effect. If it is greater, there is an option of sharing it between the steel and reinforced concrete sections, which may reduce that acting on the steel to below $0.5V_{pl, a, Rd}$. If it does not, then a reduced design yield strength is used for the shear area, as for the web of a beam. In a column, however, the shear area depends on the plane of bending considered, and may consist of the flanges of the steel section. It is assumed that shear buckling does not occur.

Clause 6.7.3.2(3)
Clause 6.7.3.2(4)

Simplified interaction curve

Clause 6.7.3.2(5) explains the use of the polygonal diagram BDCA in *Fig. 6.19* as an approximation to the interaction curve, suitable for hand calculation. The method applies to any cross-section with biaxial symmetry, not just to encased I-sections.

Clause 6.7.3.2(5)

First, the location of the neutral axis for pure bending is found, by equating the longitudinal forces from the stress blocks on either side of it. Let this be at distance h_n from the centroid of the uncracked section, as shown in *Fig. 6.19(B)* and Fig. C.2 in Appendix C. It is shown in Appendix C that the neutral axis for point C on the interaction diagram is at distance h_n on the other side of the centroid, and the neutral axis for point D passes through the centroid. The values of M and N at each point are easily found from the stress blocks shown in *Fig. 6.19*. For concrete-filled sections the factor 0.85 may be omitted.

Concrete-filled tubes of circular or rectangular cross-section

Clause 6.7.3.2(6) is based on the lateral expansion that occurs in concrete under axial compression. This causes circumferential tension in the steel tube and triaxial compression in the concrete. This increases the crushing strength of the concrete[88] to an extent that outweighs the reduction in the effective yield strength of the steel in vertical compression. The coefficients η_a and η_c given in this clause allow for these effects.

Clause 6.7.3.2(6)

This containment effect is not present to the same extent in concrete-filled rectangular tubes because less circumferential tension can be developed. In all tubes the effects of containment reduce as bending moments are applied; this is because the mean compressive strain in the concrete and the associated lateral expansion are reduced. With increasing slenderness, bowing of the member under load increases the bending moment, and therefore the effectiveness of containment is further reduced. For these reasons, η_a and η_c are dependent on the eccentricity of loading and on the slenderness of the member.

Properties of the column

For columns in a frame, some properties of each column length are needed before or during global analysis of the frame:

- the steel contribution ratio (*clause 6.7.3.3(1)*)
- the relative slenderness $\bar{\lambda}$ (*clause 6.7.3.3(2)*)
- the effective flexural stiffnesses (*clauses 6.7.3.3(3)* and *6.7.3.4(2)*)
- the creep coefficient and effective modulus for concrete (*clause 6.7.3.3(4)*).

Clause 6.7.3.3(1)
Clause 6.7.3.3(2)
Clause 6.7.3.3(3)
Clause 6.7.3.3(4)

The steel contribution ratio is explained in the comments on *clause 6.7.1(4)*.

The relative slenderness $\bar{\lambda}$ is needed to check that the column is within the scope of the simplified method, *clause 6.7.3.1(1)*. $\bar{\lambda}$ is calculated using characteristic values and the appropriate flexural stiffness is that given in *clauses 6.7.3.3(3)* and *6.7.3.3(4)*. The correction factor K_c is to allow for cracking.

As $\bar{\lambda}$ depends on the elastic critical normal force for the relevant buckling mode, the behaviour of the surrounding members needs to be taken into account. This could require a calculation of the load factor α_{cr} for elastic instability, following the procedure shown in Fig. 5.1(e). It will often be possible though to make simplifying assumptions to show that a proposed column is within the scope for the method. For example, in a frame with a high stiffness against sway it would be reasonable to calculate N_{cr} assuming the member to be pin-ended. In an unbraced continuous frame, the stiffness of each beam could be taken as that of the steel section alone, permitting N_{cr} to be determined from effective length charts that assume a beam to be of uniform stiffness. In any case, the upper limit on $\bar{\lambda}$ is somewhat arbitrary and does not justify great precision in N_{cr}.

The creep coefficient φ_t influences the effective modulus $E_{c,\,eff}$ (*clause 6.7.3.3(4)*), and hence the flexural stiffness of each column. It depends on the age at which concrete is stressed and the duration of the load. These will not be the same for all the columns in a frame. The effective modulus depends also on the proportion of the design axial load that is permanent. The design of a column is rarely sensitive to the influence of the creep coefficient on $E_{c,\,eff}$, so conservative assumptions can be made about uncertainties. Normally, a single value of effective modulus can be used for all the columns in the frame.

Verification of a column

The flow chart of Fig. 6.36 shows a possible calculation route, intended to minimize iteration, for a column as part of a frame. It is used in Example 6.10. It is assumed that the column has cross-section details that can satisfy *clauses 6.7.1(9)*, *6.7.3.1(2)* to *6.7.3.1(4)* and *6.7.5.2(1)*, and has already been shown to have $\bar{\lambda} \leq 2$, so that it is within the scope of the simplified method of *clause 6.7.3*.

The relationship between the analysis of a frame and the stability of individual members is discussed in the comments on *clauses 5.2.2(3)* to *5.2.2(7)*. Conventionally, the stability of members is checked by analysis of individual members, using end moments and forces from global analysis of the frame. Figure 6.36 follows this procedure, giving in more detail the procedures outlined in the lower part of the flow chart for global analysis (see Fig. 5.1(a)). It is assumed that the slenderness of the column, determined according to *clause 5.3.2.1(2)*, is such that member imperfections have been neglected in the global analysis. Comments are now given in the sequence of Fig. 6.36, rather than clause sequence. If bending is biaxial, the chart is followed for each axis in turn, as noted. It is assumed that loading is applied to the column only at its ends.

The starting point is the output from the global analysis, listed at the top of Fig. 6.36. The design axial compression is the sum of the forces from the two frames of which the column is assumed to be a member. If, at an end of the column (e.g. the top) the joints to beams in these frames are at a different level, they could conservatively be assumed both to be at the upper level, if the difference is small. The flow chart does not cover situations where the difference is large (e.g. a storey height). The axial force N_{Ed} is normally almost constant along the column length. Where it varies, its maximum value can conservatively be assumed to be applied at the upper end.

Clause 6.7.3.4

For most columns, the method requires a second-order analysis in which explicit account is taken of imperfections (*clause 6.7.3.4*). However, for a member subject only to end compression, *clause 6.7.3.5(2)* enables buckling curves to be used. For columns that qualify, this is a useful simplification because these curves allow for member imperfections. The reduction factor χ depends on the non-dimensional slenderness $\bar{\lambda}$. The buckling curves are also useful as a preliminary check for columns with end moment; if the resistance to the normal force N_{Ed} is not sufficient, the proposed column is clearly inadequate.

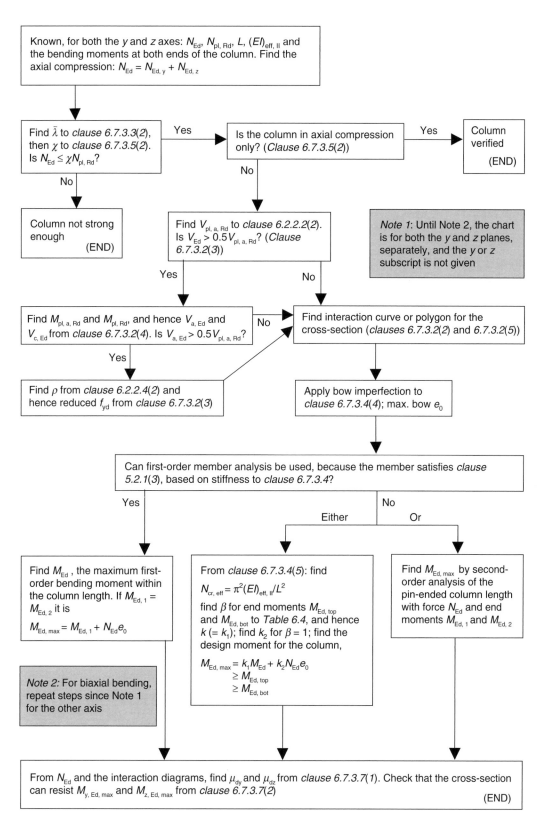

Fig. 6.36. Flow chart for verification of a column length

Comment has already been made on the calculation of $\bar{\lambda}$ when used to check the scope of the method. When $\bar{\lambda}$ is used as the basis for resistance, calculation of this parameter may still be simplified, provided the result is conservative.

Columns without end moments are exceptional, and for most members the design process continues, as shown in Fig. 6.36. Columns with transverse shear exceeding half of the shear resistance of the steel element are rare; but shear is checked next, because if it is high the interaction curve for the cross-section may be affected. Comment has been given earlier on *clauses 6.7.3.2(3)* and *6.7.3.2(4)*, on shear, and on the interaction curve or polygon.

Much of the remainder of the flow chart is concerned with finding the maximum bending moment to which the column will be subjected. In general, two calculations are necessary (*clause 6.7.3.6(1)*). The maximum bending moment may occur at one end, when the design moment equals to the larger of the two end moments; or the maximum bending moment may occur at an intermediate point along the member. This is because second-order effects and lateral load within the length of the member and initial bowing affect the bending moment.

Clause 6.7.3.4(4) If member imperfections have been neglected in the global analysis, it is necessary to include them in the analysis of the column. *Clause 6.7.3.4(4)* gives the member imperfections in *Table 6.5* as proportional to the length L of the column between lateral restraints. The imperfection is the lateral departure at mid-height of the column of its axis of symmetry from the line joining the centres of symmetry at the ends of the column. The values account principally for truly geometric imperfections and for the effects of residual stresses. They do not depend on the distribution of bending moment along the column. The curved shape is usually assumed to be sinusoidal, but use of a circular arc would be acceptable. The curve is assumed initially to lie in the plane of the frame being analysed.

The next step is to ascertain whether second-order effects need to be considered within the member length. *Clause 6.7.3.4(3)* refers to *clause 5.2.1(3)*. Second-order effects can therefore be neglected if the load factor α_{cr} for elastic instability of the member exceeds 10. Possible sway effects will have been determined by global analysis, and will already be included within the values for the end moments and forces. To calculate α_{cr}, the ends of the column are assumed to be pinned, and α_{cr} is found using the Euler formula $N_{cr, eff} = \pi^2 EI/L^2$, L being the physical length of the column. The flexural stiffness to use is $(EI)_{eff, II}$ (*clause 6.7.3.4(2)*), with the modulus of elasticity for concrete modified to take account of long-term effects (*clause 6.7.3.3(4)*). This flexural stiffness is lower than that defined in *clause 6.7.3.3(3)* because it is essentially a design value for ultimate limit states. The factor $K_{e, II}$ allows for cracking. The factor K_o is from research-based calibration studies.

The neglect of second-order effects does not mean that increase in bending moment caused by the member imperfection can also be ignored. The next box, on finding $M_{Ed, max}$, gives the example of a column in uniform single-curvature bending. If the end moments are dissimilar or of opposite sign, the maximum moment in the column, $M_{Ed, max}$, is likely to be the greater end moment.

In practice, most columns are relatively slender, and second-order effects will usually need to be included. This can be done by second-order analysis of the member, treated as pin-ended but subject to the end moments and forces given by the global analysis. Any intermediate loads would also be applied. The analysis is to obtain the maximum moment in the column, which is taken as the design moment, $M_{Ed, max}$. Formulae may be obtained from

Clause 6.7.3.4(5) the literature. Alternatively, use may be made of the factor k given by *clause 6.7.3.4(5)*.

It is assumed in Fig. 6.36 that the column is free from intermediate lateral loads. Two factors are used, written as k_1 and k_2, because two moment distributions must be considered. The first gives the equivalent moment $k_1 M_{Ed}$ in the 'perfect' column, where M_{Ed} is the larger end moment given by the global analysis. The definitions of M_{Ed} in *clause 6.7.3.4(5)* and *Table 6.4* may appear contradictory. In the text before *equation (6.43)*, M_{Ed} is referred to as a first-order moment. This is because it does not include second-order effects arising within the column length. However, *Table 6.4* makes clear that M_{Ed} is to be determined by either first-order or second-order global analysis; the choice would depend on *clause 5.2*.

The multiplier β (from *Table 6.4*) allows for the shape of the bending-moment diagram. The condition $\beta \geq 0.44$ in the table is to ensure sufficient protection against snap-through buckling in double-curvature bending.

The first-order moment from the imperfection, $N_{Ed}e_0$, has a distribution such that $\beta = 1$, from *Table 6.4*, so k_2 normally differs from k_1. The imperfection can be in any direction, so the equivalent moment $k_2 N_{Ed} e_0$ always has the same sign as $k_1 M_{Ed}$, when the two are combined.

Equation (6.43) states that k must be greater than or equal to unity, and this is correct for a single distribution of bending moment. However, for a combination of end moments and member imperfection, it could be conservative to limit all values of k in this way. At mid-length the component due to end moments depends on their ratio, r, and therefore could be small. The appropriate component is therefore $k_1 M_{Ed}$ without the limit $k \geq 1.0$, and the design moment within the column length is $(k_1 M_{Ed} + k_2 N_{Ed} e_0)$. In biaxial bending, the initial member imperfection may be neglected in the less critical plane (*clause 6.7.3.7(1)*). The limit $k \geq 1.0$ is intended to ensure that the design moment is at least the larger end moment M_{Ed}.

For uniaxial bending, the final step is to check that the cross-section can resist $M_{Ed,\,max}$ with compression N_{Ed}. The interaction diagram gives a resistance $\mu_d M_{pl,\,Rd}$ with axial load N_{Ed}, as shown in *Fig. 6.18*. This is unconservative, being based on rectangular stress blocks, as explained in the comment on *clause 3.1(1)*, so in **clause 6.7.3.6(1)** it is reduced, by the use of a factor α_M that depends on the grade of structural steel. This factor allows for the increase in the compressive strain in the cross-section at yield of the steel (which is adverse for the concrete), when the yield strength of the steel is increased.

Clause 6.7.3.6(1)

Biaxial bending

Where values of $M_{Ed,\,max}$ have been found for both axes, **clause 6.7.3.7** applies, in which they are written as $M_{y,\,Ed}$ and $M_{z,\,Ed}$. If one is much greater than the other, the relevant check for uniaxial bending, *equation (6.46)* will govern. Otherwise, the linear interaction given by *equation (6.47)* applies. If the member fails this biaxial condition by a small margin, it may be helpful to recalculate the less critical bending moment, omitting the member imperfection, as permitted by *clause 6.7.3.7(1)*.

Clause 6.7.3.7

6.7.4. Shear connection and load introduction

Load introduction

The provisions for the resistance of cross-sections of columns assume that no significant slip occurs at the interface between the concrete and structural steel components. **Clauses 6.7.4.1(1)P** and **6.7.4.1(2)P** give the principles for limiting slip to an 'insignificant' level in the critical regions: those where axial load and/or bending moments are applied to the column.

Clause 6.7.4.1(1)P
Clause 6.7.4.1(2)P

For any assumed 'clearly defined load path' it is possible to estimate stresses, including shear at the interface. In regions of load introduction, shear stress is likely to exceed the design shear strength from *clause 6.7.4.3*, and shear connection is then required (*clause 6.7.4.2(1)*). It is unlikely to be needed elsewhere, unless the shear strength τ_{Rd} from *Table 6.6* is very low, or the member is also acting as a beam, or has a high degree of double-curvature bending. **Clause 6.7.4.1(3)** refers to the special case of an axially loaded column.

Clause 6.7.4.1(3)

Few shear connectors reach their design shear strength until the slip is at least 1 mm; but this is not 'significant' slip for a resistance model based on plastic behaviour and rectangular stress blocks. However, a long load path implies greater slip, so the assumed path should not extend beyond the introduction length given in *clause 6.7.4.2(2)*.

Where axial load is applied through a joint attached only to the steel component, the force to be transferred to the concrete can be estimated from the relative axial loads in the two materials given by the resistance model. Accurate calculation is rarely practicable where the cross-section concerned does not govern the design of the column. In this partly plastic situation, the more adverse of the elastic and fully plastic models gives a safe result

Clause 6.7.4.2(1) (*clause 6.7.4.2(1)*, last line). In practice, it may be simpler to provide shear connection based on a conservative (high) estimate of the force to be transferred.

Where axial force is applied by a plate bearing on both materials or on concrete only, the proportion of the force resisted by the concrete gradually decreases, due to creep and shrinkage. It could be inferred from *clause 6.7.4.2(1)* that shear connection should be provided for a high proportion of the force applied. However, models based on elastic theory are over-conservative in this inherently stable situation, where large strains are acceptable. The application rules that follow are based mainly on tests.

In a concrete-filled tube, shrinkage effects are low, for only the autogenous shrinkage strain occurs, with a long-term value below 10^{-4}, from clause 3.1.4(6) of EN 1992-1-1. Radial shrinkage is outweighed by the lateral expansion of concrete in compression, for its inelastic Poisson's ratio increases at high compressive stress. Friction then provides significant shear *Clause 6.7.4.2(3)* connection (*clause 6.7.4.2(3)*). Friction is also the basis for the enhanced resistance of stud *Clause 6.7.4.2(4)* connectors given in *clause 6.7.4.2(4)*.

Detailing at points of load introduction or change of cross-section is assisted by the high *Clause 6.7.4.2(5)* bearing stresses given in *clauses 6.7.4.2(5)* and *6.7.4.2(6)*. As an example, the following data *Clause 6.7.4.2(6)* are assumed for the detail shown in *Fig. 6.22(B)*, with axial loading:

- steel tube with external diameter 300 mm and wall thickness 10 mm
- bearing plate 15 mm thick, with strength $f_y = f_{yd} = 355$ N/mm^2
- concrete with $f_{ck} = 45$ N/mm^2 and $\gamma_C = 1.5$.

Then, $A_c = \pi \times 140^2 = 61\,600$ mm^2; $A_1 = 15 \times 280 = 4200$ mm^2. From *equation (6.48)*,

$$\sigma_{c,\,Rd}/f_{cd} = [1 + (4.9 \times 10/300)(355/45)](14.7)^{0.5} = 8.8$$

and

$$\sigma_{c,\,Rd} = 8.8 \times 30 = 260 \text{ N/mm}^2$$

This bearing stress is so high that the fin plate would need to be at least 180 mm deep to have sufficient resistance to vertical shear.

Clause 6.7.4.2(9) *Figure 6.23* illustrates the requirement of *clause 6.7.4.2(9)* for transverse reinforcement, which must have a resistance equal to the force N_{c1}. If longitudinal reinforcement is ignored, this is given by

$$N_{c1} = A_{c2}/2nA$$

where A is the transformed area of the cross-section 1–1 of the column in *Fig. 6.23*, given by

$$A = A_s + (A_{c1} + A_{c2})/n$$

and A_{c1} and A_{c2} are the unshaded and shaded areas of concrete, respectively, in section 1–1.

Transverse shear

Clause 6.7.4.3 *Clause 6.7.4.3* gives application rules (used in Example 6.11) relevant to the principle of *clause 6.7.4.1(2)*, for columns with the longitudinal shear that arises from transverse shear. The design shear strengths τ_{Rd} in *Table 6.6* are far lower than the tensile strength of concrete. They rely on friction, not bond, and are related to the extent to which separation at the interface is prevented. For example, in partially encased I-sections, lateral expansion of the concrete creates pressure on the flanges, but not on the web, for which $\tau_{Rd} = 0$; and the highest shear strengths are for concrete within steel tubes.

Where small steel I-sections are provided, mainly for erection, and the column is mainly *Clause 6.7.4.3(4)* concrete, *clause 6.7.4.3(4)* provides a useful increase to τ_{Rd}, for covers up to 115 mm, more simply presented as

$$\beta_c = 0.2 + c_z/50 \le 2.5$$

Concern about the attachment of concrete to steel in partially encased I-sections appears *Clause 6.7.4.3(5)* again in *clause 6.7.4.3(5)*, because under weak-axis bending, separation tends to develop between the encasement and the web.

6.7.5. Detailing provisions

If a steel I-section in an environment in class X0 to EN 1992-1-1 has links in contact with its flange (permitted by *clause 6.7.5.2(3)*), the cover to the steel section could be as low as 25 mm. For a wide steel flange, this thin layer of concrete would have little resistance to buckling outwards, so the minimum thickness is increased to 40 mm in *clause 6.7.5.1(2)*. *Clause 6.7.5.1(2)*

Minimum longitudinal reinforcement (*clause 6.7.5.2(1)*), is needed to control the width of *Clause 6.7.5.2(1)* cracks, which can be caused by shrinkage even in columns with concrete nominally in compression.

Clause 6.7.5.2(4) refers to exposure class X0 of EN 1992-1-1. This is a 'very dry' *Clause 6.7.5.2(4)* environment, with 'no risk of corrosion or attack'. Buildings with 'very low air humidity' are given as an example, so some buildings, or spaces in buildings, would not qualify. The minimum reinforcement provides robustness during construction.

Example 6.10: composite column with bending about one or both axes

A composite column of length 7.0 m has the uniform cross-section shown in Fig. 6.37. Its resistance to given action effects will be found. After checking that the column is within the scope of the simplified method, the calculations follow the sequence of the flow chart in Fig. 6.36. The properties of the steel member, 254 × 254 UC89, are taken from section tables, and given here in Eurocode notation. The properties of the materials, in the usual notation, are as follows:

Structural steel: grade S355, $f_y = f_{yd} = 355$ N/mm², $E_a = 210$ kN/mm².
Concrete: C25/30; $f_{ck} = 25$ N/mm², $f_{cd} = 25/1.5 = 16.7$ N/mm²,
$0.85f_{cd} = 14.2$ N/mm², $E_{cm} = 31$ kN/mm², $n_0 = 210/31 = 6.77$.
Reinforcement: ribbed bars, $f_{sk} = 500$ N/mm², $f_{sd} = 500/1.15 = 435$ N/mm².

Geometrical properties of the cross-section
In the notation of *Fig. 6.17(a)*,

$$b_c = h_c = 400 \text{ mm} \qquad b = 256 \text{ mm} \qquad h = 260 \text{ mm}$$
$$c_y = 200 - 128 = 72 \text{ mm} \qquad c_z = 200 - 130 = 70 \text{ mm}$$

These satisfy the conditions of *clauses 6.7.3.1(2), 6.7.3.1(4)* and *6.7.5.1(2)*, so all the concrete casing is included in the calculations.

Area of reinforcement = $4 \times 36\pi = 446$ mm²

Area of concrete = $400^2 - 11\,400 - 446 = 148\,150$ mm²

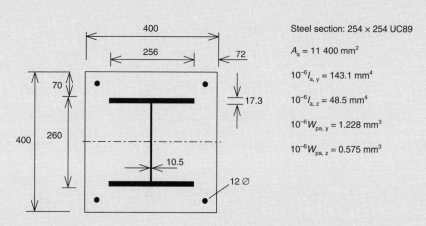

Fig. 6.37. Cross-section and properties of a composite column (dimensions in mm)

The reinforcement has area 0.301% of the concrete area, so *clause 6.7.5.2(1)* permits it to be included in calculations. For simplicity, its small contribution will be ignored, so the values are

$$A_a = \textbf{11 400 mm}^2 \qquad A_c = 400^2 - 11\,400 = \textbf{148 600 mm}^2 \qquad A_s = 0$$

For the steel section:

$$10^{-6}I_{a,y} = 143.1 \text{ mm}^4 \qquad 10^{-6}I_{a,z} = 48.5 \text{ mm}^4$$

Design action effects, ultimate limit state
For the most critical load arrangement, global analysis gives these values:

$N_{Ed} = \textbf{1800 kN}$, of which $N_{G, Ed} = 1200$ kN

$M_{y, Ed, top} = \textbf{380 kN m}$; $M_{z, Ed, top} = 0$

The bending moments at the lower end of the column and the lateral loading are zero. Later, the effect of adding $M_{z, Ed, top} = 50$ kN m is determined.

Properties of the column length
From *clause 6.7.3.2(1)*,

$$N_{pl, Rd} = A_a f_{yd} + 0.85 A_c f_{cd} = 11.4 \times 355 + 148.6 \times 14.2 = 4047 + 2109 = \textbf{6156 kN}$$

From *clause 6.7.3.3(1)*, the steel contribution ratio is

$$\delta = 4047/6156 = 0.657$$

which is within the limits of *clause 6.7.1(4)*.
For $\bar{\lambda}$ to *clause 6.7.3.3(2)*, with $\gamma_C = 1.5$,

$$N_{pl, Rk} = 4047 + 1.5 \times 2109 = \textbf{7210 kN}$$

Creep coefficient
From *clause 6.7.3.3(4)*,

$$E_c = E_{cm}/[1 + (N_{G, Ed}/N_{Ed})\varphi_t] \qquad (6.41)$$

The creep coefficient φ_t is $\varphi(t, t_0)$ to *clause 5.4.2.2*. The time t_0 is taken as 30 days, and t is taken as 'infinity', as creep reduces the stiffness, and hence the stability, of a column.
From clause 3.1.4(5) of EN 1992-1-1, the 'perimeter exposed to drying' is

$$u = 2(b_c + h_c) = 1600 \text{ mm}$$

so

$$h_0 = 2A_c/u = 297\,200/1600 = 186 \text{ mm}$$

Assuming 'inside conditions' and the use of normal cement, the graphs in Fig. 3.1 of EN 1992-1-1 give

$$\varphi(\infty, 30) = 2.7 = \varphi_t$$

The assumed 'age at first loading' has little influence on the result if it exceeds about 20 days. If, however, significant load were applied at age 10 days, φ_t would be increased to about 3.3.
From *equation (6.41)*,

$$E_{c, eff} = 31/[1 + 2.7(1200/1800)] = \textbf{11.1 kN/mm}^2$$

Elastic critical load, with characteristic stiffness
The minor axis is the more critical, so $\bar{\lambda}_z$ is needed. From *clause 6.7.3.3(3)*,

$$(EI)_{\text{eff}} = E_a I_a + K_e E_{c, \text{eff}} I_c \qquad (6.40)$$

For the concrete,

$$10^{-6} I_{c, z} = 0.4^2 \times 400^2/12 - 48.5 = 2085 \text{ mm}^4$$

From *equation (6.40)*,

$$10^{-6} (EI)_{\text{eff}, z} = 210 \times 48.5 + 0.6 \times 11.1 \times 2085 = 24\ 070 \text{ kN mm}^2$$

In this example, the end conditions for the column are assumed to be such that lateral restraint is provided, but no elastic rotational restraint, so the effective length is the actual length, 7.0 m, and

$$N_{cr, z} = \pi^2 (EI)_{\text{eff}, z}/L^2 = 24\ 070 \pi^2/49 = 4848 \text{ kN}$$

From *equation (6.39)*,

$$\overline{\lambda}_z = (N_{\text{pl, Rk}}/N_{cr, z})^{0.5} = (7210/4848)^{0.5} = \mathbf{1.22}$$

Similar calculations for the *y*-axis give

$$10^{-6} I_{c, y} = 1990 \text{ mm}^4 \qquad 10^{-6} (EI)_{\text{eff}, y} = 43\ 270 \text{ kN mm}^2$$

$$N_{cr, y} = 8715 \text{ kN} \qquad \overline{\lambda}_y = \mathbf{0.91}$$

The non-dimensional slenderness does not exceed 2.0, so *clause 6.7.3.1(1)* is satisfied.

Resistance to axial load, z-axis

From *clause 6.7.3.5(2)*, buckling curve (c) is applicable. From Fig. 6.4 of EN 1993-1-1, for $\overline{\lambda}_z = 1.22$,

$$\chi_z = 0.43$$

From *equation (6.44)*,

$$N_{\text{Ed}} \le \chi_z N_{\text{pl, Rd}} = 0.43 \times 6156 = \mathbf{2647 \text{ kN}}$$

This condition is satisfied.

Transverse shear

For $M_{y, \text{Ed, top}} = 380 \text{ kN m}$, the transverse shear is

$$V_{z, \text{Ed}} = 380/7 = 54 \text{ kN}$$

This is obviously less than $0.5 V_{\text{pl, a, Rd}}$, so *clause 6.7.3.2(3)* does not apply.

Interaction curves

The interaction polygons corresponding to *Fig. 6.19* are determined in Appendix C (see Example C.1), and reproduced in Fig. 6.38. *Clause 6.7.3.2(5)* permits them to be used as approximations to the *N–M* interaction curves for the cross-section.

First-order bending moments, y-axis

The distribution of the external bending moment is shown in Fig. 6.39(a). From *clause 6.7.3.4(4)*, the equivalent member imperfection is

$$e_{0, z} = L/200 = 35 \text{ mm}$$

The mid-length bending moment due to N_{Ed} is

$$N_{\text{Ed}} e_{0, z} = 1800 \times 0.035 = 63 \text{ kN m}$$

Its distribution is shown in Fig. 6.39(b).

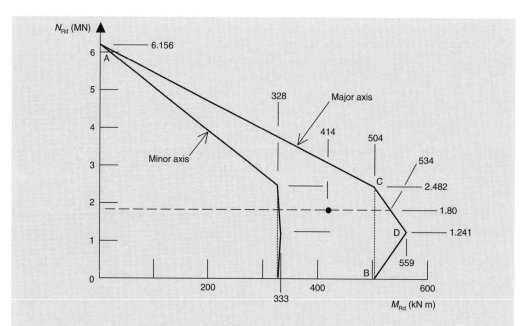

Fig. 6.38. Interaction polygons for bending about the major and minor axes

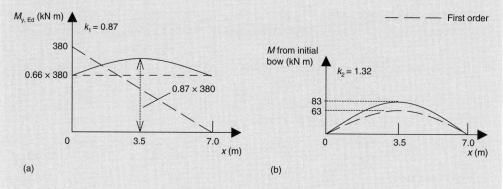

Fig. 6.39. Design second-order bending moments for a column of length 7.0 m

To check whether second-order moments can be neglected, a reduced value of N_{cr} is required, to *clause 6.7.3.4(3)*. From *equation (6.42)*,

$$(EI)_{y,\,eff,\,II} = 0.9(E_aI_a + 0.5E_cI_c) = 0.9 \times 10^6(210 \times 143.1 + 0.5 \times 11.1 \times 1990)$$
$$= 3.70 \times 10^{10}\,\text{kN mm}^2$$

Hence,

$$N_{cr,\,y,\,eff} = 37\,000\pi^2/7^2 = \textbf{7450 kN}$$

This is less than $10N_{Ed}$, so second-order effects must be considered.

Second-order bending moments, y-axis
From *clause 6.7.3.4(5)*, *Table 6.4*, for the end moments, $r = 0$, $\beta = 0.66$, and from *equation (6.43)*,

$$k_1 = \beta/(1 - N_{Ed}/N_{cr,\,y,\,eff}) = 0.66/(1 - 1800/7450) = 0.87$$

This is not increased to 1.0, as it will be combined with the effect of imperfections, so the major-axis bending moments are as shown in Fig. 6.39(a).

For the bending moment from the member imperfection, $\beta = 1.0$. From *equation (6.43)*,

$$k_2 = 1/(1 - 1800/7450) = 1.32$$

thus increasing $N_{cd}e_{0,z}$ to 83 kN m (Fig. 6.39(b)).

The total mid-length bending moment is

$$331 + 83 = 414 \text{ kN m}$$

This exceeds the greater end moment, 380 kN m, and so governs.

The point $(N_{Ed}, M_{y, Ed, max})$ is (1800, 414) on Fig. 6.38. From the values shown in the figure,

$$\mathbf{M_{y, Rd}} = 504 + (2482 - 1800) \times 55/(2482 - 1241) = \mathbf{534 \text{ kN m}}$$

This exceeds $M_{pl, y, Rd}$, so *clause 6.7.3.6(2)* is relevant.

In this case, it makes no difference whether N_{Ed} and M_{Ed} are from independent actions or not, because the point $M_{y, Rd}$ lies on line CD in Fig. 6.38, not on line BD, so the 'additional verification' to *clause 6.7.1(7)* would not alter the result.

The ratio

$$\mathbf{M_{y, Ed, max}}/\mu_{d, y}\mathbf{M_{pl, y, Rd}} = 414/534 = \mathbf{0.78}$$

This is below 0.9, so *clause 6.7.3.6(1)* is satisfied. The column is strong enough.

Biaxial bending

The effect of adding a minor-axis bending moment $M_{z, Ed, top} = 50$ kN m is as follows. It is much smaller than $M_{y, Ed}$, so major-axis failure is assumed. From *clause 6.7.3.7(1)*, there is assumed to be no bow imperfection in the x–y plane; but second-order effects have to be considered.

From *equation (6.42)*,

$$(EI)_{z, eff, II} = 0.9 \times 10^6(210 \times 48.5 + 0.5 \times 11.1 \times 2085) = 1.96 \times 10^{10} \text{ kN mm}^2$$

Hence,

$$N_{cr, z, eff} = 19\,600\pi^2/49 = \mathbf{3948 \text{ kN m}}$$

As before, $\beta = 0.66$, and from *equation (6.43)*,

$$k_1 = 0.66/(1 - 1800/3948) = 1.21$$

so

$$M_{z, Ed, max} = 1.21 \times 50 = 60.5 \text{ kN m}$$

From Fig. 6.38, for $N_{Ed} = 1800$ kN,

$$\mathbf{M_{z, Rd}} = \mu_{d, z}M_{pl, z, Rd} = \mathbf{330 \text{ kN m}}$$

From *clause 6.7.3.7(2)*,

$$\mathbf{M_{y, Ed, max}/0.9M_{y, Rd}} + \mathbf{M_{z, Ed, max}/0.9M_{z, Rd}} = 414/(0.9 \times 534) + 60.5/(0.9 \times 330)$$
$$= 0.861 + 0.204$$
$$= \mathbf{1.07}$$

This exceeds 1.0, so the check is thus not satisfied, and the column cannot resist the additional bending moment.

Example 6.11: longitudinal shear outside areas of load introduction, for a composite column

All of the data for this example are given in Example 6.10 and Fig. 6.37, and are not repeated here. The design transverse shear was found to be

$$V_{z, Ed} = 54 \text{ kN}$$

The maximum shear that can be resisted without provision of shear connection is now calculated. The critical cross-section is B–B in Fig. 6.40.

Clause 6.7.4.3(2) permits the use of elastic analysis. Creep and cracking should be considered. Creep reduces the shear stress on plane B–B, so the modular ratio $n_0 = 6.77$ is used. Uncracked section properties are used, and cracking is considered later.

The cover $c_z = 70$ mm, so from *equation (6.49)* in *clause 6.7.4.3(4)*, $\beta_c = 1.60$. From *Table 6.6*,

$$\tau_{Rd} = 0.30 \times 1.6 = 0.48 \text{ N/mm}^2$$

From Example 6.10,

$$10^{-6}I_{a, y} = 143.1 \text{ mm}^4 \qquad 10^{-6}I_{c, y} = 1990 \text{ mm}^4$$

so for the uncracked section in 'concrete' units,

$$10^{-6}I_y = 1990 + 143.1 \times 6.77 = 2959 \text{ mm}^4$$

The 'excluded area'

$$A_{ex} = 400 \times 70 = 28\,000 \text{ mm}^2$$

and its centre of area is

$$\bar{z} = 200 - 35 = 165 \text{ mm}$$

from G in Fig. 6.40. Hence,

$$V_{z, Rd} = \tau_{Rd} I_y b_c / (A_{ex}\bar{z}) = 0.48 \times 2959 \times 400/(28\,000 \times 0.165) = \mathbf{123 \text{ kN}}$$

This exceeds $V_{z, Ed}$, so no shear connection is needed. The margin is so great that there is no need to consider the effect of cracking.

Column section used as a beam

The shear strengths given in *Table 6.6* are unlikely to be high enough to permit omission of shear connection from a column member with significant transverse loading. As an example, it is assumed that the column section of Fig. 6.40 is used as a simply-supported beam of span 8.0 m, with uniformly distributed loading.

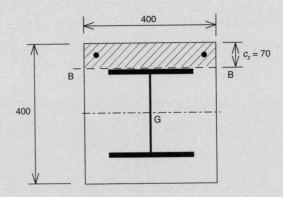

Fig. 6.40 Longitudinal shear on plane B–B in a column cross-section (dimensions in mm)

Using elastic analysis of the cracked cross-section with $n_0 = 6.77$ as before, but no axial load, the results are

$$10^{-6}I_{\text{y, cracked}} = 1441 \text{ mm}^4 \qquad V_{\text{z, Rd}} = 79 \text{ kN}$$

This corresponds to a design ultimate load of 19.7 kN/m, which is only 4.4 times the unfactored weight of the member.

6.8. Fatigue

6.8.1. General

Although fatigue verification is mainly needed for bridges, these 'general' provisions find application in some buildings; for example, where travelling cranes or fork-lift trucks are used. They refer extensively to EN 1993-1-9,[89] *Fatigue Strength*, which is also 'general'. The Eurocode methods for fatigue are quite complex. There are supplementary provisions in EN 1994-2, *Composite Bridges*.

The only complete set of provisions on fatigue in EN 1994-1-1 is for stud shear connectors. Fatigue in reinforcement, concrete, and structural steel is covered mainly by cross-reference to EN 1992 and EN 1993. Commentary will be found in the guides to those codes.[6,7]

Comments here are limited to design for a single cyclic loading: a defined number of cycles, N_E, of a loading event for which can be calculated, at a given point, either:

- a single range of stress, $\Delta\sigma_E(N_E)$ or $\Delta\tau_E(N_E)$, or
- several stress ranges, that can be represented as N^* cycles of a single 'damage equivalent stress range' (e.g. $\Delta\sigma_{E,\text{equ}}(N^*)$) by using the Palmgren–Miner rule for summation of fatigue damage.

The term 'equivalent constant-amplitude stress range', defined in clause 1.2.2.11 of EN 1993-1-9, has the same meaning as 'damage equivalent stress range', used here and in clause 6.8.5 of EN 1992-1-1.

Damage equivalent factors (typically λ, as used in bridge design) are not considered here. Reference may be made to guides in this series to Part 2 of Eurocodes 2, 3 and 4 (e.g. *Designers' Guide to EN 1994*[90]).

Fatigue damage is related mainly to the number and amplitude of the stress ranges. The peak of the stress range has a secondary influence that can be, and usually is, ignored in practice for peak stresses below about 60% of the characteristic strength. Ultimate loads are higher than peak fatigue loads, and the use of partial safety factors for ultimate-load design normally ensures that peak fatigue stresses are below this limit. This may not be so for buildings with partial shear connection, so *clause 6.8.1(3)* limits the force per stud to $0.75P_{\text{Rd}}$, or $0.6P_{\text{Rk}}$ for $\gamma_V = 1.25$.

Clause 6.8.1(4) gives guidance on the types of building where fatigue assessment may be required. By reference to EN 1993-1-1, these include buildings with members subject to wind-induced or crowd-induced oscillations. 'Repeated stress cycles from vibrating machinery' are also listed, but these should in practice be kept out of the structure by appropriate mountings.

Clause 6.8.1(3)

Clause 6.8.1(4)

6.8.2. Partial factors for fatigue assessment

Resistance factors γ_{Mf} may be given in National Annexes, so only the recommended values can be discussed here. For fatigue strength of concrete and reinforcement, *clause 6.8.2(1)* refers to EN 1992-1-1, which recommends the partial factors 1.5 and 1.15, respectively. For structural steel, EN 1993-1-9 recommends values ranging from 1.0 to 1.35, depending on the design concept and consequence of failure. These apply, as appropriate, for a fatigue failure of a steel flange caused by a stud weld.

Clause 6.8.2(1)

Fatigue failure of a stud shear connector, not involving the flange, is covered by EN 1994-1-1. The value recommended in a note to *clause 2.4.1.2(7)P*, $\gamma_{Mf,s} = 1.0$, corresponds to the value in EN 1993-1-9 for 'damage tolerant design concept' with 'low consequence of failure'. From clause 3(2) of EN 1993-1-9, the use of the damage tolerant method should be satisfactory, provided that 'a prescribed inspection and maintenance regime for detecting and correcting fatigue damage is implemented...'. A note to this clause states that the damage tolerant method may be applied where 'in the event of fatigue damage occurring a load redistribution between components of structural elements can occur'.

The second condition applies to stud connectors, but the first does not, for lack of access prevents detection of small cracks by any simple method of inspection. The recommendation of EN 1994-1-1 is based on other considerations, as follows.

Fatigue failure results from a complex interaction between steel and concrete, commencing with powdering of the highly stressed concrete adjacent to the weld collar. This displaces upwards the line of action of the shear force, increasing the bending and shear in the shank just above the weld collar, and probably also altering the tension. Initial fatigue cracking further alters the relative stiffnesses and the local stresses. Research has found that the exponent that relates the cumulative damage to the stress range may be higher than the value, five, for other welds in shear. The value chosen for EN 1994-1-1, eight, is controversial, as discussed later.

As may be expected from the involvement of a tiny volume of concrete, tests show a wide scatter in fatigue lives, which is allowed for in the design resistances. Studs are provided in large numbers, and are well able to redistribute shear between themselves.

The strongest reason for not recommending a value more conservative than 1.0 comes from experience with bridges, where stud connectors have been used for almost 50 years. Whenever occasion has arisen in print or at a conference, the first author has stated that there is no known instance of fatigue failure of a stud in a bridge, other than a few clearly attributable to errors in design. This has not been challenged. Research has identified, but not yet quantified, many reasons for this remarkable experience.[91,92] Most of them (e.g. slip, shear lag, permanent set, partial interaction, adventitious connection from bolt heads, and friction) lead to predicted stress ranges on studs lower than those assumed in design. With an eighth-power law, a 10% reduction in stress range more than doubles the fatigue life.

6.8.3. Fatigue strength

Clause 6.8.3(3)

The format of *clause 6.8.3(3)*, as in EN 1993-1-9, uses a reference value of range of shear stress at 2 million cycles, $\Delta\tau_C = 90$ N/mm². It defines the slope m of the line through this point on the log–log plot of range of stress $\Delta\tau_R$ against number of constant-range stress cycles to failure, N_R (*Fig. 6.25*).

It is a complex matter to deduce a value for m from the mass of test data, which are often inconsistent. Many types of test specimen have been used, and the resulting scatter of results must be disentangled from that due to inherent variability. Values for m recommended in the literature range from 5 to 12, mostly based on linear-regression analyses. The method of regression used (x on y, or y on x) can alter the value found by up to three.[91]

The value eight, which was also used in BS 5400: Part 10, may be too high. In design for a loading spectrum, its practical effect is that the cumulative damage is governed by the highest-range components of the spectrum (e.g. by the small number of maximum-weight lifts made by a crane). A lower value, such as five, would give more weight to the much higher number of average-range components.

While fatigue design methods for stud connectors continue to be conservative (for bridges and probably for buildings too) the precise value for m is of academic interest. Any future proposals for more accurate methods for prediction of stress ranges should be associated with re-examination of the value for m.

6.8.4. Internal forces and fatigue loadings

The object of a calculation is usually to find the range or ranges of stress in a given material at a chosen cross-section, caused by a defined event; for example, the passage of a vehicle along a beam. Loading other than the vehicle influences the extent of cracking in the concrete, and, hence, the stiffnesses of members. Cracking depends mainly on the heaviest previous loading, and so tends to increase with time. *Clause 6.8.4(1)* refers to a relevant clause in Eurocode 2. This defines the non-cyclic loading assumed to co-exist with the design value of the cyclic load, Q_{fat}: it is the 'frequent' combination, represented by

Clause 6.8.4(1)

$$\sum_{j \geq 1} G_{k,j} + P + \psi_{1,1} Q_{k,1} + \sum_{i > 1} \psi_{2,i} Q_{k,i}$$

where the Qs are non-cyclic variable actions. Often, only one G and one Q are relevant, and there is no prestress. The design combination is then

$$G_k + \psi_1 Q_k + Q_{fat} \qquad (D6.38)$$

Clause 6.8.4(2) defines symbols that are used for bending moments in *clause 6.8.5.4*. The sign convention is evident from *Fig. 6.26*, which shows that $M_{Ed,\,max,\,f}$ is the bending moment that causes the greatest tension in the slab, and is positive. *Clause 6.8.4(2)* also refers to internal forces, but does not give symbols. Analogous use of calculated tensile forces in a concrete slab (e.g. $N_{Ed,\,max,\,f}$, etc.) may sometimes be necessary.

Clause 6.8.4(2)

6.8.5. Stresses

Clause 6.8.5.1(1) refers to a list of action effects in *clause 7.2.1(1)P* to be taken into account 'where relevant'. They are all relevant, in theory, to the extent of cracking. However, this can usually be represented by the same simplified model, chosen from *clause 5.4.2.3*, that is used for other global analyses. They also influence the maximum value of the fatigue stress range, which is limited for each material (e.g. the limit for shear connectors in *clause 6.8.1(3)*). It is unusual for any of these limits to be reached in design for a building; but if there are highly stressed cross-sections where most of the variable action is cyclic, the maximum value should be checked.

Clause 6.8.5.1(1)

The provisions for fatigue are based on the assumption that the stress range caused by a given fluctuation of loading, such as the passage of a vehicle of known weight, remains approximately constant after an initial shakedown period. 'Shakedown' here includes the changes due to cracking, shrinkage and creep of concrete that occur mainly within the first year or two.

Most fatigue verifications are for load cycles with more than 10^4 repetitions. For this number in a 50 year life, the mean cycle time is less than 2 days. Thus, load fluctuations slow enough to cause creep (e.g. from the use of a tank for storing fuel oil) are unlikely to be numerous enough to cause fatigue damage. This may not be so for industrial processes with dynamic effects, such as forging, or for the charging floor for a blast furnace, but other uncertainties are likely to outweigh those from creep.

The short-term modular ratio should therefore be used when finding stress ranges from the cyclic action Q_{fat}. Where a peak stress is being checked, creep from permanent loading should be allowed for, if it increases the relevant stress. This would apply, for example, for most verifications for the structural steel in a composite beam. The effect of tension stiffening (*clauses 6.8.5.1(2)P* and *6.8.5.1(3)*), is illustrated in Example 6.12, below.

Clause 6.8.5.1(2)P

The designer chooses a location where fatigue is most likely to govern. For a vehicle travelling along a continuous beam, the critical section for shear connection may be near mid-span; for reinforcement, it is near an internal support.

Clause 6.8.5.1(3)

The extent of a continuous structure that needs to be analysed depends on what is being checked. For a fatigue check on reinforcement it would be necessary to include at least two spans of the beam, and perhaps the two adjacent column lengths; but ranges of vertical shear, as the vehicle passes, are barely influenced by the rest of the structure, so for the shear connection it may be possible to consider the beam in isolation.

For analysis, the linear-elastic method of *Section 5* is used, from *clause 6.8.4(1)*. Redistribution of moments is not permitted, *clause 5.4.4(1)*. Calculation of range of stress, or of shear flow, from the action effects is based entirely on elastic theory, following *clause 7.2.1*.

Clause 6.8.5.1(4)

For stresses in structural steel, the effects of tension stiffening may be included or neglected (*clause 6.8.5.1(4)*).

Concrete

Clause 6.8.5.2(1)

For concrete, *clause 6.8.5.2(1)* refers to clause 6.8 of EN 1992-1-1, which provides (in clause 6.8.7) for concrete subjected to a damage equivalent stress range. For a building, fatigue of concrete is unlikely to influence design, so this clause is not discussed here.

Structural steel

Clause 6.8.5.3(1)
Clause 6.8.5.3(2)

Clause 6.8.5.3(1) repeats, in effect, the concession in *clause 6.8.5.1(4)*. Where the words 'or only $M_{Ed, min, f}$' in *clause 6.8.5.3(2)* apply, $M_{Ed, max, f}$ causes tension in the slab. The use of the uncracked section for $M_{Ed, max, f}$ could then under-estimate the stress ranges in steel flanges.

Reinforcement

For reinforcement, *clause 6.8.3(2)* refers to EN 1992-1-1, where clause 6.8.4 gives the verification procedure. Its recommended value N^* for straight bars is 10^6. This should not be confused with the corresponding value for structural steel in EN 1993-1-9, 2×10^6, denoted N_C, which is used also for shear connectors (*clause 6.8.6.2(1)*).

Using the γ values recommended in EN 1992-1-1, its equation (6.71) for verification of reinforcement becomes

$$\Delta\sigma_{E, equ}(N^*) \leq \Delta\sigma_{Rsk}(N^*)/1.15 \qquad (D6.39)$$

with $\Delta\sigma_{Rsk} = 162.5$ N/mm² for $N^* = 10^6$, from Table 6.4N.

Where a range $\Delta\sigma_E(N_E)$ has been determined, the resistance $\Delta\sigma_{Rsk}(N_E)$ can be found from the S–N curve for reinforcement, and the verification is

$$\Delta\sigma_E(N_E) \leq \Delta\sigma_{Rsk}(N_E)/1.15 \qquad (D6.40)$$

Clause 6.8.5.4(1)

Clause 6.8.5.4(1) permits the use of the approximation to the effects of tension stiffening that is used for other limit states. It consists of adding to the maximum tensile stress in the 'fully cracked' section, $\sigma_{s, 0}$, an amount $\Delta\sigma_s$ that is independent of $\sigma_{s, 0}$ and of the limit state.

Clause 6.8.5.4(2)
Clause 6.8.5.4(3)

Clauses 6.8.5.4(2) and *6.8.5.4(3)* give simplified rules for calculating stresses, with reference to *Fig. 6.26*, which is discussed using Fig. 6.41. This has the same axes, and also shows a minimum bending moment that causes compression in the slab. A calculated value for the stress σ_s in reinforcement, that assumes concrete to be effective, would lie on line AOD. On initial cracking, the stress σ_s jumps from B to point E. Lines OBE are not shown in *Fig. 6.26* because *clause 7.2.1(5)P* requires the tensile strength of concrete to be neglected in calculations for σ_s. This gives line OE. For moments exceeding M_{cr}, the stress σ_s follows route EFG on first loading. Calculation of σ_s using section property I_2 gives line OC. At bending moment $M_{Ed, max, f}$ the stress $\sigma_{s, 0}$ thus found is increased by $\Delta\sigma_s$, from *equation (7.5)*, as shown by line HJ.

Tension stiffening tends to diminish with repeated loading,[93] so *clause 6.8.5.4* defines the unloading route from point J as JOA, on which the stress $\sigma_{s, min, f}$ lies. Points K and L give two examples, for $M_{Ed, min, f}$ causing tension and compression, respectively, in the slab. The fatigue stress ranges $\Delta\sigma_{s, f}$ for these two cases are shown.

Shear connection

Clause 6.8.5.5(1)P
Clause 6.8.5.5(2)

The interpretation of *clause 6.8.5.5(1)P* is complex when tension stiffening is allowed for. Spacing of shear connectors near internal supports is unlikely to be governed by fatigue, so it is simplest to use uncracked section properties when calculating the range of shear flow from the range of vertical shear (*clause 6.8.5.5(2)*). These points are illustrated in Example 6.12.

6.8.6. Stress ranges

Clause 6.8.6.1

Clause 6.8.6.1 is more relevant to the complex cyclic loadings that occur in bridges than to buildings, and relates to the provisions of EN 1992 and EN 1993. Where a spectrum

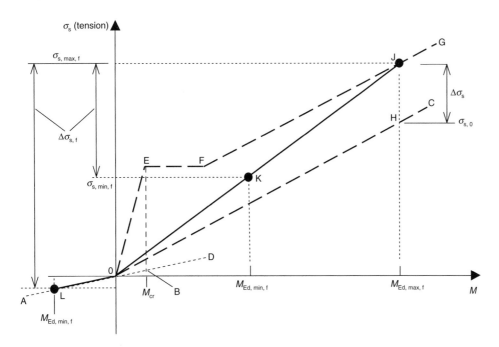

Fig. 6.41. Stress ranges in reinforcement in cracked regions

of loading is specified, the maximum and minimum stresses, as discussed above for reinforcement, are modified by the damage equivalent factor λ, a property of the spectrum and the exponent m (*clause 6.8.3(3)*). Comment and guidance will be found in the relevant guides in this series.

The need to combine global and local fatigue loading events (*clause 6.8.6.1(3)*), rarely occurs in buildings, and is outside of the scope of this guide.

Clause 6.8.6.1(3)

Where the design cyclic loading consists of a single load cycle repeated N_E times, the damage equivalent factor λ_v used in *clause 6.8.6.2* on shear connection can be found using the Palmgren–Miner rule, as follows.

Clause 6.8.6.2

Let the load cycle cause a shear stress range $\Delta\tau$ in a stud connector, for which $m = 8$. Then,

$$(\Delta\tau_E)^8 N_E = (\Delta\tau_{E,2})^8 N_C$$

where $N_C = 2 \times 10^6$ cycles. Hence,

$$\Delta\tau_{E,2}/\Delta\tau_E = \lambda_v = (N_E/N_C)^{1/8} \tag{D6.41}$$

6.8.7. Fatigue assessment based on nominal stress ranges

Comment on the methods referred to from *clause 6.8.7.1* will be found in other guides in this series.

Clause 6.8.7.1

For shear connectors, *clause 6.8.7.2(1)* introduces the partial factors. The recommended value of $\gamma_{Mf,s}$ is 1.0 (*clause 6.8.2(1)*). For γ_{Ff}, EN 1990 refers to the other Eurocodes. The recommended value in EN 1992-1-1, clause 6.8.4(1), is 1.0. No value has been found in EN 1993-1-1 or EN 1993-1-9. Clause 9.3(1) of EN 1993-2 recommends 1.0 for bridges.

Clause 6.8.7.2(1)

Clause 6.8.7.2(2) covers interaction between the fatigue failures of a stud and of the steel flange to which it is welded, when the flange is in tension. The first of *expressions (6.57)* is the verification for the flange, from clause 8(1) of EN 1993-1-9, and the second is for the stud, copied from *equation (6.55)*. The linear interaction condition is given in *expression (6.56)*.

Clause 6.8.7.2(2)

It is necessary to calculate the longitudinal stress range in the steel flange that coexists with the stress range for the connectors. The load cycle that gives the maximum value of $\Delta\sigma_{E,2}$ in the flange will not, in general, be that which gives the maximum value of $\Delta\tau_{E,2}$ in a shear connector, because the first is caused by flexure and the second by shear. Also, both $\Delta\sigma_{E,2}$ and $\Delta\tau_{E,2}$ may be influenced by whether the concrete is cracked, or not.

It thus appears that *expression (6.56)* may have to be checked four times. In practice, it is best to check first the conditions in *expression (6.57)*. It should be obvious, for these, whether the 'cracked' or the 'uncracked' model is the more adverse. Usually, one or both of the left-hand sides is so far below 1.0 that no check to *expression (6.56)* is needed.

Example 6.12: fatigue in reinforcement and shear connection

It is assumed that the imposed floor load of 7.0 kN/m² for the two-span beam in Examples 6.7 and 7.1 is partly replaced by a cyclic load. The resistance to fatigue of the reinforcement at the internal support, point B in Figs 6.23 and 6.28, and of the shear connection near the cyclic load are checked. All other data are as before.

Loading and global analysis

The cyclic load is a four-wheeled vehicle with two characteristic axle loads of 35 kN each. It travels at right angles to beam ABC, on a fixed path that is 2.0 m wide and free from other variable loads. The axle spacing exceeds the beam spacing of 2.5 m, so each passage can be represented by two cycles of point load, 0–35–0 kN, applied at point D in Fig. 6.42(a). For a 25 year design life, 20 passages per hour for 5000 h/year gives $N_{Ed} = 2.5 \times 10^6$ cycles of each point load. The partial factor γ_{Ff} is taken as 1.0.

In comparison with Example 6.7, the reduction in static characteristic imposed load is $7 \times 2.5 \times 2 = 35$ kN, the same as the additional axle load, so previous global analyses for the characteristic combination can be used. These led to the bending moments M_{Ek} at support B given in the four rows of Table 7.2. Those in rows 2 and 4 are unchanged, and $M_{Ek,B} = 263$ kN m for loading q_k. Analysis for the load Q_{fat} alone, with 15% of each span cracked, gave the results in Fig. 6.42(b), with 31 kN m at support B.

The frequent combination of non-cyclic imposed load is specified, for which $\psi_1 = 0.7$. From Table 6.2, $q_k = 17.5$ kN/m. Therefore, $\psi_1 q_k = 0.7 \times 17.5 = 12.25$ kN/m, acting on span AB and on 10 m only of span BC, giving

$$M_{Ek,B} = 0.7 \times (263 - 31) = 162 \text{ kN m}$$

Table 6.5 gives

$$M_{Ed,\,min,\,f} = 18 + 162 + 120 = \textbf{300 kN m}$$

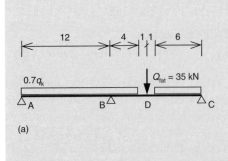

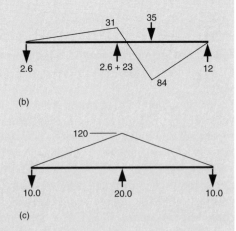

Fig. 6.42. Fatigue checks for a two-span beam. (a) Variable static and cyclic loads. (b) Design action effects, cyclic load. (c) Design action effects, shrinkage

Table 6.5. Stresses in longitudinal reinforcement at support B

Action	n	Load (kN/m)	M_{Ek} (kN m)	$10^{-6}W_{s,cr}$ (mm^3)	$\sigma_{s,0}$ (N/mm^2)
Permanent, composite	20.2	1.2	18	1.65	11
Variable, static ($\psi_1 = 0.7$)	20.2	12.25	162	1.65	98
Shrinkage	28.7	–	120	1.65	73
Cyclic load	20.2	–	31	1.65	19
Totals			331		201

From Fig. 6.42(b),

$$M_{Ed,max,f} = 300 + 31 = \textbf{331 kN m}$$

Verification for reinforcement at cross-section B

From equation (D7.5), the allowance for tension stiffening is $\Delta\sigma_s = 52$ N/mm^2. From $\sigma_{s,0}$ given in Table 6.5,

$$\sigma_{s,max,f} = 201 + 52 = 253 \text{ N/mm}^2$$

From Fig. 6.41,

$$\sigma_{s,min,f} = 253 \times 300/331 = 229 \text{ N/mm}^2$$

so

$$\Delta\sigma_{s,f} = 253 - 229 = \textbf{24 N/mm}^2$$

From clause 6.8.4 of EN 1992-1-1, for reinforcement,

$$m = 9 \text{ for } N_E > 10^6 \qquad N^* = 10^6 \qquad \Delta\sigma_{Rsk}(N^*) = 162.5 \text{ N/mm}^2$$

By analogy with equation (D6.41), the damage equivalent stress range for $N_{Ed} = 5 \times 10^6$ cycles of stress range 24 N/mm^2 is given by

$$24^9 \times 5 \times 10^6 = (\Delta\sigma_{E,equ})^9 \times 10^6$$

whence

$$\Delta\sigma_{E,equ} = 29 \text{ N/mm}^2$$

Using equation (D6.40),

$$29 \leq 162.5/1.15$$

so the reinforcement is verified.

If the axle loads had been unequal, say 35 and 30 kN, the stress range for the lighter axle would be a little higher than $24 \times 30/35 = 20.6$ N/mm^2, because its line OJ in Fig. 6.41 would be steeper. Assuming this stress range to be 21 N/mm^2, the cumulative damage check, for $\gamma_{Mf} = 1.15$, would be

$$2.5 \times 10^6 \times (24^9 + 21^9) \leq (162.5/1.15)^9 \times 10^6$$

which is

$$8.6 \times 10^{18} \leq 2.25 \times 10^{25}$$

Verification for shear connection near point D

Vertical shear is higher on the left of point D in Fig. 6.42, than on the right. From Fig. 6.42(b), $\Delta V_{Ed,f} = 23$ kN for each axle load.

Table 6.6. Fatigue of shear connectors near cross-section D

Action	$10^{-6}I_y$ (mm⁴)	$10^{-3}A_c/n$ (mm²)	$\bar{z}$ (mm)	V_{Ed} (kN)	$V_{Ed}A_c\bar{z}/nI_y$ (kN/m)
Permanent, composite	828	9.90	157	2.7	5.0
Variable, static ($\psi_1 = 0.7$)	828	9.90	157	23.8	44.7
Shrinkage	741	6.97	185	10.0	17.4
Cyclic load	828	9.90	157	23.0	43.2
Totals				59.5	110

The maximum vertical shear at this point, including 10.0 kN from the secondary effect of shrinkage, Fig. 6.42(c), is 59.5 kN, Table 6.6. The shear forces V_{Ed} are found from the loads and values M_{Ek} in Table 6.5. The resulting maximum longitudinal shear flow, for the uncracked unreinforced composite section, is 110 kN/m, of which the cyclic part is 43.2 kN/m.

Clause 6.8.1(3) limits the shear per connector under the characteristic combination to $0.75P_{Rd}$. For this combination, the shear flow from the non-cyclic variable action increases by 19 from 44.7 to 44.7/0.7 = 63.9 kN/m, so the new total is 110 + 19 = 129 kN/m. The shear connection (see Fig. 6.30), is 5 studs/m, with P_{Rd} = 51.2 kN/stud. Hence,

$$P_{Ek}/P_{Rd} = 129/(5 \times 51.2) = 0.50$$

which is below the limit 0.75 in *clause 6.8.1(3)*.

The range of shear stress is

$$\Delta\tau_E = 43\,200/(5\pi \times 9.5^2) = 30.5\ \text{N/mm}^2$$

The concrete is in density class 1.8. From *clause 6.8.3(4)*,

$$\Delta\tau_c = 90 \times (1.8/2.2)^2 = \mathbf{60\ N/mm^2}$$

From equation (D6.41),

$$\Delta\tau_{E,2} = 30.5[5 \times 10^6/(2 \times 10^6)]^{1/8} = \mathbf{34.2\ N/mm^2}$$

As $\gamma_{Mf,s} = 1.0$,

$$\Delta\tau_{c,d} = 60\ \text{N/mm}^2$$

so the shear connection is verified.

CHAPTER 7

Serviceability limit states

This chapter corresponds to *Section 7* of EN 1994-1-1, which has the following clauses:

- General   *Clause 7.1*
- Stresses   *Clause 7.2*
- Deformations in buildings   *Clause 7.3*
- Cracking of concrete   *Clause 7.4*

7.1. General

Section 7 of EN 1994-1-1 is limited to provisions on serviceability that are specific to composite structures and are not in *Sections 1, 2, 4, 5* (for global analysis) or *9* (for composite slabs), or in Eurocodes 1990, 1991, 1992 or 1993. Some of these other, more general provisions are briefly referred to here. Further comments on them are in other chapters of this book, or in other handbooks in this series.

The initial design of a structure is usually based on the requirements for ultimate limit states, which are specific and leave little to the judgement of the designer. Serviceability is then checked. The consequences of unserviceability are less serious than those of reaching an ultimate limit state, and its occurrence is less easily defined. For example, a beam with an imposed-load deflection of span/300 may be acceptable in some situations, but in others the client may prefer to spend more on a stiffer beam.

The drafting of the serviceability provisions of the EN Eurocodes is intended to give designers and clients greater freedom to take account of factors such as the intended use of a building and the nature of its finishes.

The content of *Section 7* was also influenced by the need to minimize calculations. Results already obtained for ultimate limit states are scaled or re-used wherever possible. Experienced designers know that many structural elements satisfy serviceability criteria by wide margins. For these, design checks must be simple, and it does not matter if they are conservative. For other elements, a longer but more accurate calculation may be justified. Some application rules therefore include alternative methods.

Clauses 7.1(1)P and *7.1(2)* refer to clause 3.4 of EN 1990. This gives criteria for placing a limit state within the 'serviceability' group, with reference to deformations (including vibration), durability, and the functioning of the structure.

Clause 7.1(1)P
Clause 7.1(2)

Serviceability verification and criteria

The requirement for a serviceability verification is given in clause 6.5.1(1)P of EN 1990 as

$$E_d \leq C_d$$

where E_d is the design value of the effects of the specified actions and the 'relevant' combination, and C_d is the limiting design value of the 'relevant' criterion.

From clause 6.5.3 of EN 1990, the relevant combination is 'normally' the characteristic, frequent, or quasi-permanent combination, for serviceability limit states that are, respectively, irreversible, reversible or a consequence of long-term effects. The quasi-permanent combination is also relevant for the appearance of the structure.

For buildings, these combinations are used with the partial safety factor 1.0, from clause A1.4.1 of EN 1990, 'unless differently specified' in another Eurocode. There are no departures from 1.0 in EN 1994-1-1. The same provision, with value 1.0, is given for partial safety factors for properties of materials, in clause 6.5.4(1) of EN 1990.

Clause A1.4.2 of EN 1990 refers to serviceability criteria relevant for buildings. These may be defined in National Annexes, and should be specified for each project and agreed with the client.

Clause A1.4.4 of EN 1990 says that possible sources of vibration and relevant aspects of vibration behaviour should be considered for each project and agreed with the client and/or the relevant authority. Further guidance may be found in the relevant Eurocode Part 2 (bridges) and in specialized literature.

Comments on limits to crack width are given under *clause 7.4*.

No serviceability limit state of 'excessive slip of shear connection' has been defined, but the effect of slip is recognized in *clause 7.3.1(4)* on deflection of beams. Generally, it is assumed that design of shear connection for ultimate limit states ensures satisfactory performance in service, but composite slabs can be an exception. Relevant rules are given in *clause 9.8.2*.

No serviceability criteria are specified for composite columns, so, from here on, this chapter is referring to composite beams or, in some places, to composite frames.

7.2. Stresses

Clause 7.2.1

Clause 7.2.2

Excessive stress is not itself a serviceability limit state, though stress calculations to *clause 7.2.1* are required for some verifications for deformation and cracking. For most buildings, no checks on stresses are required, *clause 7.2.2*. No stress limits for buildings are given in the Eurocodes for concrete and steel structures, other than warnings in clause 7.2 of EN 1992-1-1, with recommended stress limits in notes. The 'bridge' parts of these Eurocodes include stress limits, which may be applicable for buildings that have prestressing or fatigue loading.

7.3. Deformations in buildings

7.3.1. Deflections

Global analysis

Deflections are influenced by the method of construction, and may govern design, especially where beams designed as simpl- supported are built unpropped. For propped construction, props to beams should not be removed until all of the concrete that would then be stressed has reached a strength equivalent to grade C20/25, from *clause 6.6.5.2(4)*. Then, elastic global analysis to *Section 5* is sufficient (*clause 7.3.1(2)*).

Clause 7.3.1(1)

Where unpropped construction is used and beams are not designed as simply supported, the analysis may be more complex than is revealed by the reference to EN 1993 in *clause 7.3.1(1)*. In a continuous beam or a frame, the deflection of a beam depends on how much of the structure is already composite when the slab for each span is cast. A simple and usually conservative method is to assume that the whole of the steel frame is erected first. Then, all of the concrete for the composite members is cast at once, its whole weight being carried by the steelwork; but more realistic multi-stage analyses may be needed for a high-rise structure and for long-span beams.

Where falsework or re-usable formwork is supported from the steel beam, it will be removed after the member becomes composite. The small locked-in stresses that result can usually be ignored in buildings, but not always in bridges.

Where first-order elastic global analysis was used for ultimate limit states (ULS), it may be possible to obtain some of the results needed for serviceability limit states (SLS) by simple scaling by the ratio of the relevant loads. This ratio will depend on the method of construction, and also on which of the three serviceability load combinations is being used for the limit state considered.

As an example, suppose that for an unbraced frame at ULS, $\alpha_{cr} = 8$, so that second-order global analysis was used, from *clause 5.2.1(3)*. If most of the load on columns is from suspended floors, and these loads for SLS are 60% of those for ULS, the elastic critical load will be little altered, so for SLS, $\alpha_{cr} \approx 8/0.6 = 13$. This exceeds 10, so first-order analysis can be used.

Redistribution of moments is permitted for most framed structures at SLS by *clause 5.4.4(1)*, but the details in *paragraphs (4)* to *(7)* apply only to ULS. The relevant provisions in *Section 7* are in *clauses 7.3.1(6)* and *7.3.1(7)*, discussed below.

Limits to deflection of beams

The specification of a deflection limit for a long-span beam needs care, especially where construction is unpropped and/or the steel beam is pre-cambered. Reference should be made to the three components of deflection defined in clause A1.4.3 of EN 1990.

Depending on circumstances, it may be necessary to set limits to any one of them, or to more than one, related to a defined load level. Prediction of long-term values should take account of creep of concrete, based on the quasi-permanent combination, and may need to allow for shrinkage. Where precast floor units are used, it must be decided whether they should be cambered to compensate for creep. ***Clause 7.3.1(3)*** relates to the use of false ceilings, which conceal the sagging of a beam due to dead loading.

Clause 7.3.1(3)

Longitudinal slip

Clause 7.3.1(4) refers to the additional deflection caused by slip at the interface between steel and concrete. Its three conditions all apply. Condition (b) relates to the minimum value of the degree of shear connection, η, given as 0.4 in *clause 6.6.1.2(1)*, and gives a higher limit, 0.5.

Clause 7.3.1(4)

For use where the design is such that $0.4 \leq \eta < 0.5$, ENV 1994-1-1[49] gave the following equation for the additional deflection due to partial interaction:

$$\delta = \delta_c + \alpha(\delta_a - \delta_c)(1 - \eta) \qquad (D7.1)$$

where $\alpha = 0.5$ for propped construction and 0.3 for unpropped construction, δ_a is the deflection of the steel beam acting alone, and δ_c is the deflection for the composite beam with complete interaction; both δ_a and δ_c are calculated for the design loading for the composite member. The method comes from a summary of pre-1975 research on this subject,[94] which also gives results of relevant tests and parametric studies. Other methods are also available.[95]

Cracking in global analysis

Apart from the different loading, global analysis for serviceability differs little from that for an ultimate limit state. *Clause 5.4.1.1(2)* requires 'appropriate corrections' for cracking of concrete, and **clause 7.3.1(5)** says that *clause 5.4.2.3* applies. *Clause 5.4.2.3(2)* permits the use of the same distribution of beam stiffnesses at SLS as for ULS. *Clauses 5.4.2.3(3)* to *5.4.2.3(5)* also apply, including the reference in *clause 5.4.2.3(4)* to a method given in *Section 6* for the effect of cracking on the stiffness of composite columns.

Clause 7.3.1(5)

In the absence of cracking, continuous beams in buildings can often be assumed to be of uniform section within each span, which simplifies global analysis. Cracking reduces bending moments at internal supports to an extent that can be estimated by the method of ***clause***

Clause 7.3.1(6)

7.3.1(6), based on Stark and van Hove.[95] The maximum deflection of a given span normally occurs when no imposed load acts on adjacent spans. The conditions for the use of curve A in *Fig. 7.1* are then not satisfied, and the method consists simply of reducing all 'uncracked' moments at internal supports by 40%.

Using the new end moments, M_{h1} and M_{h2}, say, the maximum deflection can be found either by elastic theory for the span, of uncracked flexural stiffness $E_a I_1$, or by an approximate method given in BS 5950-3-1.[31] This consists of multiplying the deflection for the simply-supported span by the factor

$$1 - 0.6(M_{h1} + M_{h2})/M_0 \tag{D7.2}$$

where M_0 is the maximum sagging moment in the beam when it is simply supported.

Yielding of steel

In continuous beams built unpropped, with steel beams in Class 1 or 2, it is possible that serviceability loading may cause yielding at internal supports. This is permitted for beams in buildings, but it causes additional deflection, which should be allowed for. *Clause 7.3.1(7)* provides a method. The bending moments at internal supports are found by elastic analysis, with allowance for effects of cracking. The two values given in the clause for factors f_2 correspond to different checks. The first is for dead load only: wet concrete on a steel beam.

Clause 7.3.1(7)

According to the UK's draft National Annex to EN 1990,[96] the load combination to be used for the second check depends on the functioning of the structure. It may be the characteristic, frequent or quasi-permanent combination, with the load additional to that for the first check acting on the composite beam. For each analysis, appropriate assumptions are needed for the adjacent spans, on their loading and on the state of construction.

Local buckling

This does not influence stiffnesses for elastic analysis except for Class 4 sections. For these, *clause 5.4.1.1(6)* refers to clause 2.2 in EN 1993-1-5, which gives a design rule.

Shrinkage

In principle, shrinkage effects appear in all load combinations. For SLS, *clause 5.4.2.2(7)* refers to *Section 7*, where *clause 7.3.1(8)* enables effects of shrinkage on deflections of beams to be ignored for span/depth ratios up to 20. In more slender beams, shrinkage deflections are significantly reduced by provision of continuity at supports.

Clause 7.3.1(8)

Temperature

Clause 5.4.2.5(2), on neglect of temperature effects, does not apply. For buildings, neither ψ_0 nor ψ_1 is given as zero in clause A1.2.2 of EN 1990 (nor in the UK's draft National Annex to BS EN 1990[96]), so if temperature effects are relevant at ULS, they should be included in all SLS combinations except quasi-permanent.

Welded mesh

Clause 5.5.1(6) gives conditions for the inclusion of welded mesh in the effective section, within the rules for classification of sections.

7.3.2. Vibration

Limits to vibration in buildings are material-independent, and vibration is in clause A1.4.4 of EN 1990, not in EN 1994. Composite floor systems are lighter and have less inherent damping than their equivalents in reinforced concrete. During their design, dynamic behaviour should be checked against the criteria in EN 1990 referred to from *clause 7.3.2(1)*. These are general, and advise that the lowest natural frequency of vibration of the structure or member should be kept above a value to be agreed with the client and/or the relevant authority. No values are given for either limiting frequencies or damping coefficients.

Clause 7.3.2(1)

More specific guidance can be found in EN 1991-1-1 and the extensive literature on this subject.[97,98] These sources refer to several criteria that are likely to be specific to the individual project, and, with other aspects, should be agreed with the client. A note to clause 7.2.3 of EN 1993-1-1 says that limits to vibration of floors may be specified in a National Annex.

7.4. Cracking of concrete

7.4.1. General

In the early 1980s it was found[44,99] that for composite beams in hogging bending, the long-established British methods for control of crack width were unreliable for initial cracks, which were wider than predicted. Before this, it had been found for reinforced concrete that the appropriate theoretical model for cracking caused by restraint of imposed deformation was different from that for cracking caused by applied loading. This has led to the presentation of design rules for control of cracking as two distinct procedures:

- for minimum reinforcement, in *clause 7.4.2*, for all cross-sections that could be subjected to significant tension by imposed deformations (e.g. by effects of shrinkage, which cause higher stresses than in reinforced concrete, because of restraint from the steel beam)
- for reinforcement to control cracking due to direct loading (*clause 7.4.3*).

The rules given in EN 1994-1-1 are based on an extensive and quite complex theory, supported by testing on hogging regions of composite beams.[99,100] Much of the original literature is in German, so a detailed account of the theory has recently been published in English,[101] with comparisons with results of tests on composite beams, additional to those used originally. The paper includes derivations of the equations given in *clause 7.4*, comments on their scope and underlying assumptions, and procedures for estimating the mean width and spacing of cracks. These are tedious, and so are not in EN 1994-1-1. Its methods are simple: *Tables 7.1* and *7.2* give maximum diameters and spacings of reinforcing bars for three design crack widths: 0.2, 0.3 and 0.4 mm.

Tables 7.1 and *7.2* are for 'high-bond' bars only. This means ribbed bars with properties as in clause 3.2.2(2)P of EN 1992-1-1. The use of reinforcement other than ribbed is outside the scope of the Eurocodes.

The references to EN 1992-1-1 in *clause 7.4.1(1)* give the surface crack-width limits required for design. Concrete in tension in a composite beam or slab for a building will usually be in exposure class XC3, for which the recommended limit is 0.3 mm; however, for spaces with low or very low air humidity, Tables 4.1 and 7.1N of EN 1992-1-1 recommend a limit of 0.4 mm. The limits are more severe for prestressed members, which are not discussed further. The severe environment for a floor of a multistorey car park is discussed in Chapter 4. All these limits may be modified in a National Annex.

Clause 7.4.1(2) refers to 'estimation' of crack width, using EN 1992-1-1. This rather long procedure is rarely needed, and does not take full account of the following differences between the behaviours of composite beams and reinforced concrete T-beams. The steel member in a composite beam does not shrink or creep and has much greater flexural stiffness than the reinforcement in a concrete beam. Also, the steel member is attached to the concrete flange only by discrete connectors that are not effective until there is longitudinal slip, whereas in reinforced concrete there is monolithic connection.

Clause 7.4.1(3) refers to the methods developed for composite members, which are easier to apply than the methods for reinforced concrete members.

Clause 7.4.1(1)

Clause 7.4.1(2)

Clause 7.4.1(3)

Uncontrolled cracking

Clause 7.3.1(4) of EN 1992-1-1 (referred to from *clause 7.4.1(1)*) permits cracking of uncontrolled width in some circumstances; for example, beams designed as simply supported, with a concrete top flange that is continuous over 'simple' beam-to-column

Clause 7.4.1(4)

connections. These are flexible in bending, and rotate about a point that cannot be predicted, as its position depends on tolerances and methods of erection of the steelwork. It may then be impossible to predict the widths of cracks. Where the environment is dry and the concrete surface is concealed by a flexible finish, such as carpeting, crack widths exceeding 0.4 mm may be acceptable. Even so, the minimum reinforcement required (for other reasons) by EN 1992-1-1 may be inadequate to prevent the fracture of small-diameter bars near internal supports, or the formation of very wide cracks. Minimum areas greater than those of EN 1992-1-1 are therefore specified in *clause 7.4.1(4)* and, for composite slabs, in *clause 9.8.1(2)*.

The maximum thicknesses of slab that can be reinforced by one layer of standard welded fabric, according to these rules, are given in Table 7.1. For composite slabs, the relevant thickness is that above the profiled steel sheeting.

The maximum spacing of flexural reinforcement permitted by clause 9.3.1.1(3) of EN 1992-1-1 is $3h$, but not exceeding 400 mm, where h is the total depth of the slab. This rule is for solid slabs. It is not intended for slabs formed with profiled steel sheeting, for which a more appropriate rule is that given in *clause 9.2.1(5)*: spacing not exceeding $2h$ (and ≤ 350 mm) in both directions, where h is the overall thickness of the slab, including ribs of composite slabs.

7.4.2. Minimum reinforcement

Clause 7.4.2(1)

The only data needed when using *Tables 7.1* and *7.2* are the tensile stresses in the reinforcement, σ_s. For minimum reinforcement, σ_s is the stress immediately after initial cracking. It is assumed that the curvature of the steel beam does not change, so all of the tensile force in the concrete just before cracking is transferred to the reinforcement, of area A_s. If the slab were in uniform tension, *equation (7.1)* in *clause 7.4.2(1)* would be

$$A_s \sigma_s = A_{ct} f_{ct, eff}$$

The three correction factors in *equation (7.1)* are based on calibration work.[102] These allow for the non-uniform stress distribution in the area A_{ct} of concrete assumed to crack. 'Non-uniform self-equilibrating stresses' arise from primary shrinkage and temperature effects, which cause curvature of the composite member. Slip of the shear connection also causes curvature and reduces the tensile force in the slab.

The magnitude of these effects depends on the geometry of the uncracked composite section, as given by *equation (7.2)*. With experience, calculation of k_c can often be omitted, because it is less than 1.0 only where $z_0 < 1.2h_c$. Especially for beams supporting composite slabs, the depth of the 'uncracked' neutral axis below the bottom of the slab (excluding ribs) normally exceeds about 70% of the slab thickness, and then, $k_c = 1$.

For design, the design crack width and thickness of the slab, h_c will be known. It will be evident whether there should be one layer of reinforcement or two. Two layers will often consist of bars of the same size and spacing, which satisfies *clause 7.4.2(3)*. For a chosen bar diameter ϕ, *Table 7.1* gives σ_s, and *equation (7.1)* gives the bar spacing. If this is too high or low, ϕ is changed.

Table 7.1. Use of steel fabric as minimum reinforcement, to *clause 7.4.1(4)*

		Maximum thickness of slab (mm)	
Bar size and spacing	Cross-sectional area (mm² per m width)	Unpropped, 0.2%	Propped, 0.4%
6 mm, 200 mm	142	71	–
7 mm, 200 mm	193	96	48
8 mm, 200 mm	252	126	63

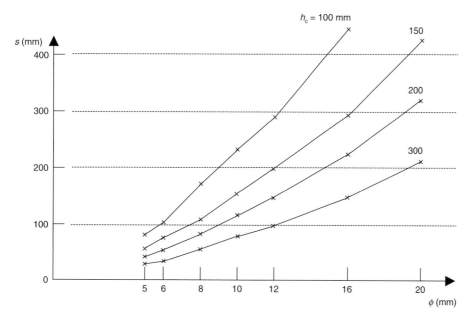

Fig. 7.1. Bar diameter and spacing for minimum reinforcement in two equal layers, for $w_k = 0.3$ mm and $f_{ct,\,eff} = 3.0$ N/mm²

A typical relationship between slab thickness h_c, bar spacing s and bar diameter ϕ is shown in Fig. 7.1. It is for two similar layers of bars, with $k_c = 1$ and $f_{ct,\,eff} = 3.0$ N/mm². *Equation (7.1)* then gives, for a slab of breadth b,

$$(\pi\phi^2/4)(2b/s) = 0.72 \times 3bh_c/\sigma_s$$

Hence,

$$h_c s = 0.727\phi^2\sigma_s \tag{D7.3}$$

For each bar diameter and a given crack width, *Table 7.1* gives $\phi^2\sigma_s$, so the product $h_c s$ is known. This is plotted in Fig. 7.1, for $w_k = 0.3$ mm, as curves of bar spacing for four slab thicknesses, which can of course also be read as slab thicknesses for four bar spacings. The shape of the curves results partly from the use of rounded values of σ_s in *Table 7.1*. The optional correction to minimum reinforcement given in *clause 7.4.2(2)* is negligible here, and has not been made. Figure 7.1 can be used for slabs with one layer of bars by halving the slab thickness.

The weight of minimum reinforcement, per unit area of slab, is proportional to ϕ^2/s, which is proportional to σ_s^{-1}, from equation (D7.3). This increases with bar diameter, from *Table 7.1*, so the use of smaller bars reduces the weight of minimum reinforcement. This is because their greater surface area provides more bond strength.

The method of *clause 7.4.2(1)* is not intended for the control of early thermal cracking, which can occur in concrete a few days old, if the temperature rise caused by the heat of hydration is excessive. The flanges of composite beams are usually too thin for this to occur. It would not be correct, therefore, to assume a very low value for $f_{ct,\,eff}$. The suggested value, 3 N/mm², was probably rounded from the mean 28 day tensile strength of grade C30/37 concrete, given in EN 1992-1-1 as 2.9 N/mm² – the value used as the basis for the optional correction given in *clause 7.4.2(2)*. The difference between 2.9 and 3.0 is obviously negligible. If there is good reason to assume a value for $f_{ct,\,eff}$ such that the correction is not negligible, it is best used by assuming a standard bar diameter ϕ, calculating ϕ^*, and then finding σ_s by interpolation in *Table 7.1*.

Clause 7.4.2(2)

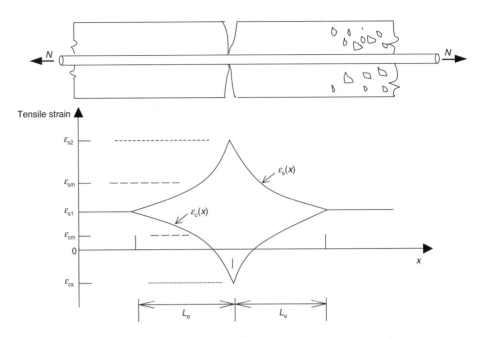

Fig. 7.2. Strain distributions near a crack in a reinforced concrete tension member

Reinforcement for encasement of a steel web

Clause 7.4.2(6) *Clause 7.4.2(6)* gives a minimum value of A_s/A_{ct} for encasement of the type shown in *Fig. 6.1*. The maximum bar size is not specified. Detailing of this reinforcement is usually determined by the requirements of *clause 5.5.3(2)* and of EN 1994-1-2, for fire resistance.

7.4.3. Control of cracking due to direct loading

Clause 7.4.3(2) *Clause 7.4.3(2)* specifies elastic global analysis to *Section 5*, allowing for the effects of cracking. The preceding comments on global analysis for deformations apply also to this analysis for bending moments in regions with concrete in tension.

Paragraph *(4)* on loading should come next, but it is placed last in *clause 7.4.3* because of the drafting rule that 'general' paragraphs precede those 'for buildings'. It specifies the quasi-permanent combination. Except for storage areas, the values of factors ψ_2 for floor loads in buildings are typically 0.3 or 0.6. The bending moments will then be much less than for the ultimate limit state, especially for cross-sections in Class 1 or 2 in beams built unpropped. There is no need to reduce the extent of the cracked regions below that assumed for global analysis, so the new bending moments for the composite members can be found by scaling values found for ultimate loadings. At each cross-section, the area of reinforcement will be already known: that required for ultimate loading or the specified minimum, if

Clause 7.4.3(3) greater; so the stresses $\sigma_{s,0}$ (*clause 7.4.3(3)*) can be found.

Tension stiffening

A correction for tension stiffening is now required. At one time, these effects were not well understood. It was thought that, for a given tensile strain at the level of the reinforcement, the total extension must be the extension of the concrete plus the width of the cracks, so that allowing for the former reduced the latter. The true behaviour is more complex.

The upper part of Fig. 7.2 shows a single crack in a concrete member with a central reinforcing bar. At the crack, the external tensile force N causes strain $\varepsilon_{s2} = N/A_s E_a$ in the bar, and the strain in the concrete is the free shrinkage strain ε_{cs}, which is negative, as shown. There is a transmission length L_e each side of the crack, within which there is transfer of shear between the bar and the concrete. Outside this length, the strain in both the steel and the concrete is ε_{s1}, and the stress in the concrete is fractionally below its tensile strength.

Within the length $2L_e$, the curves $\varepsilon_s(x)$ and $\varepsilon_c(x)$ give the strains in the two materials, with mean strains ε_{sm} in the bar and ε_{cm} in the concrete.

It is now assumed that the graph represents the typical behaviour of a reinforcing bar in a cracked concrete flange of a composite beam, in a region of constant bending moment such that the crack spacing is $2L_e$. The curvature of the steel beam is determined by the mean stiffness of the slab, not the fully cracked stiffness, and is compatible with the mean longitudinal strain in the reinforcement, ε_{sm}.

Midway between the cracks, the strain is the cracking strain of the concrete, corresponding to a stress less than 30 N/mm^2 in the bar. Its peak strain, at the crack, is much greater than ε_{sm}, but less than the yield strain, if crack widths are not to exceed 0.4 mm. The crack width corresponds to this higher strain, not to the strain ε_{sm} that is compatible with the curvature, so a correction to the strain is needed. It is presented in *clause 7.4.3(3)* as a correction to the stress $\sigma_{s,0}$ because that is easily calculated, and *Tables 7.1* and *7.2* are based on stress. The strain correction cannot be shown in Fig. 7.1 because the stress $\sigma_{s,0}$ is calculated using the 'fully cracked' stiffness, and so relates to a curvature greater than the true curvature. The derivation of the correction[101] takes account of crack spacings less than $2L_e$, the bond properties of reinforcement, and other factors omitted from this simplified outline.

The section properties needed for the calculation of the correction $\Delta\sigma_s$ will usually be known. For the composite section, A is needed to find I, which is used in calculating $\sigma_{s,0}$, and A_a and I_a are standard properties of the steel section. The result is independent of the modular ratio. For simplicity, α_{st} may conservatively be taken as 1.0, because $AI > A_a I_a$.

When the stress σ_s at a crack has been found, the maximum bar diameter or the maximum spacing are found from *Tables 7.1* and *7.2*. Only one of these is needed, as the known area of reinforcement then gives the other. The correction of *clause 7.4.2(2)* does not apply.

Influence of profiled sheeting on the control of cracking

The only references to profiled steel sheeting in *clause 7.4* are in *clause 7.4.1(4)*, '... *no account should be taken of any profiled steel sheeting*', and in the definition of h_c in *clause 7.4.2(1)*, '... *thickness ... excluding any haunch or ribs*'.

The effects of the use of profiled sheeting for a slab that forms the top flange of a continuous composite beam are as follows:

- there is no need for control of crack widths at the lower surface of the slab
- where the sheeting spans in the transverse direction, there is at present no evidence that it contributes to the control of transverse cracks at the top surface of the slab
- where the sheeting spans parallel to the beam, it probably contributes to crack control, but no research on this subject is known to the authors.

For design, the definition of 'effective tension area' in clause 7.3.4(2) of EN 1992-1-1 should be noted. A layer of reinforcement at depth $c + \phi/2$ below the top surface of the slab, where c is the cover, may be assumed to influence cracking over a depth $2.5(c + \phi/2)$ of the slab. If the depth of the concrete above the top of the sheeting, h_c, is greater than this, it would be reasonable to use the lower value, when calculating A_s from *equation (7.1)*. This recognizes the ability of the sheeting to control cracking in the lower half of the slab, and has the effect of reducing the minimum amount of reinforcement required, for the thicker composite slabs

General comments on *clause 7.4*

In regions where tension in concrete may arise from shrinkage or temperature effects, but not from other actions, the minimum reinforcement required may exceed that provided in previous practice.

Where unpropped construction is used for a continuous beam, the design loading for checking cracking is usually much less than that for the ultimate limit state, so that the quantity of reinforcement provided for resistance to load should be sufficient to control cracking. The main use of *clause 7.4.3* is then to check that the spacing of the bars is not too great.

Where propped construction is used, the disparity between the design loadings for the two limit states is smaller. If cracks are to be controlled to 0.3 mm, a check to *clause 7.4.3* is more likely to influence the reinforcement required.

For beams in frames, the preceding comments apply where semi-rigid or rigid connections are used. Where floors have brittle finishes or an adverse environment, simple beam-to-column joints should not be used, because effective control of crack width may not be possible.

Example 7.1: two-span beam (continued) – SLS

Details of this beam are shown in Fig. 6.23. All of the design data and calculations for the ultimate limit state are given in Examples 6.7 to 6.12. For data and results required here, reference should be made to:

- Table 6.2, for characteristic loads per unit length
- Table 6.3, for elastic properties of the cross-sections at the internal support (B in Fig. 6.23(c)) and at mid-span
- Table 6.4, for bending moments at support B for uniform loading on both spans
- Fig. 6.28, for bending-moment diagrams for design ultimate loadings, excluding the effects of shrinkage.

The secondary effects of shrinkage are significant in this beam, and cause a hogging bending moment at support B of 120 kN m (Example 6.7). *Clause 7.3.1(8)* does not permit shrinkage to be ignored for serviceability checks on this beam, because it does not refer to lightweight-aggregate concrete, which is used here.

Stresses

From *clause 7.2.2(1)*, there are no limitations on stress; but stresses in the steel beam need to be calculated, because if yielding occurs under service loads, account should be taken of the resulting increase in deflections, from *clause 7.3.1(7)*.

Yielding is irreversible, so, from a note to clause 6.5.3(2) of EN 1990, it should be checked for the characteristic load combination. However, the loading for checking deflections depends on the serviceability requirement.[96]

The maximum stress in the steel beam occurs in the bottom flange at support B. Results for the characteristic combination with variable load on both spans and 15% of each span cracked are given in Table 7.2. The permanent load, other than floor finishes, is assumed to act on the steel beam alone. Following *clause 5.4.2.2(11)*, the modular ratio is taken as 20.2 for all of the loading except shrinkage.

Table 7.2. Hogging bending moments at support B and stresses in the steel bottom flange, for the characteristic load combination

Loading	w (kN/m)	Modular ratio	$10^{-6}I_{y,B}$ (mm⁴)	$M_{Ek,B}$ (kN m)	$10^{-6}W_{a,bot}$ (mm³)	$\sigma_{a,bot}$ (N/mm²)
(1) Permanent (on steel beam)	5.78	–	337	104	1.50	69
(2) Permanent (on composite beam)	1.2	20.2	467	18	1.75	10
(3) Variable	17.5	20.2	467	263	1.75	150
(4) Shrinkage	–	28.7	467	120	1.75	69

Table 7.3. Deflections at 4.8 m from support A, for the frequent combination

Load	Modular ratio	Deflection (mm)
Dead, on steel beam	–	9
Dead, on composite beam	20.2	1
Imposed, on composite beam	20.2	14
Primary shrinkage	27.9	33
Secondary shrinkage	27.9	−26

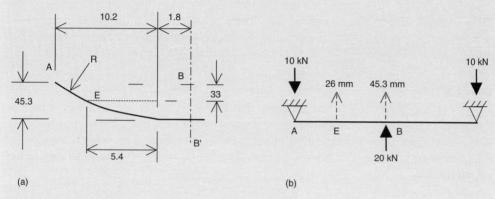

(a) (b)

Fig. 7.3. Sagging deflection at point E caused by shrinkage

The total bottom-flange compressive stress is

$$\sigma_{Ek, bot, a} = 298 \text{ N/mm}^2 \ (= 0.84f_y)$$

so no allowance is needed for yielding.

Deflections

The maximum deflection of span AB of the beam will occur at about 4.8 m from A (40% of the span), when variable load acts on span AB only. The additional deflection caused by slip of the shear connection is ignored, as *clause 7.3.1(4)(a)* is satisfied.

Calculated deflections at this point, with 15% of each span assumed to be cracked, are given in Table 7.3. The frequent combination is used, for which $\psi_1 = 0.7$, so the variable loading is

$$0.7 \times 17.5 = 12.3 \text{ kN/m}$$

The following method was used for the shrinkage deflections. From Example 6.7 and Fig. 6.27, the primary effect is uniform sagging curvature at radius $R = 1149$ m, with deflection $\delta = 45.3$ mm at support B. The secondary reaction at B is 20 kN. From the geometry of the circle, the primary deflection at point E in Fig. 7.3(a) is

$$\delta_{1, E} = 45.3 - 5.4^2 \times 1000 \times (2 \times 1149) = 33 \text{ mm}$$

The upwards displacement at E caused by the 20 kN reaction at B that moves point B′ back to B was found to be 26 mm by elastic analysis of the model shown in Fig. 7.3(b), with 15% of each span cracked. The total shrinkage deflection is only 7 mm, despite the high free shrinkage strain, but would not be negligible in a simply-supported span.

The total deflection, 31 mm, is span/390. This ratio appears not to be excessive. However, the functioning of the floor may depend on its maximum deflection relative to the supporting columns. It is found in Example 9.1 that the deflection of the composite slab, if cast unpropped, is 15 mm for the frequent combination. This is relative to the supporting beams, so the maximum floor deflection is

$$31 + 15 = 46 \text{ mm}$$

or span/260. For the characteristic combination, this increases to

$$37 + 16 = 53 \text{ mm}$$

or span/230.

The limiting deflections given in the UK's draft National Annex to EN 1990[96] depend on the serviceability requirement. For floors with partitions, they range from span/300 to span/500. For this floor, some combination of using propped construction for the composite slabs and/or the beams, and cambering the beams, will be necessary.

Reducing the modular ratio for imposed loading to 10.1 makes little difference: the value 14 mm in Table 7.3 becomes 12 mm. The extensive calculations for shrinkage lead to a net deflection of only 7 mm, because the secondary effect cancels out most of the primary effect. This benefit would not occur, of course, in a simply-supported span.

Control of crack width

Clause 7.4 applies to reinforced concrete that forms part of a composite member. In the beam considered here, the relevant cracks are those near support B caused by hogging bending of the beam, and cracks along the beam caused by hogging bending of the composite slab that the beam supports. The latter are treated in Example 9.1 on a composite slab.

Clause 7.4.1(1) refers to exposure classes. From clause 4.2(2) of EN 1992-1-1, Class XC3 is appropriate for concrete 'inside buildings with moderate humidity'. For this class, a note to clause 7.3.1(5) of EN 1992-1-1 gives the design crack width as 0.3 mm. The method of *clause 7.4.1(3)* is followed, as *clause 7.4.1(4)* does not apply.

Minimum reinforcement

The relevant cross-section of the concrete flange is as shown in Fig. 6.23(a), except that effective widths up to 2.5 m should be considered.

From *clause 5.4.1.2*, the effective width is assumed to increase from 1.6 m at support B to 2.5 m at sections more than 3 m from B. It may be difficult to show that sections 3 m from B are never 'subjected to significant tension' (*clause 7.4.2(1)*). Calculations are therefore done for both effective widths, assuming uncracked unreinforced concrete. From the definition of z_0 in that clause, $n_0 = 10.1$.

It is found for both of these flange widths that z_0 is such that $k_c > 1$, so, from *equation (7.2)*, it is taken as 1.0.

A value is required for the strength of the concrete when cracks first occur. As unpropped construction is used, there is at first little load on the composite member, so from *clause 7.4.2(1)*, conservatively, $f_{ct, \text{eff}} = 3.0 \text{ N/mm}^2$. Assuming that 10 mm bars are used for the minimum reinforcement, *Table 7.1* gives $\sigma_s = 320 \text{ N/mm}^2$. Then, from *equation (7.1)*,

$$100 A_s / A_{ct} = 100 \times 0.9 \times 1 \times 0.8 \times 3.0/320 = 0.675\%$$

However, *clause 5.5.1(5)* also sets a limit, as a condition for the use of plastic resistance moments. For this concrete, $f_{lctm} = 2.32 \text{ N/mm}^2$, and $f_{sk} = 500 \text{ N/mm}^2$. Hence, from *equation (5.8)* with $k_c = 1.0$,

$$100 \rho_s = 100 \times (355/235)(2.32/500) = \textbf{0.70\%} \tag{D7.4}$$

This limit governs; so for a slab 80 mm thick above the sheeting the minimum reinforcement is

$$A_{s, \min} = 7 \times 80 = 560 \text{ mm}^2/\text{m}$$

One layer of 10 mm bars at 125 mm spacing provides **628 mm²/m.**

Cracking due to direct loading

Only the most critical cross-section, at support B, will be considered. *Clause 7.4.3(4)* permits the use of the quasi-permanent combination, for which the variable loading is $\psi_2 q_k$, with $\psi_2 = 0.6$, from clause A1.2.2(1) of EN 1990.

From Table 7.2, the bending moment at B that stresses the reinforcement is

$$M_{E, qp, B} = 18 + 263 \times 0.6 + 127 = 303 \text{ kN m}$$

The neutral axis for the cracked section is 313 mm below the top of the slab (Table 6.12), so the section modulus for reinforcement at depth 30 mm is

$$10^{-6}W_s = 467/(313 - 30) = 1.65 \text{ mm}^3$$

Hence, from *clause 7.4.3(3)*,

$$\sigma_{s,0} = 303/1.65 = 184 \text{ N/mm}^2$$

The correction for tension stiffening, *equation (7.5)*, is now calculated, assuming that the reinforcement used in Example 6.7, 12 mm bars at 125 mm spacing, will be satisfactory. This gives $\rho_s = 0.0113$.

Using values obtained earlier,

$$\alpha_{st} = AI/A_a I_a = 11\,350 \times 467/(9880 \times 337) = 1.59$$

From *equation (7.5)*,

$$\Delta\sigma_s = 0.4 \times 2.32/(1.59 \times 0.0113) = \mathbf{52 \ N/mm^2} \tag{D7.5}$$

From *equation (7.4)*,

$$\sigma_s = 184 + 52 = 236 \text{ N/mm}^2$$

From *Table 7.1*, $\phi_s \le 16$ mm. From *Table 7.2*, the bar spacing ≤ 200 mm.

The use of **12 mm bars at 125 mm** spacing at support B satisfies both conditions. Finding the cross-sections of the beam at which this reinforcement can be reduced to the minimum found above may require consideration of the bending-moment envelopes both for ultimate loads and for the quasi-permanent combination.

CHAPTER 8

Composite joints in frames for buildings

This chapter corresponds to *Section 8* of EN 1994-1-1, which has the following clauses:

- Scope   *Clause 8.1*
- Analysis, modelling and classification   *Clause 8.2*
- Design methods   *Clause 8.3*
- Resistance of components   *Clause 8.4*

8.1. Scope

Section 8 is based on relatively recent research on beam-to-column and beam-to-beam joints of the types used in steel and composite frames for buildings, so its scope has been limited to 'frames for buildings'. The definition of composite joints to which ***clause 8.1(1)*** refers includes joints with reinforced concrete members. These could occur, for example, in a tower block with a concrete core and composite floors. However, no application rules are given for such joints.

Clause 8.1(1)

As stated in ***clause 8.1(2),*** both *Section 8* and *Annex A* are essentially extensions to the Eurocode for joints between steel members, EN 1993-1-8.[24] It is assumed that a user will be familiar with this code, especially its Sections 5 and 6.

Clause 8.1(2)

The only steel members considered in detail are I- and H-sections, which may have concrete-encased webs. Plate girders are not excluded.

The application rules of EN 1994-1-1 are limited to composite joints in which reinforcement is in tension and the lower part of the steel section is in compression (*Fig. 8.1* and *clause 8.4.1(1)*). There are no application rules for joints where the axes of the members connected do not intersect, or do so at angles other than 90°; but the basic approach is more general than the procedures prescribed in detail, and is capable of application in a wider range of situations.

Many types of joint are in use in steelwork, so that EN 1993-1-8 is around 130 pages long. The majority of the calculations needed for composite joints are specified there, and explained in the relevant guide in this series.[103] The worked examples and much of the comment in the present guide are limited to a single type of joint – the double-sided configuration shown in *Fig. 8.1* – but with an end plate, not a contact plate, and an uncased column, as shown on the left of *Fig. 8.1* and in Fig. 8.8.

Commentary on the design of this joint will be found, as appropriate, in this chapter and its examples, and in Chapter 10 on *Annex A*.

Before the Eurocodes come into regular use, it is expected that tables of resistances and stiffnesses of a wide range of steel and composite joints will become available, based on

EN 1993 and EN 1994. The extensive calculations given here will rarely be needed. Many of them serve to show that a particular property of a joint does not govern its resistance. Experience will enable such checks to be omitted.

Detailed guidance on the Eurocode methods for composite joints appeared in 1998, in the context of design to British codes.[104] An explanation of the provisions and approximations in the Eurocodes, with worked examples, was then prepared, mainly by those who drafted the codes. Its first edition[39] refers to the draft codes as they were in 1998, so some differences, mainly in symbols, will be found between it and the published EN Eurocodes. With over 200 pages, it provides much broader coverage than is possible here.

8.2. Analysis, including modelling and classification

Clause 8.2.1(1)

Clause 8.2.1(1) refers to Section 5 of EN 1993-1-8, which covers the same subjects as *clause 8.2*. Table 5.1 in clause 5.1 of EN 1993-1-8 defines the links between the three types of global analysis, elastic, rigid plastic, and elastic–plastic, and the types of models used for joints. This enables the designer to determine whether the stiffness of the joint, its resistance, or both properties, are relevant to the analysis.

Joints are classified in Section 5 by stiffness, as rigid, nominally pinned, or semi-rigid; and by strength as full-strength, nominally pinned, or partial-strength. This classification relates the property of the joint (stiffness or resistance) to that of the connected member, normally taken as the beam.

Clause 8.2.2(1)

This applies also to composite joints. The only modification, in *clause 8.2.2(1)*, concerns the rotational stiffness of a joint, S_j. This is bending moment per unit rotation, shown in Fig. 8.2(b). The symbol ϕ is used for rotation, as well as for bar diameter.

The initial elastic stiffness, $S_{j,\,ini}$, is reduced at high bending moments to allow for inelastic behaviour. For global analysis, it is divided by η, values of which, between 3.0 and 3.5, are tabulated in clause 5.1.2 of EN 1993-1-8 for various types of steel joint. These apply where the joint is composite. *Clause 8.2.2(1)* provides a further value, for contact-plate joints, as shown on the right of *Fig. 8.1* and in Fig. 8.4.

The classification of a composite joint may depend on the direction of the bending moment (e.g. sagging or hogging). This is unlikely in a steelwork joint, and so is referred to in

Clause 8.2.3(2)
Clause 8.2.3(3)

clause 8.2.3(2).

The reference in *clause 8.2.3(3)* to neglect of cracking and creep applies only to the classification of the joint according to stiffness. Its initial stiffness is to be compared with that of the connected beam, using Fig. 5.4 of EN 1993-1-8. The stiffer the beam the less likely it is that the joint can be classified as rigid.

A more precise calculation of beam stiffness is permitted by the use of 'may' in *clause 8.2.3(3)*. For example, a representative value of modular ratio, to *clause 5.4.2.2(11)*, may be used. Account could also be taken of cracked and uncracked lengths within the beam

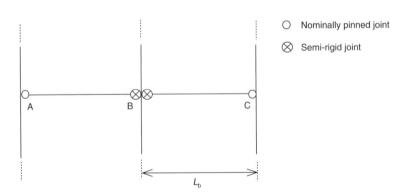

Fig. 8.1. Model for a two-span beam in a frame

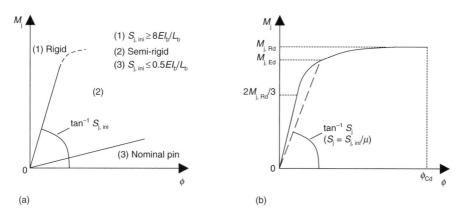

Fig. 8.2. Moment–rotation relationships for joints

in accordance with *clause 5.4.2.3*, but the additional calculation would not normally be worthwhile.

Outline of modelling of joints for global analysis

In global analysis, nominally pinned joints are represented by pins, and semi-rigid joints by rotational springs, as shown in Fig. 8.1 for a two-span beam of uniform depth, supported by three columns in a braced frame. Joints to external columns are usually designed as nominally pinned, to reduce bending moments in the columns. The use of partial-strength semi-rigid joints at point B, rather than nominally pinned joints, has advantages in design:

- possible reduction in the section sizes for beams
- reduction in the deflection of beams
- reduction in crack widths near support B.

In comparison with full-strength rigid joints, the advantages are:

- beams less susceptible to lateral–torsional buckling
- simpler construction and significant reduction in cost
- lower bending moments in columns.

The stiffness of a rotational spring, S_j, is the slope of the moment–rotation relationship for the joint (Fig. 8.2(a)). The stiffness class is determined by the ratio of the initial slope, $S_{j, ini}$, to the stiffness $E_a I_b / L_b$ of the beam adjacent to the joint, as shown.

The initial stiffness of a joint is assembled from the stiffnesses of its components, represented by elastic springs. Those for an end-plate joint with a single row of bolts in tension, between beams of equal depth are shown in Fig. 8.3, in which all elements except springs and pins are rigid. The notation for the spring stiffnesses k_i is as in EN 1993-1-8 and in Examples 8.1 and 10.1, as follows:

k_1 shear in column web
k_2 compression of column web
k_3 extension of column web
k_4 bending of column flange, caused by tension from a single row of bolts
k_5 bending of end plate, caused by tension from a single row of bolts
k_{10} extension of bolts, for a single row of bolts.

Stiffnesses in EN 1994-1-1, but not in EN 1993-1-8, are:

$k_{s, r}$ extension of reinforcement (denoted k_{13} by ECCS TC11[39])
K_{sc}/E_s slip of shear connection.

Each spring has a finite strength, governed by yield or buckling of the steel. The design method ensures that non-ductile modes, such as fracture of bolts, do not govern.

For the tension region, the weakest of the springs numbered 3, 4, 5 and 10, and of the tension reinforcement, is found. This resistance is compared with the compressive resistance of spring 2. The product of the lower of these resistances and the effective lever arm gives the plastic bending resistance of the joint. The resistance can be increased by strengthening the weakest link; for example, by the addition of column-web stiffeners.

Where the beams are of unequal depth, or $M_{Ed, 1} \neq M_{Ed, 2}$ (Fig. 8.3), rotation at the joint is increased by shearing deformation of the column web. For beams of equal depth, this is the area ABCD in Fig. 8.3. Its deformation is resisted by the spring of stiffness k_1. Depending on the out-of-balance moment $|M_{Ed, 1} - M_{Ed, 2}|$, the column web panel may govern the resistance of the joint.

8.3. Design methods

Clause 8.3.1(1)

Clause 8.3.1(1) refers to Section 6 of EN 1993-1-8, which is 40 pages long. It defines the 'basic components' of a steelwork joint, their strengths and their elastic stiffnesses. It is shown how these are assembled to obtain the resistances, rotational stiffness and rotation capacity of complete joints.

A composite joint has these additional components:

- longitudinal slab reinforcement in tension
- concrete encasement, where present, of the column web
- steel contact plates, if used (not covered in EN 1993-1-8).

In addition, account is taken of the slip of shear connection, by modifying the stiffness of the reinforcement (Fig. 8.3).

All the properties of components given in, or cross-referenced from, EN 1994-1-1 satisfy

Clause 8.3.1(2)
Clause 8.3.1(3)

the condition of *clause 8.3.1(2)*. The application of *clause 8.3.1(3)* to reinforcing bars is illustrated in Examples 8.1 and 10.1.

None of the additional components listed above influences resistance to vertical shear, so

Clause 8.3.2(1)

this aspect of design is fully covered by EN 1993-1-8 (*clause 8.3.2(1)*).

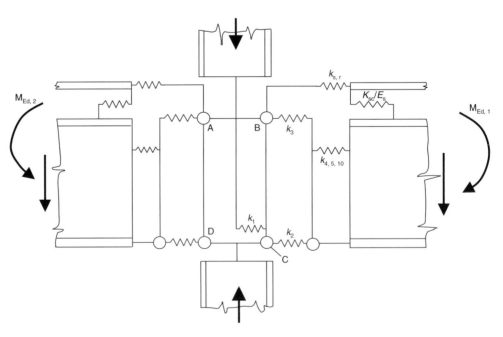

Fig. 8.3. Model for an internal beam-to-column joint

Composite joints in framed structures for buildings are almost always in regions of hogging bending, for which full shear connection is normally required, to *clauses 6.2.1.3(2)* and *8.4.2.1(2)*. The reference to shear connection in *clause 8.3.2(2)* reminds the user that no provisions are given for composite joints in regions with partial shear connection.

Clause 8.3.2(2)

The use of *Annex A* (informative) for finding rotational stiffnesses satisfies *clause 8.3.3(1)*, and is illustrated in Example 10.1.

Clause 8.3.3(1)

The coefficient ψ, referred to in *clause 8.3.3(2)*, is used in clause 6.3.1(6) of EN 1993-1-8 to define the shape of the moment-rotation curve for a joint at bending moments $M_{j,Ed}$ that exceed $2M_{j,Rd}/3$, as follows. Let $S_{j,ini}$ be the stiffness at low bending moments. For $2M_{j,Rd}/3 < M_{j,Ed} \leq M_{j,Rd}$, the stiffness is

Clause 8.3.3(2)

$$S_j = S_{j,ini}/\mu \tag{D8.1}$$

(Fig. 8.2(b)), where

$$\mu = (1.5M_{j,Ed}/M_{j,Rd})^\psi \tag{D8.2}$$

This clause gives the value for ψ for a type of joint not included in Table 6.8 of EN 1993-1-8. The table is applicable to other types of composite joint.

The rotation capacity of composite joints, ϕ_{Cd} in Fig. 8.2(b), has been extensively researched.[105] There are many relevant parameters. Analytical prediction is still difficult, and there are as yet no design rules sufficiently well established to be included in EN 1994-1-1.

So-called 'simple' joints have been widely used in composite structures. Some of them will be found to qualify as 'partial-strength' when Eurocode methods are used. The experience referred to in *clause 8.3.4(2)* is then available. It is rarely necessary in design to calculate either the available rotation capacity or the rotation required of a composite joint. Further guidance is given by ECCS TC11.[39]

Clause 8.3.4(2)

8.4. Resistance of components

This clause supplements clause 6.2 of EN 1993-1-8. The effective width of concrete flange in tension is the same at a joint as for the adjacent beam (*clause 8.4.2.1(1)*). Longitudinal bars above the beam should pass either side of the column.

Clause 8.4.2.1(1)

Clause 8.4.2.1(4) applies at an external column with a partial- or full-strength joint. The tensile force in the bars must be transferred to the column; for example, by being looped round it. This applies also at internal columns where there is a change in the tension in the bars (*Fig. 8.2, clause 8.4.2.1(3)* and Example 8.2).

Clause 8.4.2.1(4)

Clauses 8.4.2.2(1) and *8.4.3(1)* permit the same 45° spread of force in a contact plate as used in EN 1993-1-8 for an end plate. The force is assumed in EN 1993-1-8 to spread at $\tan^{-1} 2.5$ (68°) through the flange and root radius of the column. Where the compressive force relied on in design exceeds the resistance of the steel bottom flange, the length of the contact plate should allow for this (Fig. 8.4).

Clause 8.4.2.2(1)
Clause 8.4.3(1)

In EN 1994-1-1, the word 'connection' appears only in *clause 8.4.3(1)*, *clause A.2.3.2* and *Table A.1*. It means the set of components that connect a member to another member; for example, an end plate, its bolts and a column flange. Thus, a 'connection' is part of a 'joint'.

The model used in *clause 8.4.4.1(2)* is illustrated in Fig. 8.5. This figure shows an elevation of the concrete encasement of width $h - 2t_f$ (column depth less flange thicknesses) and depth z, the lever arm between the resultant horizontal forces from the beam. A shear force V is transferred through the encasement, which is of thickness $b_c - t_w$ (column width less web thickness). The concrete strut ABDEFG has width $0.8(h - 2t_f)\cos\theta$, where $\tan\theta = (h - 2t_f)/z$, so its area is

Clause 8.4.4.1(2)

$$A_c = 0.8(h - 2t_f)\cos\theta\,(b_c - t_w) \tag{8.2}$$

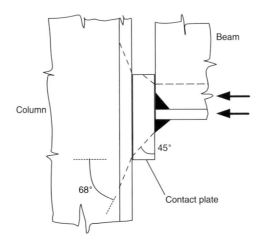

Fig. 8.4. Detail of a contact plate between a beam bottom flange and a column

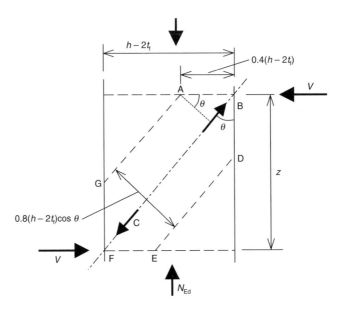

Fig. 8.5. Strut model for the shear resistance of the concrete encasement to a column web

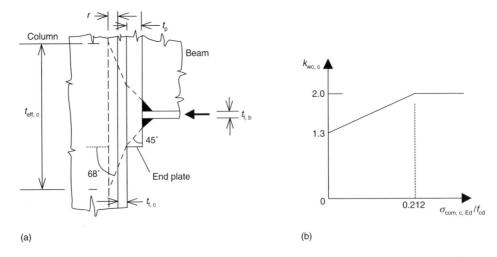

(a)   (b)

Fig. 8.6. Model for resistance to compression of the concrete encasement to a column web

Its compressive strength is $0.85\nu f_{cd}$, giving the force C in Fig. 8.5. For horizontal equilibrium at B and F, $C \sin \theta = V$. These are *equations (8.1)* to *(8.3)* in *clause 8.4.4.1*.

The shear strength of concrete is increased by compression. This is allowed for by the factor ν in *clause 8.4.4.1(3)*, which ranges from 0.55 for zero axial compression to 1.1 for $N_{Ed} \geq 0.55 N_{pl, Rd}$. *Clause 8.4.4.1(3)*

The contribution of concrete encasement to the resistance of a column web to horizontal compression is given in *clause 8.4.4.2*. For an end-plate joint to a column flange, the depth of encasement assumed to resist compression, $t_{eff, c}$, is shown in Fig. 8.6(a), with the 2.5:1 dispersion, referred to above, extending through the root radius r. *Clause 8.4.4.2*

The horizontal compressive strength of the concrete is $0.85 k_{wc, c} f_{cd}$, where $k_{wc, c}$ depends on the vertical compressive stress in the column, $\sigma_{com, c, Ed}$, as shown in Fig. 8.6(b).

Example 8.1: end-plate joints in a two-span beam in a braced frame

In development work that followed the publication of ENV 1994-1-1, a set of application rules for composite joints was prepared, more detailed than those now given in *Section 8* and *Annex A* of EN 1994-1-1. These are published by ECCS[39] as a model annex J. They provide useful guidance in this example, and are referred to, for example, as 'clause J.1.1 of ECCS TC11'.

Data

The subject of Examples 6.7 and 7.1 is a two-span beam ABC continuous over its central support (see Figs 6.23–6.28). It is now assumed that this beam is one of several similar beams in a multistorey braced frame (Fig. 8.7). Its joints with the external columns are nominal pins. The spans of the composite-slab floors are 2.5 m, as before. For simplicity, in the work on beams AB and BC, column EBF will be treated as fixed at nodes E and F. These beams are attached to the column at B by the end-plate connections shown in Fig. 8.8, which also gives dimensions of the column section. Its other properties are as follows: HEB 240 cross-section, $A_a = 10\,600$ mm^2, $f_y = 355$ N/mm^2, $10^{-6} I_y = 112.6$ mm^4, $10^{-6} I_z = 39.23$ mm^4.

The end plates are of mild steel, $f_y = 275$ N/mm^2, and relatively thin, 12 mm, to provide the plastic behaviour required. They are attached to the beam by 10 mm fillet welds to the flanges, and 8 mm welds to the web. They are each attached to the column by four Grade 8.8 M20 bolts with properties: $f_{ub} = 800$ N/mm^2, $f_{yb} = 640$ N/mm^2, net area at root of thread $A_{s, b} = 245$ mm^2 per bolt.

The only other change from the data used in Examples 6.7 and 7.1 on geometry, materials and loadings concerns the reinforcement in the slab.

Longitudinal reinforcement at support B

These partial-strength joints need rotation capacity. Its value cannot be found at this stage, but it is known to increase with both the diameter of the reinforcing bars in the slab

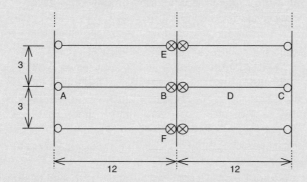

Fig. 8.7. Model for a two-span beam ABC, with an internal column EBF

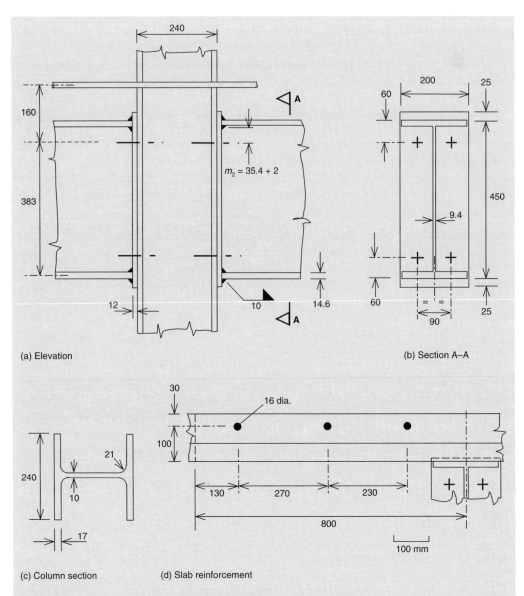

240

160

383

12

$m_2 = 35.4 + 2$

10

14.6

(a) Elevation

200   25

60

450

9.4

60

= =

90

25

(b) Section A–A

30

16 dia.

100

240

21

10

17

130   270   230

800

100 mm

(c) Column section

(d) Slab reinforcement

Fig. 8.8. Details of the beam-to-column end-plate connections

and the area of reinforcement provided. However, the amount of top reinforcement should be limited, so that the whole of the compressive force across the joint can be resisted by the beam bottom flange and the unstiffened column web.

Detailed guidance is given in Couchman and Way.[104] For a steel beam of depth 450 mm in S355 steel, the recommended minimum areas are 3000 mm^2 for bars with 5% elongation and 860 mm^2 for bars with 10% elongation. The recommended maximum amount depends on the size of the column and the details of the bolts in tension, and is about 1200 mm^2 for this example. The recommended bar diameters are 16 and 20 mm.

For these reasons, the previous reinforcement (13 No. 12 mm bars, $A_s = 1470$ mm^2) is replaced by six No. 16 mm hot-formed bars (minimum elongation 10%): $A_s = 1206$ mm^2, $f_{sk} = 500$ N/mm^2.

Classification of the joints
It is assumed initially that flexural failure of a joint will occur in a ductile manner, by yielding of the reinforcement in tension and the end-plate or column flange in bending;

and that at bottom-flange level the compressive resistance of the column web will be sufficient. As the spans are equal, it is unlikely that shear of the column web will be critical.

The joint is expected to be 'partial-strength'. This can be checked by comparing the tension resistance of the top two bolts, from Table 3.4 of EN 1993-1-8, with the force to yield the beam top flange:

$$F_{\text{T, Rd, bolts}} = 2(k_2 f_{ub} A_s / \gamma_{M2}) = 2 \times 0.9 \times 0.8 \times 245/1.25 = \textbf{282 kN} \qquad \text{(D8.3)}$$

$$F_{\text{Rd, flange}} = b_f t_f f_{yd} = 190 \times 14.6 \times 0.355 = 985 \text{ kN}$$

Thus, the resistance moment $M_{\text{j, Rd}}$ for the joint will be much less than $M_{\text{pl, Rd}}$ for the beam, and lateral buckling will be less critical than before.

There is no need to find the stiffness of the joint at this stage, because it is clearly either 'rigid' or 'semi-rigid'. Either type may be treated as 'semi-rigid'.

Approximate global analysis

Tables in Appendix B of Couchman and Way[104] enable a rough check to be made on this initial design, without much calculation. They give resistances $M_{\text{j, Rd}}$ in terms of the cross-section of the steel beam, its yield strength, the thickness and grade of the end plate, the number and size of bolts in tension, and the area of reinforcement. Even though the beam used here is an IPE section, it can be deduced that $M_{\text{j, Rd}}$ is about 400 kN m.

For both spans fully loaded, it was found in Example 6.7 that M_{Ed} at B was 536 kN m from loading (see Fig. 6.28) plus 120 kN m from shrinkage. The flexural stiffness of the joint is not yet known, but it will be between zero and 'fully rigid'. If fully rigid, the joint will obviously be 'plastic' under ultimate loading, and there will then be no secondary shrinkage moment. At mid-span, for the total load of 35.7 kN/m (see Table 6.2), the sagging bending moment is then

$$357 \times 12^2/8 - 400/2 = 443 \text{ kN m}$$

If the joint acts as a pin, the mid-span moment is

$$443 + 200 = 643 \text{ kN m}$$

It is recommended in Couchman and Way[104] that mid-span resistances should be taken as $0.85 M_{\text{pl, Rd}}$, to limit the rotation required at the joints. From Example 6.7, $M_{\text{pl, Rd}}$ with full shear connection is 1043 kN m, so the bending resistance of the beam is obviously sufficient.

Vertical shear

For $M_{\text{Ed}} = 400$ kN m at B, the vertical shear at B is

$$F_{\text{v, Ed, B}} = 35.7 \times 6 + 400/12 = \textbf{247 kN}$$

The shear resistance of the four M20 bolts is now found, using Table 3.4 of EN 1993-1-8. Two of the bolts may be at yield in tension. The shear applied to these bolts must satisfy

$$F_{\text{v, Ed}}/F_{\text{v, Rd}} + F_{\text{t, Ed}}/(1.4 F_{\text{t, Rd}}) \leq 1.0 \qquad \text{(D8.4)}$$

The net shear area of each bolt is $A_{\text{s, b}} = 245$ mm^2, so from Table 3.4 of EN 1993-1-8,

$$F_{\text{v, Rd}} = 0.6 f_{ub} A_{\text{s, b}} / \gamma_{M2} = 0.6 \times 800 \times 0.245/1.25 = 94.1 \text{ kN}$$

From equation (D8.3) with $F_{\text{t, Ed}} = F_{\text{t, Rd}}$,

$$F_{\text{v, Ed}} \leq (1 - 1/1.4) F_{\text{v, Rd}} = 27 \text{ kN}$$

For four bolts,

$$F_{\text{v, Rd}} = 2 \times (94.1 + 27) = \textbf{242 kN} \qquad \text{(D8.5)}$$

This shows that it may be necessary to add a second pair of bolts in the compression region of the joint.

Bending resistance of the joint, excluding reinforcement
Unpropped construction was used in Example 6.7. From Table 6.2, the design ultimate load for the steel beam is 7.8 kN/m. For the construction phase, this is increased to 9.15 kN/m, to allow for the higher density of fresh concrete and the construction imposed loading. For rigid joints at the internal support between two 12 m spans,

$$M_{Ed, B} = wL^2/8 = 9.15 \times 12^2/8 = 165 \text{ kN m}$$

The plastic resistance of the joint during construction is required. An upper limit is easily obtained. The lever arm from the top bolts to the centre of the bottom flange is

$$z_{bolts} = 450 - 60 - 7.3 = 383 \text{ mm} \tag{D8.6}$$

The resistance cannot exceed

$$F_{T, Rd, bolts}z_{bolts} = 282 \times 0.383 = 108 \text{ kN m} \tag{D8.7}$$

so the previous hogging bending moment of 165 kN m cannot be reached. It is assumed that the stiffness of the joint is sufficient for its plastic resistance, found later to be 83 kN m, to be reached under the factored construction loading.

Resistance of T-stubs and bolts in tension
The calculation of the bending resistance consists of finding the 'weakest links' in both tension and compression. In tension, the column flange and the end plate are each modelled as T-stubs, and prying action may occur. Some of the dimensions required are shown in Fig. 8.9. From Fig. 6.8 of EN 1993-1-8, the dimensions m overlap with 20% of the corner fillet or weld. Thus, in Fig. 8.9(a), for the end plate:

$$m = 45 - 4.7 - 0.8 \times 8 = 33.9 \text{ mm} \tag{D.8.8}$$

It is evident from the geometry shown in Fig. 8.9 that the end plate is weaker than the column flange, so its resistance is now found.

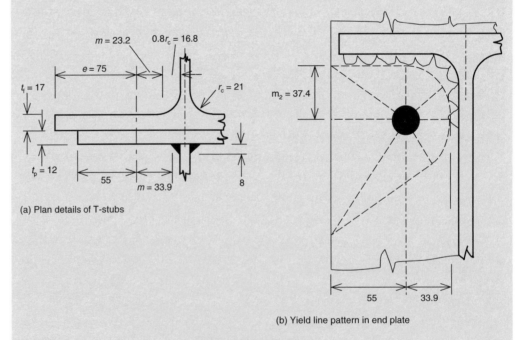

(a) Plan details of T-stubs

(b) Yield line pattern in end plate

Fig. 8.9. Dimensions of T-stubs, and the yield line pattern

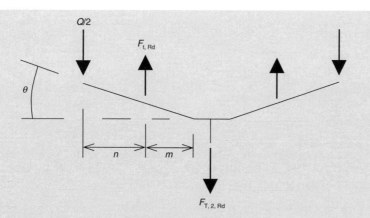

Fig. 8.10. Plan of a T-stub, showing failure mode 2

Clause 6.2.4.1 of EN 1993-1-8 gives three possible failure modes:

(1) yielding of the plate
(2) a combination of (1) and (3)
(3) failure of the bolts in tension.

Yield line theory is used for bending of the plate. The critical mechanism in this case will be either that shown in Fig. 8.9(b) or a circular fan, for which the perimeter is

$$\ell_{\text{eff, cp}} = 2\pi m$$

from Table 6.6 in clause 6.2.6.5 of EN 1993-1-8.

For the non-circular pattern, dimension m_2 in Fig. 8.8(a) is also relevant, and

$$\ell_{\text{eff, nc}} = \alpha m \qquad \leq 2\pi m$$

where α is given by Fig. 6.11 in EN 1993-1-8 or in Fig. 4.9 of Couchman and Way.[104] In this case, $\alpha = 6.8$, so the circular pattern governs for mode (1), and

$$\ell_{\text{eff, 1}} = 2\pi m = 6.28 \times 33.9 = 213 \text{ mm}$$

The plastic resistance per unit length of plate is

$$m_{\text{pl, Rd}} = 0.25 t_{\text{f}}^2 f_{\text{y}} / \gamma_{\text{M0}} = 0.25 \times 12^2 \times 0.275 / 1.0 = 9.90 \text{ kN m/m} \tag{D8.9}$$

From equation (D8.3), the tensile resistance of a pair of bolts is 282 kN.

Mode 1. For mode 1, yielding is confined to the plate. From Table 6.2 of EN 1993-1-8, the equation for this mode is

$$F_{\text{T, 1, Rd}} = 4 M_{\text{pl, 1, Rd}} / m$$

with

$$M_{\text{pl, 1, Rd}} = 0.25 \ell_{\text{eff, 1}} t_{\text{f}}^2 f_{\text{y}} / \gamma_{\text{M0}} = \ell_{\text{eff, 1}} m_{\text{pl, Rd}} = 0.213 \times 9.9 = 2.11 \text{ kN m}$$

From equation (D8.8) for m,

$$F_{\text{T, 1, Rd}} = 4 \times 2.11 / 0.0339 = \textbf{249 kN}$$

Mode 2. This mode is more complex. The equation for the tension resistance $F_{\text{T, 2, Rd}}$ is now explained. The effective length of the perimeter of the mechanism is $\ell_{\text{eff, 2}}$, and the work done for a rotation θ at its perimeter is $2m_{\text{pl, Rd}} \ell_{\text{eff, 2}} \theta$, from yield line theory. With each bolt failing in tension, the work equation is

$$F_{T, 2, Rd}(m + n)\theta = n\sum F_{t, Rd}\theta + 2m_{pl, Rd}\ell_{eff, 2}\theta \qquad (D8.10)$$

where n is shown in Fig. 8.10.

In Table 6.2 of EN 1993-1-8 there is the further condition that

$$n \le 1.25m = 1.25 \times 33.9 = 42.4 \text{ mm}$$

The effective length

$$\ell_{eff, 2} = \alpha m = 6.8 \times 33.9 = 231 \text{ mm}$$

from Table 6.6 of EN 1993-1-8. For two bolts, $\sum F_{t, Rd} = 282$ kN, from equation (D8.3). Substituting in equation (D8.10):

$$F_{T, 2, Rd} = (2m_{pl, Rd}\ell_{eff, 2} + n\sum F_{t, Rd})/(m + n)$$
$$= (2 \times 9.9 \times 231 + 42.4 \times 282)/76.3 = \mathbf{217 \text{ kN}} \qquad (D8.11)$$

Mode 3. Failure of the bolts – mode 3 – has

$$F_{T, 3, Rd} = \mathbf{282 \text{ kN}}$$

from equation (D8.3), so mode 2 governs. From Fig. 8.10, the prying force is

$$Q = 282 - 217 = 65 \text{ kN}$$

Beam web in tension

The equivalent T-stub in Fig. 8.10 applies a tensile force of 217 kN to the web of the beam. Its resistance is given in clause 6.2.6.8 of EN 1993-1-8 as

$$F_{t, wb, Rd} = b_{eff, t, wb}t_{wb}f_{y, wb}/\gamma_{M0}$$

(equation (6.22) of EN 1993-1-8), and $b_{eff, t, wb}$ is taken as the effective length of the T-stub, $\ell_{eff, 2} = 231$ mm. Hence,

$$F_{t, wb, Rd} = 231 \times 9.4 \times 0.355/1.0 = 771 \text{ kN} \qquad (D8.12)$$

so this does not govern.

Column web in tension

The effective width of the column web in tension, to clause 6.2.6.3 of EN 1993-1-8, is the length of the T-stub representing the column flange. The resistance is

$$F_{t, wc, Rd} = \omega b_{eff, t, wc}t_{wc}f_{y, wc}/\gamma_{M0}$$

where ω is a reduction factor to allow for shear in the column web. In this case, the shear is zero, and $\omega = 1$. The column web is thicker than the beam web, so from result (D8.12), its resistance does not govern.

Column web in transverse compression

The resistance is given in clause 6.2.6.2 of EN 1993-1-8. It depends on the plate slenderness λ_p and the width of the column web in compression, which is

$$b_{eff, c, wc} = t_{f, b} + 2\sqrt{2}a_p + 5(t_{fc} + s) + s_p$$

(equation (6.11) of EN 1993-1-8), where a_p is the throat thickness of the bottom-flange welds, so $\sqrt{2}a_p = 10$ mm here; s_p allows for 45° dispersion through the end plate, and is 24 mm here; and s is the root radius of the column section ($s = r_c = 21$ mm). Hence,

$$b_{eff, c, wc} = 14.6 + 20 + 5 \times (17 + 21) + 24 = 248 \text{ mm}$$

For web buckling, the effective compressed length is

$$d_{wc} = h_c - 2(t_{fc} + r_c) = 240 - 2 \times (17 + 21) = 164 \text{ mm}$$

The plate slenderness is

$$\bar{\lambda}_p = 0.932(b_{\text{eff, c, wc}}d_{\text{wc}}f_{\text{y, wc}}/E_a t_{\text{wc}}^2)^{0.5}$$
$$= 0.932 \times [248 \times 164 \times 0.355/(210 \times 100)]^{0.5} = 0.773$$

The reduction factor for plate buckling is

$$\rho = (\bar{\lambda}_p - 0.2)/\bar{\lambda}_p^2 = 0.573/0.773^2 = 0.96$$

The factor ω for web shear is 1.0, as before.

It is assumed that the maximum longitudinal compressive stress in the column is less than $0.7f_{\text{y, wc}}$, so from clause 6.2.6.2(2) of EN 1993-1-8, the reduction factor for this, k_{wc}, is 1.0. From equation (6.9) in EN 1993-1-8,

$$F_{\text{c, wc, Rd}} = \omega k_{\text{wc}}\rho b_{\text{eff, c, wc}}t_{\text{wc}}f_{\text{y, wc}}/\gamma_{\text{M1}}$$
$$= 0.96 \times 248 \times 10 \times 0.355/1.0 = \textbf{845 kN} \tag{D8.13}$$

Clearly, the tensile force of 217 kN governs the resistance of the steel connection.

Bending resistance of the steel joint, for both beams fully loaded
From equation (D8.5), the lever arm is 383 mm, so the resistance, excluding the reinforcement, is

$$M_{\text{j, Rd, steel}} = 217 \times 0.383 = \textbf{83 kN m} \tag{D8.14}$$

governed by bending of the end plate. The critical mode 2 includes failure of the top row of bolts in tension. However, the joint is closely based on a type given in Couchman and Way,[104] which is confirmed by ECCS TC11[39] as having 'ductile' behaviour.

From Example 6.7, the plastic bending resistance of the steel beam, an IPE 450 section, is

$$M_{\text{pl, a, Rd}} = 1.702 \times 355 = 604 \text{ kN m}$$

This exceeds four times $M_{\text{j, Rd}}$, so clause 5.2.3.2(3) of EN 1993-1-8 permits this joint to be classified as 'nominally pinned' for the construction stage.

Resistance of the composite joint
For the composite joint, the reinforcement is at yield in tension. Its resistance is

$$F_{\text{t, s, Rd}} = 1206 \times 0.500/1.15 = 524 \text{ kN}$$

This increases the total compressive force to

$$F_c = 217 + 524 = \textbf{741 kN} \tag{D8.15}$$

This is less than the compressive resistance of 845 kN, found above. The bars act at a lever arm of 543 mm (Fig. 8.8(a)), so the bending resistance of the composite joint is

$$M_{\text{j, Rd, comp}} = 83 + 524 \times 0.543 = 83 + 284 = \textbf{367 kN m} \tag{D8.16}$$

Check on vertical shear
For the maximum design beam load of 35.7 kN/m and a hogging resistance moment at B of 367 kN m, the vertical shear in each beam at B is 244 kN, which just exceeds the shear resistance found earlier, 242 kN. It will probably be found from elastic–plastic global analysis that the vertical shear at B is reduced by the flexibility of the joints. If necessary, two extra M20 bolts can be added in the lower half of each end plate. This has no effect on the preceding results for resistance to bending.

Maximum load on span BC, with minimum load on span AB
This loading causes maximum shear in the column web. There is an abrupt change in the tension in the slab reinforcement at B. The load acting on the steel members is equal for

the two spans, and is assumed to cause a hogging bending moment at node B equal to the resistance of the joints, 83 kN m from equation (D8.11). The ultimate loads on the composite member are 1.62 kN/m on AB and 27.9 kN/m on BC (see Table 6.2).

The flexibility of the joints and cracking of concrete both reduce hogging bending moments, so both are neglected in these checks on shear in the column web and anchorage of the reinforcement. The moment on the composite joint at B in span BC is taken as the additional resistance provided by the slab reinforcement, which is 284 kN m (equation (D8.16)). For the other three members meeting at node B, elastic analysis gives the bending moments shown in Fig. 8.11(a). The total bending moments at B, including construction, are shown in Fig. 8.11(b). The shear forces in columns DB and BE are

$$(75 + 37.5)/3 = 37.5 \text{ kN}$$

If the end plate in span AB is plastic under ultimate construction loading, the whole of the difference between the beam moments shown is caused by change of tension in the reinforcement. Thus, the relevant lever arm, z, is 543 mm.

From clause 5.3(3) of EN 1993-1-8, the shear force on the web panel is

$$V_{\text{wp, Ed}} = (M_{\text{b1, Ed}} - M_{\text{b2, Ed}})/z - (V_{\text{c1, Ed}} - V_{\text{c2, Ed}})/2$$
$$= (367 - 217)/0.543 - [37.5 - (-37.5)]/2 = 276.2 - 37.5 = \mathbf{239 \text{ kN}}$$

The sign convention used here is given in Fig. 5.6 of EN 1993-1-8. It is evident from Fig. 8.11(b) and the equation above that the web shear from the beams, 276 kN, is reduced by the shear forces in the column. The change of force in the reinforcement is **276 kN**.

Shear resistance of the column web
From clause 6.2.6.1(1) of EN 1993-1-8, the shear resistance of an unstiffened column web panel is

$$V_{\text{wp, Rd}} = 0.9 f_{\text{y, wc}} A_{\text{vc}}/(\sqrt{3}\gamma_{\text{M0}})$$

where A_{vc} is the shear area of the column web. This is given in EN 1993-1-1, and is 3324 mm² here. Hence,

$$V_{\text{wp, Rd}} = 0.9 \times 0.355 \times 3324/(\sqrt{3} \times 1.0) = \mathbf{613 \text{ kN}} \qquad (> V_{\text{wp, Ed}})$$

This load arrangement therefore does not govern the design of the joint.

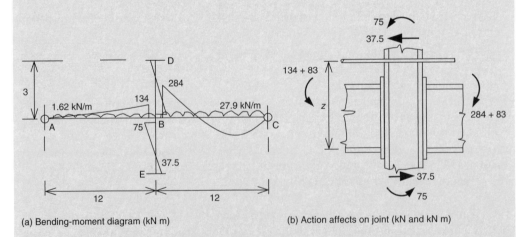

(a) Bending-moment diagram (kN m)   (b) Action affects on joint (kN and kN m)

Fig. 8.11. Analyses for unequal design loadings (ultimate limit state) on spans AB and BC

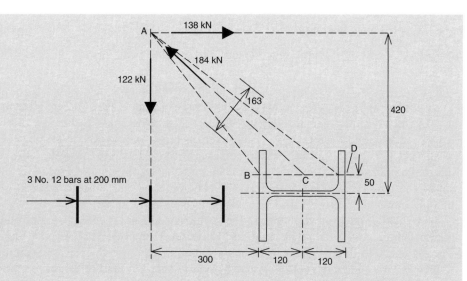

Fig. 8.12. Strut-and-tie model for anchorage of unbalanced tension in slab reinforcement

Table 8.1. Initial stiffnesses of joints, $S_{j,\,ini}$ (kN m/mrad)

	No shear	Joint BA, with shear	Joint BC, with shear
Steel joint	61.1	–	–
Composite joint, elastic	146	118	48.8
Composite joint, no top bolts	110	118	38.6

Anchorage of the force from the reinforcement

The force of 276 kN (above) has to be anchored in the column. The strut-and-tie model shown in *Fig. 8.2* requires transverse reinforcement to resist the force F_{tq} shown in the figure, and the force depends on the directions chosen for the struts.

The mean distance of the three 16 mm bars shown in Fig. 8.8(d) from the centre-line of the column is 420 mm. The two concrete struts AB and AD shown in Fig. 8.12 can, for calculation, be replaced by line AC. Resolution of forces at point A gives the strut force as 184 kN. The depth of concrete available is 80 mm. With $f_{ck} = 25$ N/mm^2, the total width of the struts is

$$b_c = (184 \times 1.5)/(0.08 \times 0.85 \times 25) = 163 \text{ mm}$$

This width is shown to scale in Fig. 8.12, and is obviously available.

The existing transverse reinforcement (Example 6.7) is 12 mm bars at 200 mm spacing. Insertion of three more bars ($A_s = 339$ mm^2) at 200 mm spacing provides an extra resistance

$$T_{Rd} = 339 \times 0.5/1.15 = 147 \text{ kN}$$

which exceeds the tie force of 122 kN shown in Fig. 8.12. Three extra bars are provided on each side of the column.

The available area of column flange to resist bearing stress is

$$80 \times (120 + 115) = 18\,800 \text{ mm}^2$$

so the mean stress is

$(276/2)/18.8 = 7.34 \text{ N/mm}^2$

well below the design compressive strength of the concrete.

Stiffness of the joints and rotation capacity, ultimate limit state
The initial stiffnesses of these joints are calculated in Example 10.1, and are given in Table 8.1. In the preceding global analyses, the joints were assumed to be rigid until their resistance $M_{j,\,Rd}$ was reached, and to act as hinges for further loading. This neglect of the elastic rotation of the joints at moments below $M_{j,\,Rd}$ leads to overestimation of the hogging bending moments at the joints. The mid-span moments therefore exceed those calculated. This method is safe for the verification of the joints, and is appropriate where there is ample bending resistance at mid-span, as in this example.

There is little inelastic curvature in the regions of sagging moment, so the rotation at the joints is much less than that required for the development of mid-span plastic hinges. The typical joint details given in Couchman and Way,[104] which were used here, were shown to have adequate rotation capacity by a calculation method[19] supported by tests (*clause 8.3.4(3)*) or are those '*which experience has proved have adequate properties*' (*clause 8.3.4(2)*), so no further verification of rotation capacity is required.

Serviceability checks
The preceding analyses are inadequate for serviceability checks on deflections or crack width. Account must be taken of the flexibility of each joint, as given by equations (D8.1) and (D8.2). From clause 6.3.1(6) of EN 1993-1-8 or clause J.4.1(5) of ECCS TC11,[39] $\Psi = 2.7$ for bolted end-plate joints. Thus, where $M_{j,\,Ed} = M_{j,\,Rd}$, from equation (D8.2),

$$\mu = 1.5^{2.7} = 2.99 \tag{D8.17}$$

This dependence of the joint stiffness S_j on $M_{j,\,Ed}$ leads to iterative analysis, so simplifications are given in clause 5.1.2 of EN 1993-1-8 and in section 9.5 of ECCS TC11[39] for use in elastic frame analysis, as follows:

- for a composite beam-to-column joint with a flush end-plate connection, and 'usual cases', a nominal stiffness $S_j = S_{j,\,ini}/2$ may be used, for moments up to $M_{j,\,Rd}$ (i.e. $\mu = 2$)

- where joints are required to behave within their elastic range, the stiffness $S_{j,\,ini}$ should be used, and $M_{j,\,Ed}$ should not exceed $2M_{j,\,Rd}/3$.

Here, the joints are included in conventional elastic analyses as follows. From Fig. 8.8, a pair of joints (see Fig. 8.1) has an overall length of $240 + 2 \times 12 = 264$ mm, so each joint is represented by a beam-type member of length $L_j = 132$ mm and second moment of area I_j. For a bending moment M_j, the rotation is

$$\phi = M_j/S_j$$

For the 'beam', it is

$$\phi = M_j L_j/E_a I_j$$

Eliminating ϕ/M_j,

$$I_j = (L_j/E_a)S_j$$

Hence,

$$10^{-6}I_j = (132/210)S_j = 0.63S_j \tag{D8.18}$$

with I_j in units of mm^4 and S_j in units of kN m/mrad.

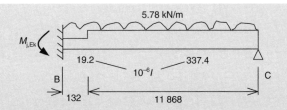

Fig. 8.13. Analysis for steel beams, serviceability limit state

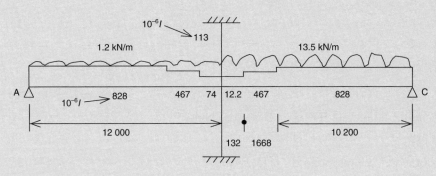

Fig. 8.14. Analysis for composite beams, serviceability limit state

Maximum deflection, with imposed load on span BC only
Separate calculations are required for the steel joints and the composite joints. The load at the end of construction, 5.78 kN/m, is applied to both spans. From Table 8.1 and equation (D8.18), with $\mu = 2$,

$$10^{-6}I_{\mathrm{j}} = 0.63 \times 61.1/2 = 19.2 \text{ mm}^4$$

For the beam,

$$10^{-6}I_{\mathrm{ay}} = 337.4 \text{ mm}^4$$

so the calculation model for the steel joints is as shown in Fig. 8.13, with I in units of mm⁴. The results are:

- bending moment in the connection in span BC: 67.7 kN m, which is 82% of $M_{\mathrm{j, Rd, steel}}$
- maximum deflection of span BC: 13.8 mm.

The calculation model for the composite phase takes account of cracking, and uses the modular ratio $n = 20.2$. The floor finishes, 1.2 kN/m, act on both spans, and the frequent value of the imposed load, $0.7 \times 17.5 = 12.3$ kN/m, acts on span BC only.

For the joint in span BC, $\mu = 2$. There is a little unused tensile resistance from the steel connection. If this is neglected, then for the composite joint in span BC, $S_{\mathrm{j, ini}} = 39.6$ kN m/mrad (Table 8.1) and

$$10^{-6}I_{\mathrm{j, BC}} = 0.63 \times 39.6/2 = 12.5 \text{ mm}^4$$

(The effect of including the full stiffness of the steel joint ($S_{\mathrm{j, ini}} = 48.8$ kN m/mrad, not 38.6 kN m/mrad) is small; it reduced the deflection by less than 1 mm.)

The moment in the connection in span BA is low, so $\mu = 1$. From Table 8.1,

$$10^{-6}I_{\mathrm{j, BA}} = 0.63 \times 118 = 74 \text{ mm}^4$$

For the column,

$$10^{-6}I_{\mathrm{y}} = 113 \text{ mm}^4$$

The calculation model is shown in Fig. 8.14, with I in units of mm⁴. The results are:

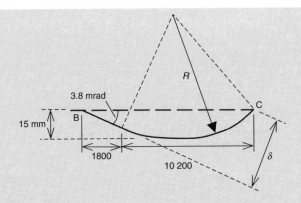

Fig. 8.15. Primary shrinkage deformation of span BC

- bending moment at B in span BC: 70.2 kN m
- maximum deflection of span BC: 17.9 mm.

The total deflection of span BC is therefore

$$13.8 + 17.9 = 31.7 \text{ mm}$$

or span/380. These two components exceed the values found for the fully continuous beam (see Table 7.3) by 4.8 and 2.9 mm, respectively.

The imposed-load deflection is about 17 mm, or span/700, for the frequent loading. The modular ratio used allows for some creep. The additional deflection of the composite slabs, relative to that of the beams, is discussed in Example 7.1.

The effect of shrinkage of concrete.
Accurate calculation is difficult where semi-rigid joints are used, but estimates can be made, as follows. The primary shrinkage deformations for the 24 m length of beam are shown in Fig. 6.27(b). Calculations in Example 6.7 found that $R = 1149$ m and $\delta = 45.3$ mm. The most conservative assumption is that the flexibility of the joints reduces the secondary shrinkage moment (which reduces deflections) to zero. Fig. 8.15 shows the same primary curvature as in Fig. 6.27(b), but with compatibility restored by rotation of the joint at B, rather than by secondary bending of the beam. From the geometry of Fig. 8.15, this rotation is found to be 3.8 mrad for each joint. The mid-span shrinkage deflection is then about 15 mm. The direction shown for δ is consistent with that in Fig. 6.1(b), and is not important, as these angles of slope are very small.

The preceding calculation for the composite joint found $M_{j, Ek} = 70$ kN m, and used $S_j = 38.6/2 = 19.3$ kN m/mrad, giving a rotation of 70/19.3 = 3.6 mrad. Thus, shrinkage imposes a significant increase of rotation on each joint, and the resulting increase of hogging moment at B, while far less than the 120 kN m found for the fully continuous beam, will decrease the 15 mm deflection found above. The result for the fully continuous beam was 7 mm (see Table 7.3). It is concluded that the shrinkage deflection lies in the range 10–12 mm, additional to the 31.7 mm found above.

Cracking of concrete
Elastic analysis of the composite frame for service (frequent) loading acting on both spans, otherwise similar to those outlined above, found the hogging bending moment at B to be 133 kN m. The lever arm for the reinforcement, of area 1206 mm², is 543 mm (Fig. 8.8(a)), so the tensile stress is

$$\sigma_s = 133/(0.543 \times 1.206) = 203 \text{ N/mm}^2$$

The mean spacing of the 16 mm bars is about 250 mm (see Fig. 8.8(d)), which happens to be the limiting value for a crack width of 0.3 mm given in *Table 7.2* of EN 1994-1-1. The alternative condition in *Table 7.1* is satisfied by a wide margin.

However, the strain field in the slab is disturbed locally by the column and by the concentrated rotations associated with the joints. The values in *Tables 7.1* and *7.2* take no account of this situation. It can be concluded that the top reinforcement is unlikely to yield in service, and that very wide cracks will not occur.

CHAPTER 9

Composite slabs with profiled steel sheeting for buildings

This chapter corresponds to *Section 9* of EN 1994-1-1, which has the following clauses:

9.1. General

Scope

The form of construction and the scope of *Section 9* are defined in ***clause 9.1.1***. The shape of the steel profile, with ribs running in one direction, and its action as tensile reinforcement for the finished floor, result in a system that effectively spans in one direction only. The slab can also act as the concrete flange of a composite beam spanning in any direction relative to that of the ribs. Provision is made for this in the clauses on design of beams in *Sections 5, 6* and *7*.

Clause 9.1.1

The ratio of the gap between webs to the web spacing, b_r/b_s in ***clause 9.1.1(2)P***, is an important property of a composite slab. This notation is as in *Fig. 9.2* and Fig. A.1 in Appendix A. If the troughs are too narrow, the shear strength of stud connectors placed within them is reduced (*clause 6.6.4*), and there may be insufficient resistance to vertical shear. If the web spacing is too wide, the ability of the slab to spread loads across several webs may be inadequate, especially if the thickness of the slab above the sheeting is minimized, to save weight.

Clause 9.1.1(2)P

Such a wide range of profiles is in use that it was necessary to permit the limit to b_r/b_s to be determined nationally. It should probably be a function of the thickness of the slab above the sheeting. As a guide, it should normally be less than about 0.6.

No account is taken of any contribution from the top flange of the sheeting to resistance to transverse bending.

The design methods for composite slabs given in *Section 9* are based on test procedures described in *clause B.3*. Although the initial loading is cyclic, the test to failure is under static loading. Thus, if dynamic effects are expected, the detailed design for the particular project

Clause 9.1.1(3)P
Clause 9.1.1(4)P
Clause 9.1.1(5)

must ensure that the integrity of the composite action is maintained (**clauses 9.1.1(3)P** and **9.1.1(4)P**).

Guidance on the degree of lateral restraint provided to steel beams (**clause 9.1.1(5)**) is available in EN 1993-1-1 and elsewhere.[106] Inverted U-frame action relies also on flexural restraint. This subject is covered in comments on *clause 6.4.2*.

Because of the wide range of profiles used, resistance to longitudinal shear has always been based on tests. Slabs made with some profiles have a brittle mode of failure, which is penalized in *clause B.3.5(1)*.

Types of shear connection

Clause 9.1.2.1

As for other types of composite member, bond is not accepted in **clause 9.1.2.1** as a reliable method of shear connection. Sheeting without local deformations of profile is permitted where the profile is such that some lateral pressure will arise from shrinkage of the concrete (*Fig. 9.1(b)*). Here, the distinction between 'frictional interlock' and 'bond' is, in effect, that the former is what remains after the 5000 cycles of loading specified in *clause B.3.4*.

The quality of mechanical interlock is sensitive to the height or depth of the small local deformations of the sheeting, so tight tolerances (*clause B.3.3(2)*) should be maintained on these during manufacture, with occasional checking on site.

Clause 9.1.2.2

These two standard forms of interlock are sometimes insufficient to provide full shear connection, as defined in **clause 9.1.2.2**. They can be augmented by anchorages at the ends of each sheet, as shown in *Fig. 9.1*, or design can be based on partial shear connection.

9.2. Detailing provisions

Clause 9.2.1.(1)P
Clause 9.2.1(2)P

The limits to thickness given in **clauses 9.2.1(1)P** and **9.2.1(2)P** are based on satisfactory experience of floors with these dimensions. No limits are given for the depth of the profiled sheeting. Its minimum depth will be governed by deflection. For a slab acting compositely with a beam, the minimum depths are increased (*clause 9.2.1(2)P*) to suit the detailing rules for stud connectors, such as the length of stud that extends above the sheeting and the concrete cover. A slab used as a diaphragm is treated similarly.

Where a slab spans onto a hogging moment region of a composite beam, the minimum reinforcement transverse to its span is governed by the rules for the flange of the beam (e.g.

Clause 9.2.1(4)
Clause 9.2.3

Table 7.1), not by the lower amount given in **clause 9.2.1(4)**.

The minimum bearing lengths (*clause 9.2.3*) are based on accepted good practice. The lengths for bearing onto steel or concrete are identical to those given in BS 5950: Part 4.[107]

9.3. Actions and action effects

Profiled sheeting

Clause 9.3.1(2)P

Where props are used for profiled sheeting (*clause 9.3.1(2)P*), care should be taken to set these at the correct level, taking account of any expected deflection of the surface that supports them. If verification relies on the redistribution of moments in the sheeting due to local buckling or yielding, this must be allowed for in the subsequent check on deflection of the completed floor; but this is, of course, less likely to be critical where propping is used.

Clause 9.3.2(1)

For the loading on the profiled sheeting, *clause 9.3.2(1)* refers to clause 4.11 of EN 1991-1-6.[108] For working personnel and small site equipment, a note to clause 4.11.1(3) proposes a characteristic distributed load of 1 kN/m^2. Further guidance may be given in the National Annex.

For the weight density of normal-weight concrete, Annex A of EN 1991-1-1[9] recommends 24 kN/m^3, increased by 1 kN/m^3 for 'normal' reinforcement and by another 1 kN/m^3 for unhardened concrete. In addition to self-weight, clause 4.11 of EN 1991-1-6 specifies an imposed load of 10% of the weight of the concrete, but not less than 0.75 kN/m^2 (which

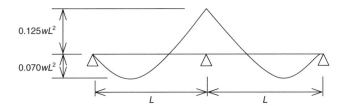

Fig. 9.1. Bending moments for a two-span beam or slab for uniform loading; elastic theory without redistribution

usually governs), applied to a working area of 3×3 m, and 0.75 kN/m² outside this area. This corresponds to a layer of normal-weight concrete about 35 mm thick, to allow for the mounding that occurs during delivery of fresh concrete. Guidance on the avoidance of overload during construction is available elsewhere.[109]

Partial factors for ultimate limit states are recommended in Table A1.2(B) of EN 1990, as 1.35 for permanent actions and 1.5 for variable actions. It would be reasonable to use 1.35 for the whole of the weight density of 26 kN/m³, explained above, even though the extra 1 kN/m³ for unhardened concrete is not strictly 'permanent'.

Sometimes, to increase the speed of construction, the profiled sheeting is not propped. It then carries all these loads. This condition, or the check on the deflection of the finished floor, normally governs its design.

For the serviceability limit state, the deflection of the sheeting when the concrete hardens is important, for use when checking the total deflection of the floor in service. The construction load and the extra loading from mounding are not present at this time, so the deflection is from permanent load only, and the ψ factors for serviceability, given in Table A.1 of EN 1991-1-6, are not required.

Clause 9.3.2(1) refers to 'ponding', and ***clause 9.3.2(2)*** gives a condition for its effects to be ignored. Where profiled sheeting is continuous over several supports, this check should be made using the most critical arrangement of imposed load.

Clause 9.3.2(2)

Composite slab

The resistances of composite slabs are determined by plastic theory or by empirical factors based on tests in which all of the loading is resisted by the composite section (*clause B.3.3(6)*). This permits design checks for the ultimate limit state to be made under the whole of the loading (***clause 9.3.3(2)***).

Clause 9.3.3(2)

9.4. Analysis for internal forces and moments

Profiled steel sheeting

Clause 9.4.1(1) refers to EN 1993-1-3,[25] which gives no guidance on global analysis of continuous members of light-gauge steel. ***Clause 9.4.1(2)*** rules out plastic redistribution where propping is used, but not where the sheeting extends over more than one span, as is usual. Subsequent flexure over a permanent support will be in the same direction (hogging) as during construction, whereas at the location of a prop it will be in the opposite direction.

Clause 9.4.1(1)
Clause 9.4.1(2)

Elastic global analysis can be used, because a safe lower bound to the ultimate resistance is obtained. Elastic moments calculated for uniform stiffness are normally greatest at internal supports, as shown in Fig. 9.1 for a two-span slab under distributed loading. The reduction in stiffness due to parts of the cross-section yielding in compression will be greatest in these regions, which will cause redistribution of moment from the supports to mid-span. In a technical note from 1984,[110] and in a note to clause 5.2 of BS 5950-4,[107] the redistribution is given as between 5 and 15%. This suggests that redistribution exceeding about 10% should not be used in absence of supporting evidence from tests.

Composite slab

As the steel sheets are normally continuous over more than one span, and the concrete is cast over this length without joints, the composite slab is in reality continuous. If elastic global analysis is used based on the uncracked stiffness, the resulting moments at internal supports are high, as in the example in Fig. 9.1. To resist these moments may require heavy reinforcement. This can be avoided by designing the slab as a series of simply-supported spans (*clause 9.4.2(5)*), provided that crack-width control is not a problem. Other approaches that reduce the quantity of hogging reinforcement needed are the use of redistribution of moments (*clause 9.4.2(3)*), and of plastic analysis (*clause 9.4.2(4)*).

Clause 9.4.2(3)
Clause 9.4.2(4)

Numerical and experimental research on continuous slabs has been reported.[111] With typical relative values of moment resistance at internal supports and at mid-span, the maximum design loads calculated by elastic analysis with limited redistribution were found to be less than those obtained by treating each span as simply supported. This arises because the large resistance to sagging moment is not fully utilized.

If the slab is to be treated as continuous, plastic analysis is more advantageous. The studies showed that no check on rotation capacity need be made provided the conditions given in *clause 9.4.2(4)* are satisfied.

Effective width for concentrated point and line loads

The ability of composite slabs to carry masonry walls or other heavy local loads is limited. The rules of *clause 9.4.3* for the effective widths b_m, b_{em} and b_{ev} are important in practice. They are based on a mixture of simplified analysis, test data and experience,[107] and are further discussed, with a worked example, in Johnson.[81] The effective width depends on the ratio between the longitudinal and transverse flexural stiffnesses of the slab. The nature of these slabs results in effective widths narrower than those given in BS 8110[17] for solid reinforced concrete slabs.

Clause 9.4.3

The nominal transverse reinforcement given in *clause 9.4.3(5)* is not generous for a point load of 7.5 kN, and should not be assumed to apply for the 'largely repetitive' loads to which *clause 9.1.1(3)P* refers.

Clause 9.4.3(5)

9.5–9.6. Verification of profiled steel sheeting as shuttering

Clause 9.5(1)

The design checks before composite action is established are done to EN 1993-1-3. *Clause 9.5(1)* refers to the loss of effective cross-section that may be caused by deep deformations of the sheeting. This loss and the effects of local buckling are both difficult to determine theoretically. Design recommendations provided by manufacturers are based in part on the results of loading tests on the sheeting concerned.

Clause 9.6(2)

The maximum deflection of $L/180$ given in the note to *clause 9.6(2)* is accepted good practice. Deflection from ponding of wet concrete is covered in *clause 9.3.2(2)*.

9.7. Verification of composite slabs for the ultimate limit states

9.7.1. Design criterion
No comment is needed.

9.7.2. Flexure

Clause 9.7.2(3)

The rules in *clause 9.7.2* are based on research reported in Stark and Brekelmans.[111] *Clause 9.7.2(3)* says that deformed areas of sheeting should be ignored in calculations of section properties, unless tests show otherwise. No guidance on relevant testing is given. Test results are also influenced by local buckling within the flat parts of the steel profile, and by the enhanced yield strength at cold-formed corners.

For a composite slab in sagging bending, tests can be done in which the shear span is long enough, or the end anchorage is sufficient, for flexural failure to occur. If the strengths of the materials are known, the effective area of the sheeting, when in tension, can be calculated from the moment resisted, and may be close to the gross area of the sheeting.

For a composite slab in hogging bending, the contribution from the sheeting is usually ignored, because it may not be continuous. Where it is continuous, the area of tensile reinforcement is usually small compared with the effective area of the sheeting, so that a conservative estimate of the latter (e.g. excluding embossed areas) may reduce only slightly the calculated resistance to bending. Alternatively, a value found from a bending test on the sheeting alone could be used.

The effective widths in *clause 9.7.2(4)* for local buckling take account of the restraint provided to one side of the sheeting by the concrete.

Clause 9.7.2(4)

Bending resistances of composite slabs are based on rectangular stress blocks (*clauses 9.7.2(5)* to *9.7.2(7)*). In design of reinforced concrete beams, the compressive strain in concrete is limited, to prevent premature crushing of the concrete before the reinforcement yields. There is no similar restriction for composite slabs. The design yield strength of the profiled sheeting, typically between 280 and 420 N/mm^2 (lower than that of reinforcement), and its own bending resistance make composite slabs less sensitive to premature crushing of concrete. However, it could be a problem where stronger sheeting is used.

Clause 9.7.2(5)

For stress in concrete, the 0.85 factor is included, as discussed in comments on *clause 3.1(1)*. When the neutral axis is within the sheeting, theory based on stress blocks as in *Fig. 9.6* becomes very complex for some profiles so simplified equations are given in *clause 9.7.2(6)*. Their derivation is on record.[111] As shown in *Fig. 9.6*, the bending resistance is

Clause 9.7.2(6)

$$M_{Rd} = M_{pr} + N_{c,f} z \qquad (D9.1)$$

where z and M_{pr} are given by *equations (9.5)* and *(9.6)*.

The concrete in compression within the trough is neglected. When

$$N_{c,f} = A_{pe} f_{yp,d}$$

and the sheeting is entirely in tension, the neutral axis is at its top edge. *Equation (9.5)* then correctly gives the lever arm as

$$z = h - h_c/2 - e.$$

9.7.3. Longitudinal shear for slabs without end anchorage

Design of composite slabs for longitudinal shear is based on the results of tests. The specification for these involves a compromise between exploring interactions between the many relevant parameters and limiting the cost of testing to a level such that the use of new profiles is not prevented. The tests on composite slabs are defined in *clause B.3*, on which comments are given in Chapter 11 of this guide. The tests are suitable for finding the design resistance to longitudinal shear by either of the methods referred to in *clause 9.7.3(2)*.

Clause 9.7.3(2)

The m–k method, and existing tests

An empirical '*m–k* method' has long been established. It is difficult to predict the effect of changes from test conditions using this method, because of the lack of analytical models, especially for slabs with 'non-ductile' behaviour. A model for ductile behaviour is given in Appendix B. The *m–k* test is included in EN 1994-1-1 in a modified form, to provide continuity with earlier practice; but values of *m* and *k*, determined in accordance with codes such as BS 5950: Part 4,[107] cannot be used in design to EN 1994-1-1, as explained in comments on *clause B.3.5*. Subject to sufficient test data being available, it may be possible to convert the former values to 'Eurocode' values.

A study for the European Convention for Constructional Steelwork[112] found many differences between methods of testing used. Conversion can be difficult, both for the *m–k*

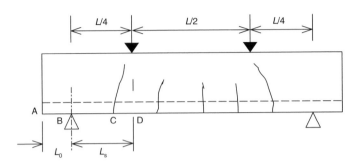

Fig. 9.2. Shear spans for a composite slab with two-point loading

method and for the partial-connection method, and the range of applicability of the values found may be uncertain. Further details are given in Examples 11.1 and 11.2.

Clause 9.7.3(4)   For the *m–k* method, resistance to longitudinal shear is presented in *clause 9.7.3(4)* in terms of vertical shear because of the way in which *m* and *k* are defined. Shear–bond failure is characterized by the formation of a major crack in the slab at between one-quarter and one-third of the span from a support, as shown in Fig. 9.2. It is over the length AC from this point to the end of the sheeting that significant slip occurs between the concrete and the sheeting, so this is the length over which the resistance to longitudinal shear is mobilized.

The location of point C is unknown, and the finite widths of both the applied load and the support are further complications. The definition of 'shear span' L_s for use with the *m–k*
Clause 9.7.3(5)   method is treated in *clause 9.7.3(5),* which gives values for common load arrangements. For the two-point loading in Fig. 9.2, it is the length BD. For the partial-interaction method, calculation of the mean shear strength τ_u is based on the length $L_s + L_0$.

In *clauses 9.7.3(3)* and *9.7.3(5)*, *L* is the span of a simply-supported test specimen, which
Clause 9.7.3(6)   differs from its use in *clause 9.7.3(6)*. In *clause 9.7.3(6)*, the 'isostatic span' is the approximate length between points of contraflexure in a continuous span of length *L* between supports.

The partial connection method

To avoid the risk of sudden failure, profiled sheeting should have ductile behaviour in longitudinal shear. For plain sheeting, the ultimate shear resistance is not significantly greater than that for initial slip. Such behaviour is not 'ductile' to *clause 9.7.3(3)*, and is referred to as 'brittle' in *clause B.3.5(1)*. The partial shear connection method is not applicable to slabs with this behaviour (*clause 9.7.3(2)*). The *m–k* method may still be used, but with an additional partial safety factor of 1.25, expressed by the reduction factor 0.8 in *clause B.3.5(1)*.

For profiles with deformations, the expected ultimate behaviour involves a combination of friction and mechanical interlock after initial slip, giving a relationship between load and deflection that should satisfy the definition of 'ductile' in *clause 9.7.3(3)*.

Clause 9.7.3(7)   Design data from test results should be found by the partial connection method of *clauses 9.7.3(7)* to *9.7.3(10)*. The analytical model, now given, is similar to that used for composite beams, *clause 6.2.1.3*, and has been verified for slabs by full-scale tests.[113,114] It is used in Example 11.2.

For an assumed flexural failure at a cross-section at a distance L_x from the nearest support, the compressive force N_c in a slab of breadth *b* is assumed to be given (*equation (9.8)*) by

$$N_c = \tau_{u,\,Rd}bL_x \tag{D9.2}$$

where the design shear strength $\tau_{u,\,Rd}$ is found by testing, to *clause B.3*. Its derivation takes account of the difference between the perimeter of a cross-section of sheeting and its overall breadth, *b*. By its definition in *equation (9.8)*, force N_c cannot exceed the force for full interaction, $N_{c,\,f}$. Hence, there are two neutral axes, one of which is within the steel profile.

In *clause B.3.6(2)* the degree of shear connection is defined as

$$\eta = N_c/N_{c,f} \tag{D9.3}$$

The longitudinal forces that determine the partial-interaction bending resistance M_{Rd} are all known, for given η, but calculation of the resistance moment by the method used for partial interaction in composite beams is difficult. The line of action of the longitudinal force in the sheeting (shown in Fig. 11.5) depends on its complex geometry.

A simplified method is given in *clause 9.7.3(8)*. It consists of using *equation (9.5)* of *clause 9.7.2(6)*, with $N_{c,f}$ replaced by $\eta N_{c,f}$ and $0.5h_c$ replaced by $0.5x_{pl}$, to determine the lever arm z:

Clause 9.7.3(8)

$$z = h - 0.5x_{pl} - e_p + (e_p - e)\eta N_{c,f}/A_{pe}f_{yp,d} \tag{9.9}$$

The reason for these changes is that where x_{pl} is much less than h_c, the method gives too low a value for M_{Rd}, because *equation (9.5)* assumes that the line of action of the force N_c in the slab is at depth $h_c/2$. The correct value is $\eta x_{pl}/2$, where x_{pl} is the full-interaction value as shown in *Fig. 9.5*.

It is not clear in EN 1994-1-1 whether the symbol x_{pl} in *equation (9.9)* means the full-interaction value, or the reduced value, which in this guide is written ηx_{pl}. The reduced value corresponds to the model used, gives the higher value for z, and is recommended.

The value of the last two terms in *equation (9.9)* increases from $-e_p$ to $-e$ as η is increased from 0 to 1. For profiled sheeting, the plastic neutral axis is usually above the centroidal axis (i.e. $e_p > e$), and $(e_p - e) \ll z$. It can then be assumed, for simplicity, that the force N_c in the sheeting acts at height e_p above its bottom fibre, giving a lever arm that is correct for $\eta = 0$, and slightly too low for $\eta < 1$.

With these changes, *equation (9.9)* becomes

$$z = h - 0.5\eta x_{pl} - e_p \tag{D9.4}$$

The bending resistance M_{Rd} of the slab, not stated in *clause 9.7.3*, can be deduced from *Fig. 9.6* (and Fig. 11.5 in this guide). It is

$$M_{Rd} = M_{pr} + N_c z \tag{D9.5}$$

Calculations for a range of values of L_x thus give the curve relating resistance M_{Rd} to the distance to the nearest support. The design is satisfactory for longitudinal shear if the corresponding curve for M_{Ed} lies entirely within the one for M_{Rd}, as shown in Example 9.1 and Fig. 9.12.

In tests, the resistance to longitudinal shear is increased by the friction associated with the reaction at the adjacent end support. If this is allowed for when calculating $\tau_{u,Rd}$, a lower value is obtained. *Clause 9.7.3(9)* provides compensation by using the same effect in the structure being designed, μR_{Ed}, to contribute to the shear resistance required. The value recommended for the coefficient of friction μ is based on tests.

Clause 9.7.3(9)

Additional reinforcement

Reinforcing bars may be provided in the troughs of the profiled sheeting, and this reinforcement may be taken into account when calculating the resistance of the slab by the partial connection method, *clause 9.7.3(10)*.

Clause 9.7.3(10)

The analytical model assumes that the total resistance is that from composite action of the concrete with both the sheeting and the bars, as for reinforced concrete, determined by plastic analysis of the cross-section. The value of $\tau_{u,Rd}$ is obtained, as before, by testing of specimens without additional reinforcement, *clause B.3.2(7)*.

If the m–k method were to be used, reinforcement in troughs would be an additional variable, which would require a separate test series (*clause B.3.1(3)*), with evaluation based on measured strength of the reinforcement.

9.7.4. Longitudinal shear for slabs with end anchorage

Clause 9.7.4 refers to the two types of end anchorage defined in *clause 9.1.2.1*. The anchorage provided by studs is ductile. It is preferable to that provided by deformed ribs of re-entrant profiles, where poor compaction of concrete may occur.

Clause 9.7.4

Clause 9.7.4(2)
Clause 9.7.4(3)

In the partial-connection method, the anchorage force is used as a contribution to the total force N_c (*clause 9.7.4(2)*). For through-deck-welded studs it can be calculated, to *clause 9.7.4(3)*. The model is based on the weld collar pulling through the end of the sheeting. Further comments are given in *clause 6.6.6.4*. It is not clear how a contribution from deformed ribs should be determined, as end anchorage is not used in the test specimens (*clause B.3.2(7)*).

For the *m–k* method, end anchorage of either type may be included in the test specimens, but each type is an additional variable (*clause B.3.1(3)*), and would require a separate test series.

9.7.5. Vertical shear

Clause 9.7.5

Clause 9.7.5 refers to EN 1992-1-1, where resistance to vertical shear depends on the effective depth d of the section. In a composite slab, where the sheeting is the reinforcement, d is the distance d_p to the centroid of the profile, shown in *Fig. 9.6*.

9.7.6. Punching shear

Clause 9.7.6(1)

The critical perimeter for punching shear (*clause 9.7.6(1)*) has rounded corners, as does that used in EN 1992-1-1. It is therefore shorter than the rectangular perimeter used in BS 5950: Part 4. It is based on dispersion at 45° to the centroidal axis of the sheeting in the direction parallel to the ribs, but only to the top of the sheeting in the less stiff transverse direction.

Clause 6.4.4 of EN 1992-1-1 gives the shear resistance as a stress, so one needs to know the depth of slab on which this stress is assumed to act. For a concrete slab this would be the appropriate effective depth in each direction. For a composite slab, no guidance is given. BS 5950-4[107] takes the effective depth in both directions as that of the concrete above the top of the profiled steel sheeting, to be used in conjunction with BS 8110.[17]

9.8. Verification of composite slabs for serviceability limit states

9.8.1. Cracking of concrete

Clause 9.8.1(1)

Clause 9.8.1(1) refers to EN 1992-1-1, where, from clause 7.3.1(4),

> Cracks may be permitted to form without any attempt to control their width, provided that they do not impair the functioning of the structure.

Clause 9.8.1(2)

For this situation, the provisions for minimum reinforcement above internal supports of composite slabs (*clause 9.8.1(2)*) are the same as those for beams in *clause 7.4.1(4)*, where further comment is given. Crack widths should always be controlled above supports of slabs subjected to travelling loads. The methods of EN 1992-1-1 are applicable, neglecting the presence of the sheeting.

9.8.2. Deflection

Clause 9.8.2(1)

Clause 9.8.2(1) refers to EN 1990, which lists basic criteria for the verification of deformations.

Clause 9.8.2(2)

For the construction phase, *clause 9.8.2(2)* refers to EN 1993-1-3, where clause 7.3(2) says that elastic theory should be used, with the characteristic load combination (clause 7.1(3)). This corresponds to an 'irreversible' limit state, which is appropriate for the deflection of sheeting due to the weight of the finished slab. Where it can be assumed that when the slab hardens, the imposed load on it is negligible, the remaining deflection of the sheeting due to construction loads should also be negligible; but this assumption, if made, should be based on relevant experience.

The prediction of construction loads may also be difficult. If in doubt, the deflection of the sheeting at this time should be determined for the characteristic combination, even though the less adverse frequent combination is permitted for reversible deflections.

Clause 7.3.(4) of EN 1993-1-3 refers to a clause in EN 1993-1-1 which says that limits to deflection of sheeting 'should be agreed', and may be given in a National Annex. Further comment is given under *clause 9.3.2*, and in Examples 7.1 and 9.1.

For the composite member, *clause 9.8.2(3)* refers to *Section 5* for global analysis, where the comments made on continuous beams apply. Restraint of bending of slabs from the torsional stiffness of supporting members is usually ignored, but situations arise where it could cause cracking.

Clause 9.8.2(3)

The rules in *clause 9.8.2(4)* permit calculation of deflections to be omitted if two conditions are satisfied. The first refers to limits to the ratio of span to effective depth given in EN 1992-1-1. These are 20 for a simply-supported slab, 26 for an external span of a continuous slab and 30 for an internal span. The effective depth should be that given in the comment on *clause 9.7.5*.

Clause 9.8.2(4)

The second condition, *clause 9.8.2(6)*, applies to external spans only, and relates to the initial slip load found in tests – information which may not be available to the designer. Two-point loading is used for testing, so the 'design service load' must be converted to a point load. This can be done by assuming that each point load equals the end reaction for a simply-supported span under service loading.

Clause 9.8.2(6)

Where the initial slip load in the tests is below the limit given in *clause 9.8.2(6)*, *clause 9.8.2(7)* provides a choice. Either the slip should be allowed for, which means estimating the deflection from the test results, or 'end anchors should be provided'. There is no guidance on how much end anchorage is required. Its effectiveness would have to be found by testing and analysis by the *m–k* method, because *clause B.3.2(7)* does not permit end anchors to be used in tests for the partial-connection method.

Clause 9.8.2(7)

Tied-arch model

The situation that is covered by *clause 9.8.2(8)* seems likely to arise only where:

Clause 9.8.2(8)

- a high proportion of the shear connection is provided by welded studs
- its amount is established by calculation to *clause 9.7.4*
- no test data are available.

If the end anchorage is provided by deformed ribs, then experimental verification is essential, and the slip behaviour will be known.

In the tied-arch model proposed, the whole of the shear connection is provided by end anchorage. Accurate calculation of deflection is difficult, but the arch will be so shallow that the following simplified method is quite accurate.

The tie shown in Fig. 9.3(a) consists of the effective area of the steel sheeting. Line AB denotes its centroid. The thickness h_c of the arch rib must be such that at the relevant bending moment its compressive stress at mid-span is not excessive. There is interaction between its assumed thickness h_c and the lever arm h_a, so a little trial-and-error is needed. Longitudinal forces at mid-span are now known, and the strains ε_c and ε_t in the concrete and steel members can be found, taking appropriate account of creep. In Fig. 9.3(b), curve CB represents the arch rib. The ratio L/h_a is unlikely to be less than 20, so both the curve length and the chord length CB can be taken as $L/2$, and

$$\operatorname{cosec} \alpha \approx \cot \alpha = L/2h_a$$

As shown in the figure, the changes in length of the members are

$$e_t = \varepsilon_t L/2$$

and

$$e_c = \varepsilon_c L/2$$

so the deflection δ is given by

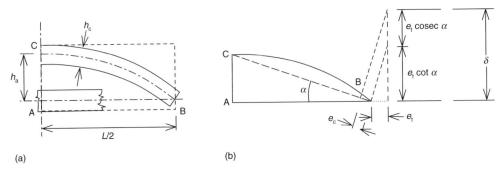

Fig. 9.3. Tied-arch model for deflection of a composite slab with an end anchorage

$$\delta/L = (\varepsilon_t + \varepsilon_c)(L/4h_a) \qquad\qquad\text{(D9.6)}$$

with both strains taken as positive numbers.

Example 9.1: two-span continuous composite slab

Data

Details of the geometry assumed for this composite slab are shown in Fig. 9.4(a). The properties of the concrete and reinforcement are as used in the worked example on a two-span beam in Chapters 6 and 7, where further information on them is given. The spacing of the supporting composite beams is different, 3.0 m rather than 2.5 m. Their top-flange width is 190 mm.

The cross-section assumed for the sheeting satisfies the condition of *clause 9.1.1* for 'narrowly spaced webs'. It provides shear connection by embossments, in accordance with *clause 9.1.2.1(a)*. Its dimensions h_c and h_p in *Fig. 9.2* are defined in *clause 1.6*. From Fig. 9.4(a), they are $h_c = 75$ mm (concrete above the 'main flat surface' of the sheeting) and $h_p = 70$ mm ('overall depth' of the sheeting). Thus, for profiles of this type, the thickness of the slab, 130 mm here, is less than $h_c + h_p$. For flexure of the composite slab, h_c is the appropriate thickness, but for flexure of the composite beam supporting the sheeting, or for in-plane shear in the slab, the relevant thickness is, for this sheeting, $h_c - 15$ mm. Some of the design data used here have been taken from the relevant manufacturer's brochure.

For simplicity, it is assumed that the reinforcement above the supporting beams, which affects the properties of the composite slab in hogging bending, is not less than that determined in Example 6.7 on the two-span beam, as follows:

- in regions where the beam resists hogging bending, as determined by resistance to distortional lateral buckling: $A_s = 565$ mm²/m and 12 mm bars at 200 mm spacing
- in other regions, as determined by resistance to longitudinal shear: $A_s \geq 213$ mm²/m.

It is assumed that A252 mesh is provided ($A_s = 252$ mm²/m), resting on the sheeting. This has 8 mm bars at 200 mm spacing, both ways.

These details satisfy all the requirements of *clause 9.2.1*.

At the outset, two assumptions have to be made that affect the verification of a composite slab:

- whether construction will be unpropped or propped
- whether the spans are modelled as simply supported or continuous.

Here, it will be assumed that unpropped construction will be used wherever possible. The sheeting is provided in 6 m lengths, so no 3 m span can have sheeting continuous at both ends. For a building 9 m wide, there will also be spans where 3 m lengths of sheeting are used, so several end-of-span conditions will be considered.

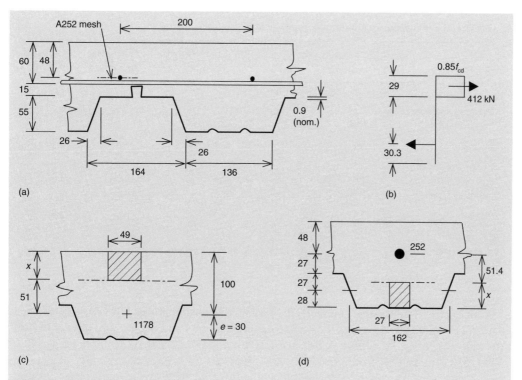

Fig. 9.4. Composite slab. (a) Dimensions. (b) $M_{pl, Rd}$, sagging. (c) Second moment of area, sagging. (d) Second moment of area, hogging

Some of the design checks on a composite slab are usually satisfied by wide margins. These checks will be simplified here by making conservative assumptions.

Properties of materials and profiled sheeting
Lightweight-aggregate concrete: grade LC25/28; $\rho \le 1800$ kg/m³; $0.85f_{cd} = 14.2$ N/mm²; $E_{lctm} = 20.7$ kN/mm²; $n_0 = 10.1$; $f_{lctm} = 2.32$ N/mm².
  Creep is allowed for by using $n = 20.2$ for all loading (*clause 5.4.2.2(11)*).
  Reinforcement: $f_{sk} = 500$ N/mm², $f_{sd} = 435$ N/mm².
  Profiled sheeting: nominal thickness including zinc coating, 0.9 mm; bare-metal thickness, 0.86 mm; area, $A_p = 1178$ mm²/m; weight, 0.10 kN/m²; second moment of area, $10^{-6}I_{y, p} = 0.548$ mm⁴/m; plastic neutral axis, $e_p = 33$ mm above bottom of section (see *Fig. 9.6*); centre of area, $e = 30.3$ mm above bottom of section; $E_a = 210$ kN/mm²; yield strength, $f_{yk, p} = 350$ N/mm², $\gamma_{M, p} = 1.0$; plastic moment of resistance in hogging and sagging bending, $M_{pa} = 6.18$ kN m/m – this value is assumed to take account of the effect of embossments (*clause 9.5(1)*).
  Composite slab: 130 mm thick; volume of concrete, 0.105 m³/m².

Loading for profiled sheeting
From clause 11.3 of EN 1992-1-1, the design density of the reinforced concrete is 1950 kg/m³, which is assumed to include the sheeting. The dead weight of the floor is

$$g_{k1} = 1.95 \times 9.81 \times 0.105 = 2.01 \text{ kN/m}^2$$

From Note 2 to clause 4.11.1(7) of EN 1991-1-6:[108] for fresh concrete the weight density should be increased by 1 kN/m³, so for initial loading on the sheeting,

$$g_{k1} = 2.01 \times 20.5/19.5 = 2.11 \text{ kN/m}^2$$

Table 9.1. Loadings per unit area of composite slab (kN/m^2)

Type of load	Characteristic, maximum	Characteristic, minimum	Ultimate, maximum	Ultimate, minimum
During concreting				
Sheeting and concrete	2.11	0.10	2.85	0.13
Imposed load	1.00	0	1.50	0
Total	3.11	0.10	4.35	0.13
For composite slab				
Slab and floor finish	2.01 + 0.48	2.49	3.36	3.36
Imposed load	7.00	0	10.5	0
Total	9.49	2.49	13.9	3.36
For deflection of composite slab (frequent)	$0.7 \times 7 + 0.48 = 5.38$	0.48	NA	NA

For construction loading, *clause 9.3.2(1)* refers to clause 4.11.2 of EN 1991-1-6. Clause 4.11.2(1) of EN 1991-1-6 gives the actions from personnel and equipment, q_k, as '10% of the self weight of the concrete, but not less than 0.75 and not more than 1.5 kN/m^2'. EN 12812[115] may also be relevant.

The mounding of concrete during placing is referred to in *clause 9.3.2(1)*, but not in EN 1991-1-6, although its clause 4.11.1(2) refers to 'storage of materials'. Here, to demonstrate the method of calculation, q_k will be taken as 1.0 kN/m^2. The National Annex may specify a different value.

Loading for composite slab
Floor finish (permanent): $g_{k2} = 0.48$ kN/m^2.
Variable load (including partitions, services, etc.): $q_k = 7.0$ kN/m^2.

The loads per unit area are summarized in Table 9.1, using $\gamma_{F, g} = 1.35$ and $\gamma_{F, q} = 1.5$.

Verification of sheeting
Ultimate limit state
From *clause 9.2.3(2)*, the minimum width of bearing of the sheeting on a steel top flange is 50 mm. Assuming an effective support at the centre of this width, and a 190 mm steel flange, the effective length of a simply-supported span is

$$3.0 - 0.19 + 0.05 = 2.86 \text{ m}$$

Hence,

$$M_{Ed} = 4.35 \times 2.86^2/8 = 4.45 \text{ kN m/m}$$

This is only 72% of $M_{pl, Rd}$, so there is no need to consider bending moments in the continuous slab, or to check rotation capacity to *clause 9.4.2.1(1)(b)*.

Excluding effects of continuity, for vertical shear:

$$V_{Ed} = 4.35 \times 1.43 = 6.22 \text{ kN/m}$$

There are 6.7 webs of depth 61 mm per metre width of sheeting, at an angle $\cos^{-1} 55/61$ to the vertical. In the absence of buckling, their shear resistance is given by EN 1993-1-3 as

$$(61/55)V_{Rd} = 6.7 \times 61 \times 0.9 \times 0.350/\sqrt{3}$$

whence

$$V_{Rd} = 74.3 \text{ kN/m}$$

The slenderness of each web is $61/0.9 = 68$, which is close to the limit at which buckling must be considered; but V_{Ed} is so far below V_{Rd}, as is usual for the construction stage, that no calculation is needed.

Deflection

A note to *clause 9.6(2)* recommends that the deflection should not exceed span/180. The worst case is where a span is simply-supported. Then,

$$\delta = 5wL^4/(384E_aI_y) = 5 \times 2.01 \times 2.86^4 \times 1000/(384 \times 210 \times 0.548) = 15.2 \text{ mm}$$

For fresh concrete, this is increased to

$$15.2 \times 20.5/19.5 = 16.0 \text{ mm}$$

From *clause 9.3.2(1)*, allowance should be made for ponding if the deflection exceeds 1/10th of the slab thickness (13 mm), as it does here. The specified thickness of the additional concrete is 0.7δ. Its weight, for fresh concrete, is

$$0.7 \times 0.016 \times 20.5 = 0.23 \text{ kN/m}^2$$

This increases the deflection to

$$16 \times 2.34/2.01 = 17.7 \text{ mm}$$

which is span/161, and so exceeds span/180.

It follows that where the sheeting is not continuous at either end of a 3 m span, propping should be used during construction.

The effects of continuity at one end of a span are now considered. The most adverse condition occurs when the concrete in one span hardens (with no construction load present) before the other span is cast. The loadings are then 2.01 kN/m on one span and 0.10 kN/m on the other. The spans should be taken as slightly longer than 2.84 m, to allow for the hogging curvature over the width of the central support. The appropriate length is

$$(2.86 + 3.0)/2 = 2.93 \text{ m}$$

It can be shown by elastic analysis of a continuous beam of uniform section, with uniformly distributed loading, that the deflection δ at the centre of a span is

$$\delta = \delta_0[1 - 0.6 (M_1 + M_2)/M_0]$$

where the hogging end moments are respectively M_1 and M_2, and δ_0 and M_0 are the deflection and mid-span moment of the span when the end moments are zero.

From elastic analysis for a span of 2.93 m, $M_0 = 2.16$ kN m, $M_1 = 1.13$ kN m, $M_2 = 0$ and $\delta_0 = 16.7$ mm. Hence,

$$\delta = 16.7[1 - 0.6 \times (1.13/2.16)] = 11.5 \text{ mm}$$

When the other span is cast, this deflection is reduced; but if the concrete in the first span has already hardened, the reduction is small. The deflection is less than span/180.

Properties of the composite slab

Plastic resistance moment

For sagging bending, the plastic neutral axis is likely to be above the sheeting, so *clause 9.7.2(5)* applies. The tensile force in the sheeting, when at yield, is

$$F_{y, p} = A_p f_{yp, d} = 1178 \times 0.35 = 412 \text{ kN/m} \tag{D9.7}$$

The depth of slab in compression is

$$412/14.2 = 29 \text{ mm} \tag{D9.8}$$

The lever arm is

$130 - 30.3 - 29/2 = 85$ mm

(Fig. 9.4(b)), so

$$M_{\text{pl, Rd}} = 412 \times 0.085 = \textbf{35 kN m/m} \tag{D9.9}$$

Second moments of area

For sagging bending, the transformed width of concrete is $1000/20.2 = 49$ mm/m. For an elastic neutral axis at depth x (Fig. 9.4(c)), first moments of area give

$$1178(100 - x) = 49x^2/2$$

whence $x = 49$ mm. Hence

$$10^{-6}I_y = 0.548 + 1178 \times 0.051^2 + 49 \times 0.49^2/3 = 5.53 \text{ mm}^4/\text{m}$$

For hogging bending with sheeting present, each trough in the sheeting is replaced by a rectangle of width 162 mm. There is one trough per 300 mm, so the transformed width of concrete is

$$49 \times 162/300 = 27 \text{ mm/m}$$

For a neutral axis at height x above the bottom of the slab (Fig. 9.4(d)),

$$252(82 - x) = 1178(x - 30) + 27x \, (x/2)$$

whence $x = 30.6$ mm. Thus, the neutral axis almost coincides with the centre of area of the sheeting, and

$$\mathbf{10^{-6}}\textbf{\textit{I}}_{\textbf{y}} = 0.548 + (252 \times 51.4^2 + 27 \times 30.6^3/3) \times 10^{-6} = \textbf{1.47 mm}^{\textbf{4}}\textbf{/m}$$

Verification of the composite slab

Deflection

This is considered first, as it sometimes governs the design. *Clause 9.8.2(4)* gives conditions under which a check on deflection may be omitted. It refers to clause 7.4 of EN 1992-1-1. Table 7.4 in that clause gives the limiting ratio of span to effective depth for an end span as 26. The depth to the centroid of the sheeting is 100 mm, so the ratio is $2.93/0.1 = 29.3$, and the condition is not satisfied.

Deflection is a reversible limit state, for which a note to clause 6.5.3(2) of EN 1990 recommends use of the frequent combination. The ψ_1 factor for this combination depends on the floor loading category. From Table A1.1 in EN 1990, it ranges from 0.5 to 0.9, and is here taken as 0.7, the value for 'shopping' or 'congregation' areas. From Table 9.1, the maximum and minimum loadings are 5.38 and 0.48 kN/m, respectively. For a simply-supported loaded span of 2.93 m, with $I_y = 5.53 \times 10^6$ mm^4/m, the deflection is 4.4 mm. The region above the central support is likely to be cracked. A more accurate calculation for the two-span slab, assuming 15% of each span to be cracked, and with 0.48 kN/m on the other span, gives the deflection of the fully loaded span as 3.5 mm. Hence, the total deflection of the slab, if cast unpropped, is

$$\delta_{\text{total}} = 11.5 + 3.5 = 15 \text{ mm}$$

which is span/195. This value is not the total deflection, as it is relative to the levels of the supporting beams. In considering whether it is acceptable, account should also be taken of their deflection (Example 7.1). If it is found to be excessive, propped construction should be used for the composite slab.

Ultimate limit states: flexure

From Table 9.1, the maximum loading is 13.9 kN/m. For a simply-supported span,

$$M_{\text{Ed}} = 13.9 \times 2.93^2/8 = 14.9 \text{ kN m}$$

This is so far below the plastic moment of resistance, 35 kN m/m, that there is no need, for this check, to consider continuity or the resistance to hogging bending.

Where it is necessary to consider continuity, *clause 9.4.2* on global analysis and *clause 9.7.2(4)* on resistance to hogging bending are applicable.

Longitudinal shear by the m–k *method*

For longitudinal shear, it is assumed that there is no end anchorage, so that *clause 9.7.3* is applicable. The shear properties of this sheeting are determined and discussed in Examples 11.1 and 11.2 and Appendix B.

It is assumed that tests have shown that the sheeting provides 'ductile' shear connection to *clause 9.7.3(3)*, and that the values for use in the *m–k* method are $m = 184$ N/mm^2 and $k = 0.0530$ N/mm^2. From *clause 9.7.3(4)*, the design shear resistance is

$$V_{l,\mathrm{Rd}} = bd_\mathrm{p}/\gamma_{\mathrm{VS}}[(mA_\mathrm{p}/bL_\mathrm{s}) + k]$$

where d_p is the depth to the centroidal axis of the sheeting, 100 mm; A_p is the cross-sectional area of breadth b of the sheeting, 1178 mm^2/m; L_s is span/4, or 0.73 m, from *clause 9.7.3(5)*; and γ_{VS} is the partial safety factor, with a recommended value of 1.25. These values give: $V_{l,\mathrm{Rd}} = 28.0$ kN/m, which must not be exceeded by the vertical shear in the slab.

For a simply-supported span,

$$V_{\mathrm{Ed}} \approx 1.5 \times 13.9 = 20.9 \text{ kN/m}$$

For the two-span layout, it will be a little higher at the internal support, but clearly will not exceed 28 kN/m.

Vertical shear

Clause 9.7.5 refers to clause 6.2.2 of EN 1992-1-1. This gives a formula for the resistance in terms of the 'area of tensile reinforcement', which is required to extend a certain distance beyond the section considered. The sheeting is unlikely to satisfy this condition at an end support, but its anchorage has already been confirmed by the check on longitudinal shear. Treating the sheeting as the 'reinforcement', the clause gives the resistance to vertical shear as 49 kN/m, which far exceeds V_{Ed}, found above.

Serviceability limit state – cracking

Clause 9.8.1(1) is for 'continuous' slabs. This slab can be assumed to satisfy the condition of *clause 9.8.1(2)*: to have been designed as simply supported in accordance with *clause 9.4.2(5)*. To control cracking above intermediate supports, that clause requires the provision of reinforcement to *clause 9.8.1*.

The amount required, for unpropped construction, is 0.2% of the area of concrete 'on top of the steel sheet'. For this purpose, the mean concrete thickness is relevant. This is close to 75 mm, so the area required is 150 mm^2/m, and the A252 mesh used here is sufficient.

However, if any spans are constructed propped, to reduce deflections, then the required area is doubled, and A252 mesh is not sufficient.

Longitudinal shear resistance by the partial-connection method

In Example 11.2 it is deduced from tests on slabs with the sheeting used here that its design shear strength was

$$\tau_{\mathrm{u,Rd}} = 0.144 \text{ N/mm}^2 \tag{D9.10}$$

Other conditions for the use of this result in design to EN 1994-1-1, based on *clause B.3.1(4)*, are now compared with the data for this example, which are given in parentheses, with ✓ indicating compliance:

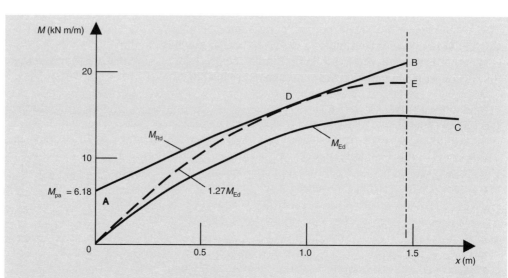

Fig. 9.5. Design partial-interaction diagram

(a) thickness of sheeting ≥ 0.9 mm, including coating ($t = 0.86$ mm, plus coating; ✓)
(b) concrete strength, $f_{ck} \geq 0.8f_{cm} = 0.8 \times 29.8 = 23.8$ N/mm² (C25/30 concrete; ✓)
(c) steel yield strength, $f_{yp} \geq 0.8 f_{yp, m} = 0.8 \times 376 = 301$ N/mm² ($f_{yp} = 350$ N/mm²; ✓)
(d) concrete density, measured 1.5 h after mixing: 1944 kg/m³ (design density ≤ 1800 kg/m³; ?)
(e) slab thickness, $h = 170$ mm, as in tests 1 to 4 ($h = 130$ mm; ✗).

Clause B.3.1(3) defines concrete density and slab thickness as 'variables to be investigated'. *Section 9* gives no guidance on what allowance should be made, if any, for differences between test and design values of these variables.

The density, measured at an early age, takes no account of subsequent loss of moisture. The concrete strength, item (b), is acceptable, and the difference of density, item (d), is small, so its effects can be ignored.

The difference in slab thickness, item (e), is significant. Its effect is discussed more generally in Appendix B. The test results on thinner slabs led to a higher value of $\tau_{u, Rd}$, for reasons explained in Example 11.2. It is assumed that the value for $\tau_{u, Rd}$ given in equation (D9.7) can be used here.

Design partial-interaction diagram
To satisfy *clause 9.7.3(7)* it is necessary to show that throughout the span (coordinate x) the curve of design bending moment, $M_{Ed}(x)$, nowhere lies above the curve of design resistance, $M_{Rd}(x)$, which is a function of the degree of shear connection, $\eta(x)$. These two curves are now constructed.

From Table 9.1, the design ultimate load for the slab is 13.9 kN/m², assumed to act on the composite member. The verification for flexure assumed simply-supported spans of 2.93 m, which gives $M_{Ed, max}$ as 14.9 kN m/m, at mid-span. The parabolic bending-moment diagram is plotted, for a half span, in Fig. 9.5.

From *equation (9.8)* in *clause 9.7.3(8)*, the compressive force in the slab at distance x m from an end support (i.e. with $L_x = x$) is

$$N_c = \tau_{u, Rd}bx = 0.144 \times 1000x = 144x \text{ kN/m}$$

From equation (D9.4),

$$N_{c, f} = A_p f_{yp, d} = 412 \text{ kN/m}$$

The length of shear span needed for full interaction is therefore

$L_{s,f} = 412/144 = 2.86$ m

This exceeds span/2 (1.47 m), so full interaction is not achieved in a span of this length. From equation (D9.5), the depth of the full-interaction stress block in the slab is $x_{pl} = 29$ mm. With partial interaction, this value gives a slightly conservative result for z, and is used here for simplicity.

With $h = 130$ mm, $e_p = 33$ mm and $e = 30.3$ mm, as before, *equation (9.9)* for the lever arm gives

$$z = 130 - 29/2 - 33 + (33 - 30.3) \times 144x/412 = 82 + 1.05x \text{ mm}$$

The reduced bending resistance of the composite slab is given by *equation (9.6)* with $N_{c,f}$ replaced by N_c and $M_{pa} = 6.18$ kN m/m, as before:

$$M_{pr} = 1.25 \times 6.18 \times (1 - 144x/412) = 7.72 - 2.7x \leq 6.18$$

so

$$x \geq 1.54/2.7 = 0.570 \text{ m}$$

From *Fig. 9.6*, the plastic resistance is

$$M_{Rd} = N_c z + M_{pr} = 0.144x \times (82 + 1.05x) + 7.72 - 2.7x$$
$$= 7.72 + 9.11x + 0.151x^2 \qquad \text{for } 0.57 \leq x \leq 1.47 \text{ m}$$

For $x < 0.57$ m,

$$M_{Rd} = 0.144x \times (82 + 1.05x) + 6.18 = 6.18 + 11.8x + 0.151x^2$$

The curve $M_{Rd}(x)$ is plotted as AB in Fig. 9.5. It lies above the curve 0C for M_{Ed} at all cross-sections, showing that there is sufficient resistance to longitudinal shear.

This result can be compared with that from the *m–k* method, as follows. Curve 0C is scaled up until it touches curve AB. The scale factor is found to be 1.27 (curve 0DE), with contact at $x = 1.0$ m. Shear failure thus occurs along a length of 1.0 m adjacent to an end support. The vertical reaction at that support is then

$$V_{Ed} = 1.27 \times 13.9 \times 2.93/2 = 25.9 \text{ kN/m}$$

This is 8% lower than the 28 kN/m found by the *m–k* method. It is concluded in Example 11.2 that its result for $\tau_{u,Rd}$ is probably too low because the test span was too long. The two methods therefore give consistent results, for this example. No general comparison of them is possible, because the partial shear-connection method involves the bending-moment distribution, while the *m–k* method does not.

The calculations summarized in this example illustrate provisions of EN 1994-1-1 that are unlikely to be needed for routine design. They are relevant to the preparation of design charts or tables for composite slabs using sheeting of a particular thickness and profile. These are normally prepared by specialists working on behalf of the manufacturer.

CHAPTER 10

Annex A (Informative). Stiffness of joint components in buildings

This chapter corresponds to *Annex A* in EN 1994-1-1, which has the following clauses:

- Scope   *Clause A.1*
- Stiffness coefficients   *Clause A.2*
- Deformation of the shear connection   *Clause A.3*

Annex A is needed for the application of *clause 8*. It is 'informative' because the 'component' approach to the design of steel and composite joints continues to be developed. Its content is based on the best available research, much of which is recent. It is informed by and generally consistent with two reports prepared on behalf of the steel industry.[39,104]

A.1. Scope

This annex supplements the provisions on stiffness of steel joints in clause 6.3 of EN 1993-1-8.[24] Its scope is limited (*clause A.1(1)*). It covers conventional joints in regions where the longitudinal slab reinforcement is in tension, and the use of steel contact plates in compression. As in EN 1993-1-8, stiffness coefficients k_i are determined (*clause A.1(2)*), with dimensions of length, such that when multiplied by Young's elastic modulus for steel, the result is a conventional stiffness (force per unit extension or compression). For a known lever arm z between the tensile and compressive forces across the joint, the rotational stiffness is easily found from these coefficients.

Clause A.1(1)

Clause A.1(2)

As in EN 1993-1-8, stiffnesses of components are combined in the usual way, for example:

$$k = k_1 + k_2 \qquad \text{(for two components in parallel)}$$
$$1/k = 1/k_1 + 1/k_2 \qquad \text{(for two components in series)} \tag{D10.1}$$

Stiffness coefficients k_1 to k_{16} are defined in Table 6.11 of EN 1993-1-8. Those relevant to composite joints are listed in Section 8.2 of this guide. Of these, only k_1 and k_2 are modified here, to allow for steel contact plates and for the encasement of a column web in concrete (*clause A.1(3)*).

Clause A.1(3)

A.2. Stiffness coefficients

The background to this clause is available.[116] The coefficients have been calibrated against test results. For longitudinal reinforcement in tension, *clause A.2.1.1(1)* gives formulae for the coefficient $k_{s,r}$ in terms of the bending moments $M_{Ed,1}$ and $M_{Ed,2}$, shown in *Fig. A.1* and

Clause A.2.1.1(1)

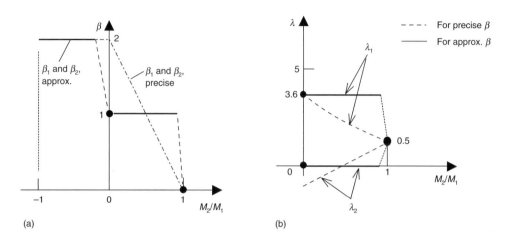

Fig. 10.1. Flexibility of reinforcement. (a) Transformation parameter, β. (b) Flexibility of reinforcement, represented by λ_1 and λ_2, for $M_1 \geq M_2$

Fig. 8.3. Subscripts 1 and 2 are used here also for the properties of the connections on which these moments act. The concrete slab is assumed to be fully cracked.

The transformation parameters β_1 and β_2 allow for the effects of unequal bending moments applied to the pair of connections on either side of a column. They are given in clause 5.3(9) of EN 1993-1-8, with simplified values in clause 5.3(8). The latter are discontinuous functions of $M_{\mathrm{Ed},\,2}/M_{\mathrm{Ed},\,1}$, as shown in Fig. 10.1(a). The sign convention in EN 1993-1-8 is that both moments are positive when hogging, with $M_{\mathrm{Ed},\,1} \geq M_{\mathrm{Ed},\,2}$. The range covered by EN 1993-1-8 is

$$-1 \leq M_{\mathrm{Ed},\,2}/M_{\mathrm{Ed},\,1} \leq 1$$

However, the stiffness coefficients $k_{\mathrm{s,\,r}}$ in *Table A.1* are based on reinforcement in tension, and composite joints with $M_{\mathrm{Ed},\,2} < 0$ are outside the scope of EN 1994-1-1.

A typical stiffness coefficient is

$$k_{\mathrm{s,\,r}} = A_{\mathrm{s,\,r}}/\lambda h \tag{D10.2}$$

where h is the depth of the steel section of the column, and λ_1 and λ_2 (for the connections on sides 1 and 2 of the column) are functions of β_1 and β_2, respectively. Based on both the precise and the simplified values for the βs given in EN 1993-1-8, they are plotted against the moment ratio M_2/M_1 (using this notation for $M_{\mathrm{Ed},\,2}$ and $M_{\mathrm{Ed},\,1}$) in Fig. 10.1(b). For the simplified βs, they are discontinuous at $M_2/M_1 = 0$ and 1.

It is the extension of a length λh of reinforcement that is assumed to contribute to the flexibility of the joint. The figure shows that when $M_2 = M_1$, this length for connection 1 is $h/2$, increasing to $3.6h$ when $M_2 = 0$. This is the value in *Table A.1* for a single-sided joint. The flexibility $1/k_{\mathrm{s,\,r}}$ for connection 2 becomes negative for $M_2 < 0.5M_1$.

Clause A.2.1.2 The 'infinite' stiffness of a steel contact plate (*clause A.2.1.2*) simply means that one term in an equation of type (D10.1) is zero.

Clause A.2.2.1 In *clause A.2.2.1*, the stiffness of a column web panel in shear is reduced below the value in EN 1993-1-8 because the force applied by a contact plate may be more concentrated than would occur with other types of end-plate connection.

Clause A.2.2.2 Similarly, the stiffness for a web in transverse compression has been reduced in *clause A.2.2.2*, where the value 0.2 replaces 0.7 in EN 1993-1-8.

Concrete encasement

Encasement in concrete increases the stiffness of the column web in shear, which is given for an uncased web in EN 1993-1-8 as

$$k_1 = 0.38A_{\mathrm{vc}}/\beta z$$

The addition to k_1 given in *clause A.2.3.1(1)* has a similar form:

$$k_{1,c} = 0.06(E_{cm}/E_a)b_c h_c/\beta z$$

where E_{cm}/E_a is the modular ratio and $b_c h_c$ is the area of concrete.

For the column web in compression (*clause A.2.3.2*), the relationship with the stiffness of the steel web is similar to that for the web in shear. The coefficient in the additional stiffness $k_{2,c}$ is 0.5 for an end plate, but reduces to 0.13 for a contact plate, because of the more concentrated force.

Clause A.2.3.1(1)

Clause A.2.3.2

A.3. Deformation of the shear connection

The background to the rather complex provisions of *clause A.3* is given in Appendix 3 of ECCS TC11[39] and in COST-C1.[117] They are based on linear partial-interaction theory for the shear connection. *Equations (A.6)* to *(A.8)* are derived as equations (7.26) and (7.28) in Aribert.[118]

Clause A.3

Equation (A.5) in *clause A.3(2)* can be rearranged as follows:

$$1/k_{slip}k_{s,r} = (K_{sc} + E_s k_{s,r})/K_{sc}k_{s,r} = E_s/K_{sc} + 1/k_{s,r}$$

This format shows that the flexibility E_s/K_{sc} has been added to that of the reinforcement, $1/k_{s,r}$, to give the combined stiffness, $k_{slip}k_{s,r}$. It also shows that, unlike the k_i, K_{sc} is a conventional stiffness, force per unit extension.

The definition of the stiffness of a shear connector in *clause A.3(3)* assumes that the mean load per connector will be a little below the design strength, P_{Rk}/γ_{VS} (typically $0.8P_{Rk}$). Where the slab is composite, the tests should ideally be 'specific push tests' to *clause B.2.2(3)*. In practice, the approximate value given in *clause A.3(4)* for 19 mm studs, 100 kN/mm, may be preferred. Its use is limited to slabs in which the reduction factor k_t (*clause 6.6.4.2*) is unity. It may not apply, therefore, to pairs of studs in each trough, as used in Example 6.7.

Clause A.3(3)

In fact, this stiffness, the *connector modulus*, can vary widely. Johnson and Buckby[37] refer to a range from 60 kN/mm for 16 mm studs to 700 kN/mm for 25 mm square bar connectors; and an example in Johnson[81] uses 150 kN/mm for 19 mm studs. The value 100 kN/mm is of the correct magnitude, but designs that are sensitive to its accuracy should be avoided.

Further comments on stiffness
These are found in Chapter 8 and in the following example.

Example 10.1: elastic stiffness of an end-plate joint
The rotational stiffness $S_{j,ini}$, modified to give S_j, is needed for elastic or elastic–plastic global analysis, both for finding the required rotation of the joint, and for checking deflection of the beams. The stiffnesses k_i shown in Fig. 8.3 are now calculated. Formulae for the steel components are given in Table 6.11 of EN 1993-1-8. Dimensions are shown in Figs 8.8 and 8.9.

Column web in shear
From Table 6.11 of EN 1993-1-8,

$$k_1 = 0.38A_{vc}/\beta z$$

It was shown in Example 8.1 that the relevant lever arm, z, is 543 mm. This stiffness is relevant only for unequal beam loading, for which the transformation parameter β is 1.0 (Fig. 10.1). The shear area of the column web is 3324 mm², so

$$k_1 = 0.38 \times 3324/543 = \textbf{2.33 mm} \tag{D10.3}$$

Column web in compression, unstiffened
From Table 6.11 of EN 1993-1-8,

$$k_2 = 0.7 b_{eff, c, wc} t_{wc}/d_c$$

From Example 8.1, the width of the web, $b_{eff, c, wc}$, is 248 mm; $t_{wc} = 10$ mm, and

$$d_c = 240 - 2 \times (21 + 17) = 164 \text{ mm}$$

so

$$k_2 = 0.7 \times 248 \times 10/164 = \textbf{10.6 mm}$$

Column web in tension, unstiffened
From Table 6.11 of EN 1993-1-8,

$$k_3 = 0.7 b_{eff, t, wc} t_{wc}/d_c$$

where $b_{eff, t, wc}$ is the smallest of the effective lengths ℓ_{eff} found for the column T-stub. These are given in Table 6.4 of EN 1993-1-8. The smallest is $2\pi m$, with $m = 23.2$ mm (Fig. 8.9), so $\ell_{eff} = 146$ mm. Hence,

$$k_3 = 0.7 \times 146 \times 10/164 = \textbf{6.22 mm}$$

Column flange in bending
From Table 6.11 of EN 1993-1-8,

$$k_4 = 0.9 \ell_{eff} (t_{fc}/m)^3$$

where $\ell_{eff} = 2\pi m$ as above, so

$$k_4 = 0.9 \times 146 \times (17/23.2)^3 = \textbf{51.7 mm}$$

End plate in bending
From Table 6.11 of EN 1993-1-8,

$$k_5 = 0.9 \ell_{eff} (t_p/m)^3$$

The smallest ℓ_{eff} for the end plate was 213 mm (Example 8.1), and from Fig. 8.9, $m = 33.9$ mm. Hence,

$$k_5 = 0.9 \times 213 \times (12/33.9)^3 = \textbf{8.50 mm}$$

Bolt in tension
From Table 6.11 of EN 1993-1-8,

$$k_{10} = 1.6 A_s/L_b$$

where L_b is the grip length (29 mm) plus an allowance for the bolt head and nut; total 44 mm. The tensile stress area is 245 mm², so

$$k_{10} = 1.6 \times 245/44 = \textbf{8.91 mm}$$

per row of two bolts.

Slab reinforcement in tension
Let λh be the length of reinforcing bar assumed to contribute to the flexibility of the joint. There are two cases:

(a) beams equally loaded, for which $\lambda_1 = \lambda_2 = 0.5$, from Fig. 10.1
(b) beams unequally loaded, for which $\lambda_1 = 3.6$ and $\lambda_2 = 0$.

From equation (D10.2),

$$k_{s,r} = A_{s,r}/\lambda h$$

where $A_{s,r}$ = 1206 mm^2 and h = 240 mm. It follows that

$$k_{s,r(a)} = 1206/(0.5 \times 240) = 10.05 \text{ mm}$$

for both joints,

$$k_{s,r(b)} = 1206/(3.6 \times 240) = 1.40 \text{ mm}$$

for the joint in span BC and

$$k_{s,r(b)} \rightarrow \infty$$

for the joint in span AB. This result is revised later.

Deformation of the shear connection
In the notation of *clause A.3*:

- hogging length of beam: $\ell = 0.15 \times 12 = 1.80$ m
- distance of bars above centre of compression: $h_s = 543$ mm from Fig. 8.8(a)
- distance of bars above centroid of steel beam: $d_s = 325$ mm from Fig. 8.8
- second moment of area of steel beam: $10^{-6}I_a = 337$ mm^4.

Allowance will be made for the possible reduced stiffness of pairs of studs in a trough of sheeting by taking N, the number in length ℓ, as the equivalent number of single studs. In Example 6.7, 19.8 equivalent studs were spread along a 2.4 m length of beam each side of support B (see Fig. 6.30). In Example 8.1, the area of tension reinforcement was reduced from 1470 to 1206 mm^2, but the shear connection is now assumed to be as before.
For $\ell = 1.8$ m,

$$N = 19.8 \times 1.8/2.4 = 14.85 \text{ studs}$$

From *equation (A.8)*,

$$\xi = E_a I_a/d_s^2 E_s A_s = 210 \times 337/(0.325^2 \times 200 \times 1206) = 2.778$$

From *equation (A.7)*,

$$\nu = [(1 + \xi)Nk_{sc}\ell d_s^2/E_a I_a]^{1/2}$$
$$= [3.778 \times 14.85 \times 0.100 \times 1.8 \times 325^2/(210 \times 337)]^{1/2} = 3.88$$

From *equation (A.6)*,

$$K_{sc} = Nk_{sc}/[\nu - (\nu - 1)(h_s/d_s)/(1 + \xi)]$$
$$= 14.85 \times 100/[3.88 - 2.88 \times (543/325)/3.778] = 570 \text{ kN/mm}$$

From *equation (A.5)*, the reduction factor to be applied to $k_{s,r}$ is

$$k_{slip} = 1/(1 + E_s k_{s,r}/K_{sc}) = 1/(1 + 210k_{s,r}/570)$$

The symbol $k_{s,red}$ is used for the reduced value. For $k_{s,r} = 10.05$ mm, $k_{slip} = 0.213$, whence

$$k_{s,red} = k_{s,r}k_{slip} = \textbf{2.14 mm}$$

for beams equally loaded. For $k_{s,r} = 1.40$ mm, $k_{slip} = 0.660$, whence

$$k_{s,red} = \textbf{0.924 mm} \tag{D10.4}$$

for joint 1, unequal loading. For $k_{s,r} \rightarrow \infty$, $k_{slip} = 0$. Hence, $k_{s,red}$ is indeterminate. This is an anomaly in the code. Research has found that the steel tension zone of the joint that resists the lower bending moment should be treated as rigid, so in this case, for joint BA,

$$\boldsymbol{k}_{s,red} \rightarrow \infty \tag{D10.5}$$

Stiffness of joints, for both beams fully loaded
The rules for assembly of stiffnesses in Table 6.10 of EN 1993-1-8 are extended on p. B3.7 of ECCS TC11[39] to allow for the slab reinforcement.

Stiffness in tension
Stiffnesses 3, 4, 5 and 10 are in series (see Fig. 8.3). For these,

$1/k_t = 1/6.22 + 1/51.7 + 1/8.5 + 1/8.91 = 0.410$ mm^{-1}

$k_t = 2.44$ mm

The lever arm for k_t is $z_2 = 0.383$ m. The lever arm for the reinforcement is $z_1 = 0.543$ m, and $k_{s, red} = 2.14$ mm. The equivalent lever arm is

$$z_{eq} = (k_{s, red}z_1^2 + k_t z_2^2)/(k_{s, red}z_1 + k_t z_2)$$
$$= 0.989/2.096 = 0.472 \text{ m} \tag{D10.6}$$

The equivalent stiffness in tension is

$$k_{eq} = (k_{s, red}z_1 + k_t z_2)/z_{eq}$$
$$= 2.096/0.472 = 4.44 \text{ mm} \tag{D10.7}$$

Stiffness in compression
Only the stiffness for the column web is required: $k_2 = 10.6$ mm.

Stiffness of joints
From clause 6.3.1 of EN 1993-1-8, the initial stiffness of each composite joint is

$$S_{j, ini} = E_a z_{eq}^2/(1/k_{eq} + 1/k_2)$$
$$= 210 \times 0.472^2/(1/4.44 + 1/10.6) = 146 \text{ kN m/mrad} \tag{D10.8}$$

If, during construction, the end plates yield in tension, the stiffness represented by k_t is ineffective for actions on the composite member. Then, for the stiffness of the composite joint, $k_t = 0$, $z_{eq} = z_1$ and $k_{eq} = k_{s, red} = 2.14$ mm, and equation (D10.8) becomes

$$S_{j, ini} = E_a z_1^2/(1/k_{s, red} + 1/k_2)$$
$$= 210 \times 0.543^2/(1/2.14 + 1/10.6) = 110 \text{ kN m/mrad} \tag{D10.9}$$

For each joint during construction, $k_{s, red} = 0$, $z = z_2$ and $k_{eq} = k_t$, so

$$S_{j, ini, steel} = 210 \times 0.383^2/(1/2.44 + 1/10.6) = 61.1 \text{ kN m/mrad} \tag{D10.10}$$

Stiffness of joints, for imposed load on span BC only
The flexibility of the column web in shear, $1/k_1$ (equation (D10.3)), must now be included, and the values of $k_{s, red}$ are different for the two joints. There are two cases: either the end plate is elastic, or it has yielded in the tension zone, so that $k_t = 0$.
    For the connection in span BC, with z_1 and z_2 as above, from equations (D10.6) and (D10.7),

$$z_{eq} = (0.924 \times 0.543^2 + 2.44 \times 0.383^2)/(0.924 \times 0.543 + 2.44 \times 0.383)$$
$$= 0.630/1.436 = 0.439 \text{ m}$$

$$k_{eq} = 1.436/0.439 = 3.27 \text{ mm}$$

Including $1/k_1$ in equation (D10.8),

$$S_{j, ini, BC} = 210 \times 0.439^2/(1/2.33 + 1/10.6 + 1/3.27) = 48.8 \text{ kN m/mrad} \tag{D10.11}$$

If $k_t = 0$, then from equations (D10.6) and (D10.7), $z_{eq} = z_1$, and $k_{eq} = k_{s, red} = 0.924$ mm. From equation (D10.8),

$$S_{j, ini, BC} = 210 \times 0.543^2/(1/2.33 + 1/10.6 + 1/0.924) = 38.6 \text{ kN m/mrad} \tag{D10.12}$$

For the joint in span AB, with $k_{\text{s, red}} \to \infty$, then $z_{\text{eq}} = z_1$ and $k_{\text{eq}} \to \infty$, and equation (D10.8) gives

$$S_{\text{j, ini, BA}} = 210 \times 0.543^2/(1/2.33 + 1/10.6) = \mathbf{118\ kN\ m/mrad} \tag{D10.13}$$

This use of equation (D10.8) where there is shear in the web panel includes an approximation that leads to a small overestimate of the deflection of span BC. The shear deformation of the column web panel, of stiffness k_1 (2.33 mm here), causes clockwise rotation of end B of span AB, and hence increases the hogging bending moment at this point. The effective stiffness $S_{\text{j, ini, BA}}$ therefore exceeds 118 kN m/rad. The resulting increase in the hogging moment at B in span BC is small, and so is the associated decrease in the mid-span deflection.

Results (D10.8) to (D10.13) are repeated in Table 8.1, for use in Example 8.1.

CHAPTER 11

Annex B (Informative). Standard tests

B.1. General

Annex B is 'informative', not 'normative', because test procedures for products are strictly outside the scope of a design code. From the note to *clause B.1(1)*, they should be given in a European standard or in guidelines for European technical approvals, which are not yet available.

One of the objectives of standard tests is to provide guidance to designers in situations where calculation models are not sufficient. This commonly occurs for two components of composite structures: shear connectors and profiled steel sheeting. Existing design rules for both shear connection and composite slabs are based mainly on test data obtained over many decades using various procedures and types of test specimen, for which there has been no international standard.

There are many national standards, and there is some international consensus on details of the *m–k* test for resistance of composite slabs to longitudinal shear. However, evidence has accumulated over the past 20 years that both this test and the UK's version of the push test for shear connectors have significant weaknesses. These restrict the development of new products, typically by giving results that are over-conservative (push test) or misleading (*m–k* test). A full set of *m–k* tests for a new profile is also expensive and time-consuming.

When the specification for an existing test is changed, past practice should, in principle, be re-evaluated. This is one reason why the UK's push test has survived so long in its present form. The new push test (*clause B.2*) has been in drafts of Eurocode 4 for 15 years, and was based on research work in the preceding decade. Almost all non-commercial push tests since that time have used slabs wider than the 300 mm of the specimen that is defined, for example, in BS 5400: Part 5.[82]

The new test generally gives higher results, and so does not raise questions about past practice. It costs more, but gives results that are more consistent and relevant to the behaviour of connectors in composite beams and columns.

For profiled sheeting, most research workers have concluded that the empirical *m–k* test procedure should be phased out. This method, as given in BS 5950: Part 4,[107] does not distinguish sufficiently between profiles that fail in a ductile manner and those that fail suddenly, and does not exploit the use of end anchorage or the ability of many modern profiles to provide partial shear connection.[113,119] However, its use has been the principal basis world-wide for the design of composite slabs for longitudinal shear. Re-testing of the scores (if not hundreds) of types of composite slabs used in existing structures is impracticable.

Clause B.3 therefore sets out in detail a method of testing that can be used with what is essentially the existing *m–k* procedure, though with a tighter specification relating to the mode of failure, and other changes based on recent experience of its use. The test method is intended also for use with the more rational partial-interaction design of composite slabs, which is to be preferred for reasons given in comments on *clauses 9.7* and *B.3*.

Properties of materials

Ideally, the strengths of the materials in a test specimen should equal the characteristic values specified for the application concerned. This is rarely possible in composite test specimens that include three different materials. It is therefore necessary to adjust resistances found by testing, or to limit the range of acceptable measured strengths of a material so that any adjustment would be negligible. Relevant provisions are given within *clauses B.2* and *B.3*.

The influence of cracking of concrete may be assumed to be allowed for in the test procedures. Tests that fully reproduce the effects of shrinkage and creep of concrete are rarely practicable; but these effects can normally be predicted once the behaviour in a short-term test has been established, and have little influence on ultimate strength except in slender composite columns.

B.2. Tests on shear connectors

General

The property of a shear connector that is needed for design is a curve that relates longitudinal slip, δ, to shear force per connector, P, of the type shown in *Fig. B.2*. No reliable method has been found for deducing such curves from the results of tests on composite beams, mainly because bending resistance is insensitive to the degree of shear connection, as shown by curve CH in Fig. 6.4(a).

Almost all the load-slip curves on which current practice is based were obtained from push tests, which were first standardized in the UK in 1965, in CP117: Part 1. A metricated version of this test is given in BS 5400: Part 5,[82] and referred to in clause 5.4.3 of BS 5950: Part 3.1[31] without comment on the need to modify it when profiled sheeting is present. This test has two variants, because the slab and reinforcement 'should be either as given in [the code] ... or as in the beams for which the test is designed'. This distinction is maintained in EN 1994-1-1 (*clause B.2.2(1)*). A 'standard' specimen is specified in *clause B.2.2(2)* and *Fig. B.1*, and a specimen for 'specific push tests' is defined in more general terms in *clause B.2.2(3)*. The principal differences between the 'standard' tests of EN 1994-1-1 and BS 5400 (the 'BS test') are summarized below, with reference to Fig. 11.1, and reasons for the changes are given.

Clause B.2.2(1)
Clause B.2.2(2)

The standard test is intended for use

> where the shear connectors are used in T-beams with a concrete slab of uniform thickness, or with haunches complying with 6.6.5.4. ... In other cases, specific push tests should be used.

It can be inferred from *clause B.2.2(1)* that separate 'specific' push tests should be done to determine the resistance of connectors in columns and in L-beams, which commonly occur at external walls of buildings and adjacent to large internal holes in floors. This is rarely, if ever, done, although a connector very close to a free edge of a slab is likely to be weaker and have less slip capacity than one in a T-beam.[79] This problem can be avoided by appropriate detailing, and is the reason for the requirements of *clauses 6.6.5.3* (on longitudinal splitting) and *6.6.5.4* (on the dimensions of haunches).

Push tests to clause B.2, compared with the BS test

Welded headed studs are the only type of shear connector for which large numbers of tests have been done in many countries, so all reported studies of push testing (e.g. see Johnson and Oehlers,[67] Stark and van Hove[72] and Oehlers[120]) are based on these tests. It has been

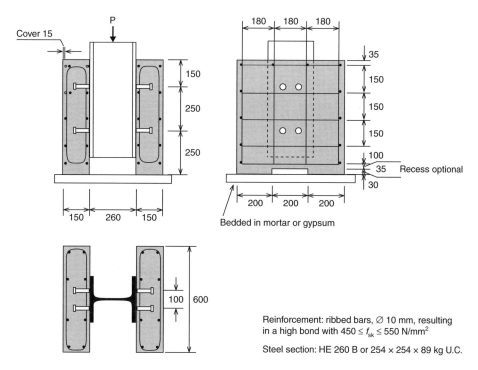

Fig. 11.1. Test specimen for the standard push test (dimensions in mm)

found that the results of the tests are widely scattered.[76] To obtain realistic characteristic values, it is necessary to separate inherent variability from that due to differences in the test specimens, the methods of casting and testing, and the ultimate tensile strength of the connectors.

The BS specimen was probably designed to give results at the lower edge of the band of uncertainty that existed 40 years ago, because it has very small slabs, prone to split longitudinally because the mild steel reinforcement is light and poorly anchored. It has connectors at only one level, which in effect prevents redistribution of load from one slab to the other[92] and so gives the resistance of the weaker of the two pairs of connectors. The changes from this test are as follows:

(1) The slabs have the same thickness, but are larger (650 × 600 mm, cf. 460 × 300 mm). This enables reinforcement to be better anchored, and so avoids low results due to splitting. The bond properties of the reinforcement are more important than the yield strength, which has little influence on the result. Limits are given in *Fig. B.1*.

(2) The transverse reinforcement is 10 high-yield ribbed bars per slab, instead of four mild steel bars of the same diameter, 10 mm, so the transverse stiffness provided by the bars is at least 2.5 times the previous value. In T-beams, the transverse restraint from the in-plane stiffness of the slab is greater than in a push specimen. The reinforcement is intended to simulate this restraint, not to reproduce the reinforcement provided in a beam.

(3) Shear connectors are placed at two levels in each slab. This enables redistribution of load to occur, so that the test gives the mean resistance of eight stud connectors, and better simulates the redistribution that occurs within the shear span of a beam.

(4) The flange of the steel section is wider (> 250 mm, cf. 146 mm), which enables wider block or angle connectors to be tested; and the lateral spacing of pairs of studs is standardized. The HE 260B section (*Fig. B.1*) is 260 × 260 mm, 93 kg/m.

(5) Each concrete slab must be cast in the horizontal position, as it would be in practice (*clause B.2.3(1)*). In the past, many specimens were cast with the slabs vertical, with the risk that the concrete just below the connectors would be poorly compacted.

Clause B.2.3(1)

Clause B.2.3(3)
Clause B.2.3(4) (6) Unlike the BS test, details of concrete curing are specified, in **clauses B.2.3(3)** and **B.2.3(4)**.

(7) The strength of the concrete measured at the time the push test is done must satisfy

$$0.6 \leq f_{cm}/f_{ck} \leq 0.8 \tag{D11.1}$$

where f_{ck} is the specified strength in practice (*clause B.2.3(5)*). The corresponding rule for the BS test is

$$0.86 \leq f_{cm}/f_{cu} \leq 1.2$$

where f_{cu} is 'the cube strength of the concrete in the beams'. For both codes, the two strength tests must be done using the same type of specimen, cylinder or cube.

Condition (D11.1) is now explained. It is essentially

$$f_{cm} = 0.7 f_{ck}$$

The resistance of a stud is usually found from *equation (6.19)*:

$$P_{Rd} = 0.29 \alpha d^2 (f_{ck} E_{cm})^{0.5}/\gamma_V$$

In the push test, f_{ck} is in effect replaced by $0.7f_{ck}$. Then,

$$P_{Rd} = 0.29 \alpha d^2 (0.7 f_{ck} E_{cm})^{0.5}/\gamma_V = 0.29 \alpha d^2 (f_{ck} E_{cm})^{0.5}/1.5 \tag{D11.2}$$

when $\gamma_V = 1.25$. This shows that the purpose of condition (D11.1) is to compensate for the use of a γ_V factor of 1.25, lower than the value 1.5 normally used for concrete, and the likelihood that the quality of the concrete in the laboratory may be higher than on site.

Clause B.2.4(1) (8) The loading is cycled 25 times between 5 and 40% of the expected failure load (*clause B.2.4(1)*). The BS test does not require this. Stresses in concrete adjacent to shear connectors are so high that, even at 40% of the failure load, significant local cracking and inelastic behaviour could occur. This repeated loading ensures that if the connector tested is susceptible to progressive slip, this will become evident.

Clause B.2.4(3)
Clause B.2.4(4) (9) Longitudinal slip and transverse separation are measured (*clauses B.2.4(3)* and *B.2.4(4)*), to enable the characteristic slip and uplift to be determined, as explained below. The BS test does not require this.

Evaluation of results of push tests

Normally, three tests are conducted on nominally identical specimens to determine the characteristic resistance P_{Rk} for concrete and connector material of specified strengths f_{ck} and f_u, respectively. Let P_m be the mean and P_{min} the lowest of the three measured resistances per connector, and f_{ut} be the measured ultimate strength of the connector material. If all Clause B.2.5(1) three results are within 10% of P_m, then, from *clause B.2.5(1)*,

$$P_{Rk} = 0.9 P_{min} \tag{D11.3}$$

Clause B.2.5(2) refers to Annex D of EN 1990 (Informative) for the procedure to be followed if the scatter of results exceeds the 10% limit.

A method to clause D.8 of EN 1990 for the deduction of a characteristic value from a small number of test results, which took no account of prior knowledge, would severely penalize a three-test series. It is necessary to rely also on the extensive past experience of push testing. Clause D.8.4 is relevant. For three tests it sets the condition that all results must be within 10% of the mean, P_m. This appears in *clause B.2.5(1)*. Clause D.8.4 then gives the characteristic resistance as a function of P_m and of V_r, 'the maximum coefficient of variation observed in previous tests', in which the '10% from the mean' condition was satisfied.

Most of the previous results were from research programmes, with many different types of test specimen. The results for studs in profiled sheeting, for example, have been found to be samples from seven different statistical populations.[76] It has not been possible to establish the value of V_r. The method of *clause B.2.5(1)*, of reducing the lowest of the three results by 10%, is mainly based on previous practice. It can be deduced from clause D.8.4 that for a set of three results with the lowest 10% below the mean, the method of *clause B.2* implies that $V_r = 11\%$.

Clause B.2.5(1) gives a penalty that applies when $f_{ut} > f_u$. This is appropriate where the resistance of a connector is governed by its own material, usually steel, but in practice the resistance of a connector can depend mainly on the strength of the concrete, especially where lightweight aggregate is used. The correction then seems over-conservative, because f_u is limited to 500 N/mm² by *clause 6.6.3.1(1)*, and the strength of the material can exceed 600 N/mm² for studs.

In the BS test, a 'nominal' strength P_u is calculated from

$$P_u = (f_{ck}/f_c)P_{min}$$

and, then,

$$P_{Rd} = P_u/1.4$$

It so happens that $1.25/0.9 = 1.4$, so from equation (D11.3) the two methods give a similar relationship between P_{min} and P_{Rd}, except that the Eurocode result is corrected for the strength of the steel, and the BS result is corrected for the strength of the concrete. This is probably because the results of the BS test are rarely governed by the strength of the steel, as the slabs are so likely to split.

Clause B.2.5(3) finds application for connectors such as blocks with hoops, where the block resists most of the shear, and the hoop resists most of the uplift.

Clause B.2.5(3)

The classification of a connector as ductile (*clause 6.6.1.1(5)*) depends on its characteristic slip capacity, which is defined in *clause B.2.5(4)*. From the definition of P_{Rk} (*clause B.2.5(1)*), all three test specimens will have reached a higher load, so the slips δ_u in *Fig. B.2* are all taken from the falling branches of the load–slip curves. It follows that a push test should not be terminated as soon as the maximum load is reached.

Clause B.2.5(4)

B.3. Testing of composite floor slabs

General

The most usual mode of failure of a composite slab is by longitudinal shear, loss of interlock occurring at the steel–concrete interface. Resistance to longitudinal shear is difficult to predict theoretically. The pattern and height of indentations or embossments and the shape of the sheeting profile all have significant effect. There is no established method to calculate this resistance, so the methods of EN 1994-1-1 rely on testing.

Tests are needed for each new shape of profiled sheet. They are normally done by or for the manufacturer, who will naturally be concerned to minimize their cost. Their purpose (*clause B.3.1(1)*) is to provide values for either the factors m and k for the 'm–k method', or the longitudinal shear strength required for the partial shear connection method. These procedures for verifying resistance to longitudinal shear are given in *clauses 9.7.3* and *9.7.4*. Comments on them are relevant here.

Clause B.3.1(1)

The tests also determine whether the shear connection is brittle or ductile (*clause B.3.1(2)*). There is a 20% penalty for brittle behaviour (*clause B.3.5(1)*). In view of the purpose of the tests, failure must be in longitudinal shear (*clauses B.3.2(6)* and *B.3.2(7)*).

Clause B.3.1(2)

Number of tests

The list of relevant variables in *clause B.3.1(3)* and the concessions in *clause B.3.1(4)* define the number of tests required. As an example, it is assumed that a manufacturer seeks to determine shear resistance for a new profile, as the basis for design data for a range of sheet thicknesses, slab thicknesses and spans, and concrete strengths, with both lightweight and normal-weight concrete. How many tests are required?

Clause B.3.1(3)
Clause B.3.1(4)

In view of the penalty for brittle behaviour (*clause B.3.5(1)*), it is assumed that the new profile is found to satisfy *clause 9.7.3(3)* on ductility. The partial-connection method is more versatile than the *m–k* method, and is recommended. Its calculations are straightforward on a spreadsheet. From *clause B.3.2(7)*, its tests are done in groups of four. The variables are now considered in turn, to find the minimum number of values needed for each one, and, hence, the number of tests needed for a full set.

(a) Thickness of sheeting: test the thinnest sheeting. As interlock is dependent on the local bending of individual plate elements in the sheeting profile, the results may not be applied to thinner or significantly weaker sheets, which would be more flexible . . . (1)
(b) Type of sheeting, meaning the profile, including any overlap details, and the specification of embossments and their tolerances. Ensure that the embossments on sheets tested satisfy *clause B.3.3(2)*, and standardize the other details . . . . (1)
(c) Steel grade: test the highest and lowest grades to be used. The materials standards listed in *clause 3.5* include several nominal yield strengths . . . . (2)
(d) Coating: this should be standardized, if possible . . . . (1)
(e) Density of concrete: test the lowest and highest densities. . . . . (2)
(f) Grade of concrete: test with a mean strength not exceeding 1.25 times the lowest value of f_{ck} to be specified (see *clause B.3.1(4)*). The results will be slightly conservative for stronger concretes. . . . . (1)
(g) Slab thickness: test the thinnest and thickest slabs . . . . (2)
   The use of a single thickness is not permitted because the effectiveness of shear connection may depend on the stiffness of the concrete component. Conclusions from a theoretical model for the effect of slab thickness, given in Appendix B of this guide, are summarized below.
(h) Shear span: account is taken of this in the provisions for use of the test results.

This gives a total of

$4 \times 1^4 \times 2^3 = 32$ tests

If it is suspected that the results for parameters (a) and (g) will be over-conservative for thick sheets and strong concrete, respectively, even more tests would be needed. If an alternative coating is to be offered, it should be possible to compare its performance with that of the standard coating in a few tests, rather than another full set.

For the *m–k* method, tests are in groups of six, so the number rises from 32 to 48.

The main conclusions from Appendix B of this guide are as follows;

• for the partial-interaction method, interpolation between results from tests on slabs of the same shear span and two thicknesses is valid for slabs of intermediate thickness
• for the *m–k* method, results from tests on two shear spans are applicable for shear spans between those tested.

The status of Annex B, and use of fewer tests

Annex B is informative. From notes to *clauses 9.7.3(4)* and *9.7.3(8)*, its test methods '*may be assumed to meet the basic requirements*' of the relevant design method for longitudinal shear. These requirements are not defined; they have to be inferred, mainly from *Annex B*.

This implies that where the testing does not conform to the extensive scheme outlined above, some independent body, such as the relevant regulatory authority or its nominee, must be persuaded that the evidence presented does satisfy the 'basic requirements' of one or both of the two design methods. Where this is done, the design can presumably claim to be in accordance with Eurocode 4, in this respect; but that would not apply internationally.

Annex B may eventually be superseded by a European standard on the determination of the shear resistance of composite slabs. Until then, the situation is unsatisfactory. Development of better theoretical models would help. At present, research workers cannot validate these because manufacturers rarely release their detailed test results.

Where a new profile is a development from an existing range, it should be possible to use the results of earlier tests to predict the influence of some of the parameters, and so reduce the number of new tests required.

Testing arrangement

Loading is applied symmetrically to a simply-supported slab of span L, at points distant $L/4$ from each support (*clause B.3.2(2)*). Crack inducers are placed beneath the loads (*clause B.3.3(3)*), to reduce the effect of local variations in the tensile strength of the concrete. The failure loading is much heavier than the slabs, so the shear spans L_s (*Fig. B.3*) are subjected to almost constant vertical shear. This differs from the test details in BS 5950: Part 4, in which vertical shear is not constant over the length between a crack inducer and the nearer support.

Clause B.3.2(2)

As the shear span is a fixed proportion of the span, specimens for regions such as A and B for the *m–k* method (*clause B.3.2(6)* and *Fig. B.4*) are obtained by altering the span L. As this method is empirical, it is good practice to ensure that the tests also encompass the range of spans required for use in practice.[107]

Clause B.3.2(6)

For sheeting with ductile behaviour and where design will use the partial-interaction method, the number of tests in a series, for specimens of given thickness h_t, can be reduced from six to four (*clause B.3.2(7)*).

Clause B.3.2(7)

Clauses B.3.3(1) and *B.3.3(2)* are intended to minimize the differences between the profiled sheeting used in the tests and that used in practice. The depth of embossments has been found to have a significant effect on the resistance.

Clause B.3.3(1)
Clause B.3.3(2)

Propped construction increases the longitudinal shear. It is required for the test specimens to enable the results to be used with or without propping (*clause B.3.3(6)*).

Clause B.3.3(6)

From *clause B.3.3(8)*, the specimens for the determination of concrete strength, defined in *clause B.3.3(9)*, should be cured under the same conditions as the test slabs. This cannot of course be the curing under water normally used for standard cubes and cylinders. When deviation of strength from the mean is significant, the concrete strength is taken as the maximum value (*clause B.3.3(9)*).This causes the applicability of the test results to be more restricted (*clause B.3.1(4)*).

Clause B.3.3(8)
Clause B.3.3(9)

The test procedure for the strength of the profiled sheeting (*clause B.3.3(10)*) is given elsewhere.[121]

Clause B.3.3(10)

The initial loading test is cyclic (*clauses B.3.4(3)* and *B.3.4(4)*), to destroy any chemical bond between the sheeting and the concrete, so that the subsequent test to failure gives a true indication of the long-term resistance to variations of longitudinal shear. The number of cycles, 5000, is fewer than that required by BS 5940: Part 4, but has been judged to be adequate for these purposes.

Clause B.3.4(3)
Clause B.3.4(4)

Design values for m and k

Clause B.3.5(1) gives a design rule for the possibility that the two end reactions may differ slightly, and applies an additional factor of safety of 1.25 to compensate for brittle behaviour, in the form of a reduction factor of 0.8.

Clause B.3.5(1)

The method of *clause B.3.5(2)* is applicable to any set of six or more test results, irrespective of their scatter. An 'appropriate statistical model' will penalize both the scatter and the number of results, if small, and may be that given in EN 1990, to which *clause B.3.5(3)* refers.

Clause B.3.5(2)

Clause B.3.5(3)

Where a series consists of six tests and the results are consistent, *clause B.3.5(3)* provides a simple method for finding the design line shown in *Fig. B.4*, and hence values for m and k. These are in units of N/mm^2.

These methods differ from that of BS 5950: Part 4, both in the determination of the line that gives the values of m and k (see Fig. 11.3) and in their definition. In BS 5950, k is proportional to the square root of the concrete strength, which causes complications with units, and the two sets of three results could be from slabs with different concrete strengths. It has been found that the deliberate use of very different strengths for the specimens in regions A and B in Fig. 11.3 can lead to unsafe applications of the method, when m and k are defined as in BS 5950: Part 4. All the results in a diagram such as *Fig. B.4* are required by *clause B.3.3(8)* to be from specimens with nominally identical concrete, so there is no need to include concrete strength in the functions plotted in this figure.

The formula for vertical shear in *clause 9.7.3(4)* and the definitions of *m* and *k* in *clause B.3.5* are dimensionally correct, and can be used with any consistent set of units. However, analyses of a given set of test results by the Eurocode method give values for *m* and *k* different to those found by the BS method, and *k* even has different dimensions. The conversion of BS values to Eurocode values is illustrated in Example 11.1. The applicability of sets of test results not in accordance with *Annex B* are discussed in Appendix B of this guide.

Design values for $\tau_{u,\,Rd}$

Clause B.3.6(1) *Clause B.3.6(1)* refers to the partial-interaction curve shown in *Fig. B.5*. This is for sagging bending, and is determined for a group of tests on specimens with nominally identical cross-sections as follows:

(a) The measured values of the required dimensions and strengths of materials are determined, and used to calculate the full-interaction plastic moment of resistance of a test specimen, $M_{p,\,Rm}$ and the corresponding compressive force in the concrete slab, $N_{c,\,f}$.

(b) A value is chosen for $\eta\ (= N_c/N_{c,\,f})$, which determines a value N_c, the partial-interaction compressive force in the slab at the section where flexural failure is assumed to occur. The corresponding value of the bending resistance *M* is then calculated from

$$M = M_{pr} + N_c z$$

with M_{pr} from *equation (9.6)*, with N_c replacing $N_{c,\,f}$, and *z* from *equation (9.9)*. This gives a single point on the curve in *Fig. B.5*, which assumes that an undefined slip can occur at the interface between the sheeting and the concrete. This necessitates ductile behaviour.

(c) By repeating step (b) with different values of η, sufficient points are found to define the partial-interaction curve.

Clause B.3.6(2) From *clause B.3.6(2)*, a bending moment *M* is found from each test. This is M_{test} in *Fig. B.5*, and leads to a value η_{test}, and hence τ_u from *equation (B.2)*.

For the test arrangement shown in *Fig. B.3*, there will be an overhang L_0 beyond the shear span L_s, along which slip will occur. This is allowed for in *equation (B.2)*, which assumes that the shear strength is uniform along the total length $(L_s + L_0)$. In reality, the strength includes a contribution from friction at the interface between the sheeting and the concrete, arising from the transmission of the vertical load across the interface to the support. In *clause B.3.6(2)*, this effect is included in the value found for τ_u.

Clause B.3.6(3) A more accurate equation for τ_u is given in *clause B.3.6(3)*, for use with the alternative method of *clause 9.7.3(9)*, where relevant comment is given.

From *clause B.3.2(7)*, a group of four tests on specimens of given span and slab thickness gives three values of τ_u, and evidence on ductility (*clause B.3.2(7)*). All the values of τ_u are
Clause B.3.6(4) used in a single calculation of the lower 5% fractile value, to *clause B.3.6(4)*. This is divided by γ_{VS} to obtain the design value used in *clause 9.7.3(8)*.

The shape of the partial-interaction curve depends on the slab thickness, so a separate one is needed for each thickness. The need for tests at different thicknesses is discussed at the end of Appendix B of this guide.

Example 11.1: *m–k* tests on composite floor slabs

In this example, values of *m* and *k* are determined from a set of tests not in accordance with *clause B.3*, '*Testing of composite floor slabs*'. These tests, done in accordance with the relevant Netherlands standard, RSBV 1990, were similar to 'specific tests' as specified in clause 10.3.2 of ENV 1994-1-1, which has been omitted from EN 1994-1-1.

This set of tests on eight simply-supported composite slabs has been fully reported.[122] The cross-section of the profiled sheeting is shown in Fig. 9.4. The values of *m* and *k*

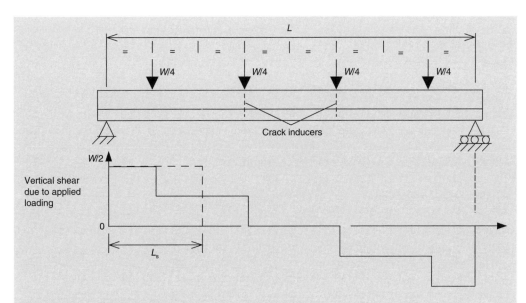

Fig. 11.2. Loading used in the tests on composite slabs

determined here are used in Example 9.1, 'Two-span continuous composite slab', which includes the results of tests on the non-composite sheeting.

Test specimens and procedure

All of the composite slabs had the same breadth, 915 mm, which satisfies *clause B.3.3(5)*, and were cast using the same mix of lightweight-aggregate concrete, with propped construction (*clause B.3.3(6)*). (Where a clause number is given without comment, as here, it means that the clause was complied with.) The tests to failure were done between the ages of 27 and 43 days, when the strengths of test specimens stored with slabs (*clause B.3.3(8)*) were as given in Table 11.1. Steel mesh with 6 mm bars at 200 mm spacing was provided in each slab (*clause B.3.3(7)*).

For specimens 1–4, the overall thickness and span were $h_t = 170$ mm and $L = 4500$ mm, where the notation is as in *Fig. B.3*. For specimens 5–8, $h_t = 120$ mm and $L = 2000$ mm. The distance between the centre-line of each support and the adjacent end of each slab was 100 mm (*clause B.3.2(4)*). The surfaces of the sheeting were not degreased (*clause B.3.3(1)*).

The tensile strength and the yield strength of the sheeting were found from coupons cut from its top and bottom flanges (*clause B.3.3(10)*). The mean values were $f_u = 417$ N/mm^2 and $f_{y, 0.2} = 376$ N/mm^2. The stress 376 N/mm^2, measured at the 0.2% proof strain, is significantly higher than the yield strength found in another series of tests,[123] which was 320 N/mm^2. The nominal yield strength for this sheeting, now 350 N/mm^2, was then 280 N/mm^2, which is only 74% of 376 N/mm^2, so *clause B.3.1(4)* is not complied with. This is accepted, because small changes of yield strength have little influence on resistance to longitudinal shear.

There is a similar '80%' rule in *clause B.3.1(4)* for the strength of the concrete. Applying it to the mean cube strength for this series, 34.4 N/mm^2, gives a cube strength of 27.5 N/mm^2, which is below the value used in Example 9.1, so the rule is satisfied.

The slabs were tested under four-point loading, as shown in Fig. 11.2, and crack inducers were provided at distances $L/8$ each side of mid-span. This is not in accordance with *Fig. B.3*; *clause B.3.2(3)* specifies two-point loading. An appropriate value of L_s has to be found, for use in the determination of m and k. A shear–force diagram for two-point loading is found (the dashed line in Fig. 11.2) that has the same area as the actual shear–force diagram, and the same maximum vertical shear. Here, $L_s = L/4$, as it is in *Annex B*.

Cyclic loading

Clause B.3.4 specifies 5000 cycles of loading between $0.2W_t$ and $0.6W_t$, where W_t is a static failure load. In these tests, W_t for specimen 1 was 75.5 kN, and the range of loading in tests 2–4, for 10 000 cycles, was from $0.13W_t$ to $0.40W_t$. For specimens 5–8, with a mean failure load of 94.4 kN, the fatigue loading in tests 6–8 ranged from $0.19W_t$ to $0.57W_t$, close to the range specified. These divergences are not significant.

Results of tests to failure

To satisfy *clause 9.7.3(3)* on ductility, it is necessary to record the total load on the specimen, including its weight, at a recorded end slip of 0.1 mm, at a deflection (δ) of span/50, and at maximum load. These are given in Table 11.1.

The failure load, as defined in *clause 9.7.3(3)*, is for all these tests the value when $L/50$. These loads all exceed the load at a slip of 0.1 mm by more than 10%, the least excess being 13%. All failures are therefore 'ductile'. From *clause B.3.5(1)*, the representative vertical shear force V_t is taken as half the failure load.

Determination of m and k

In the original report[122] the axes used for plotting the results were similar to those in BS 5950: Part 4 (Fig. 11.3(a)). They are

$$X = A_p/[bL_s(0.8f_{cu})^{0.5}] \qquad Y = V_t/[bd_p(0.8f_{cu})^{0.5}] \qquad \text{(D11.4)}$$

where f_{cu} is the measured cube strength. The other symbols are in Eurocode notation. Values of X and Y were calculated from the results and are given in Table 11.1. From these, the following values were determined:

$$m = 178 \text{ N/mm}^2 \qquad k = 0.0125 \text{ N}^{0.5} \text{ mm} \qquad \text{(D11.5)}$$

For m and k as defined in EN 1994-1-1, the relevant axes (Fig. 11.3(b)) are

$$x = A_p/bL_s \qquad y = V_t/bd_p$$

so that

$$x = X(0.8f_{cu})^{0.5} \qquad y = Y(0.8f_{cu})^{0.5} \qquad \text{(D11.6)}$$

Approximate values for m and k to EN 1994-1-1 can be found by assuming that m to BS 5950: Part 4 is unchanged, and k is $(0.8f_{cu,m})^{0.5}$ times the BS value, given above, where $f_{cu,m}$ is the mean cube strength for the series. These values are

Table 11.1. Results of tests on composite floor slabs

Test No.	f_{cu} (N/mm^2)	Load at 0.1 mm slip (kN)	Load at $\delta = L/50$ (kN)	Maximum load (kN)	$10^3 X$ ((1/N$^{0.5}$)mm)	$10^3 Y$ (N$^{0.5}$mm)	$10^3 x$	$10^3 y$ (N/mm^2)
1	31.4	63.3	75.5	75.5	0.222	58.6	1.115	294
2	30.4	65.3	75.5	75.5	0.226	59.6	1.115	294
3	32.1	64.3	73.9	73.9	0.220	56.7	1.115	287
4	34.2	66.8	75.4	75.4	0.213	56.1	1.115	293
5	35.3	52.2	94.0	94.2	0.472	108.2	2.51	575
6	37.4	54.2	90.9	94.0	0.459	104.9	2.51	574
7	37.2	52.2	91.7	93.9	0.460	105.0	2.51	573
8	36.9	56.2	94.7	95.4	0.462	107.2	2.51	582

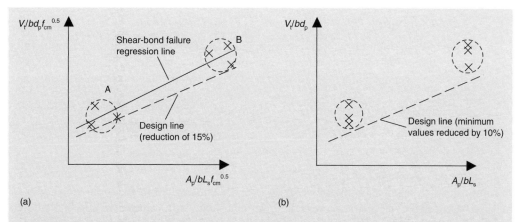

Fig. 11.3. Evaluation of the results of tests on composite slabs. (a) BS 5950: Part 4. (b) EN 1994-1-1

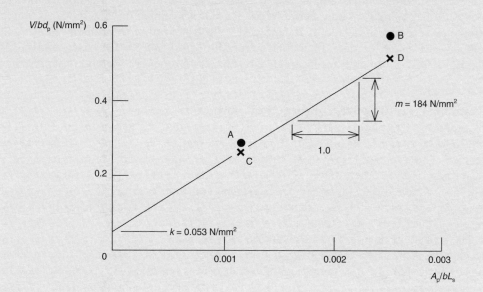

Fig. 11.4. Determination of m and k

$$m = 178 \text{ N/mm}^2 \qquad k = 0.066 \text{ N/mm}^2 \tag{D11.7}$$

These results are approximate because f_{cu} is different for each test, and the procedure of *Annex B* for finding characteristic values differs from the BS procedure. The correct method is to calculate x and y for each test, plot a new diagram, and determine m and k from it in accordance with *clause B.3.5*, as follows.

The values of x and y for these tests, from equations (D11.6), are given in Table 11.1. The differences within each group of four are so small that, at the scale of Fig. 11.4, each plots as a single point: A and B. *Clause B.3.5(3)*, on variation within each group, is satisfied. Using the simplified method of that clause, the characteristic line is taken to be the line through points C and D, which have y coordinates 10% below the values for specimens 3 and 7, respectively. This line gives the results

$$m = 184 \text{ N/mm}^2 \qquad k = 0.0530 \text{ N/mm}^2 \tag{D11.8}$$

which are used in Example 9.1.

For these tests, the approximate method gives a small error in m, –3%, and a larger error in k, +25%. From *clause 9.7.3(4)*, the design shear resistance is

$$V_{\ell,\mathrm{Rd}} = (bd_\mathrm{p}/\gamma_{\mathrm{VS}})[(mA_\mathrm{p}/bL_\mathrm{s}) + k] \tag{D11.9}$$

The second term in square brackets is much smaller than the first, and in this example the errors in m and k almost cancel out. In Example 9.1, $V_{\ell,\mathrm{Rd}}$ was found to be 28.0 kN/m. Using the approximate values of equations (D11.7) for m and k changes it only to 28.3 kN/m.

Similar comparisons are needed with other sets of test results, before any general conclusion can be drawn about the accuracy of the approximate method of calculation.

Note on the partial-interaction method

A composite slab using sheeting of the type tested was designed in Example 9.1. The m–k method was used for the verification for longitudinal shear, with values of m and k calculated from test results, as shown in Example 11.1.

To illustrate the partial-interaction method of *clauses 9.7.3(7)* to *9.7.3(9)*, an attempt will be made in the following Example 11.2 to use it in an alternative verification of the same composite slab, using the same set of test results.[122] It is assumed that the reader is familiar with the two examples referred to. Example 11.2 illustrates potential problems in using this method with existing test data, shows that a procedure given in ENV 1994-1-1,[49] and omitted from EN 1994-1-1, can give unconservative results, and proposes a method to replace it.

Example 11.2: the partial-interaction method

It is shown in Example 11.1 that in the eight tests reported,[122] the behaviour of the slabs was 'ductile' to *clause 9.7.3(3)*. For the partial-interaction method, *clause B.3.2(7)* then requires a minimum of four tests on specimens of the same overall depth h_t: three with a long shear span, to determine τ_u, and one with a short shear span, but not less than $3h_\mathrm{t}$. The tests available satisfy the $3h_\mathrm{t}$ condition, but not that for uniform depth. The four long-span slabs were all thicker than the four short-span slabs. The purpose of the single short-span test is to verify ductility, which is satisfactory here.

The maximum recorded end slips in the long-span tests (Nos. 1 to 4), only 0.3 mm, reveal a problem. These tests were discontinued when the deflections reached span/50, so it is unlikely that the maximum longitudinal shear was reached. The specimens had the high span/depth ratio of 26.5, and probably failed in flexure, not longitudinal shear. This is confirmed by the results that follow: the shear strength from tests 1–4 is about 30% lower than that from the short-span tests 5–8, where the end slips at maximum load were from 1 to 2 mm and the span/depth ratio was 16.7.

Clause B.3.2(7) requires the shear strength to be determined from the results for the long-span slabs. Its condition for a shear span 'as long as possible while still providing failure in longitudinal shear' was probably not satisfied here, so that the final design value $\tau_{\mathrm{u,Rd}}$ is lower than it would have been if a shorter span had been used for tests 1–4. In the absence of guidance from previous tests, this condition is difficult to satisfy when planning tests.

Other aspects of these tests are compared with the provisions of *Annex B* in Example 11.1.

The partial-interaction diagram

Measured cube strengths and maximum loads for the eight tests are given in Table 11.1. The mean measured yield strength and cross-sectional area of the sheeting were 376 N/mm² and 1145 mm²/m, respectively.[122] For full shear connection, the plastic neutral axes are above the sheeting, so *clause 9.7.2(5)* applies.

The longitudinal force for full interaction is

$$N_{\mathrm{c,f}} = A_\mathrm{p}f_{\mathrm{yp}} = 1145 \times 0.376 = 431 \text{ kN/m} \tag{D11.10}$$

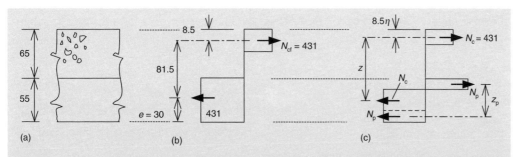

Fig. 11.5. Stress blocks for bending resistance of composite slab with partial interaction (dimensions in mm)

and the stress blocks are as shown in Fig. 11.5(b). The mean cube strength for specimens 5–8, 36.7 N/mm², corresponds to a cylinder strength f_{cm} of 29.8 N/mm², so that the depth of the concrete stress block is

$$x_{pl} = 431/(0.85 \times 29.8) = 17.0 \text{ mm} \tag{D11.11}$$

With full interaction, the force $N_{c,f}$ in the sheeting acts at its centre of area, 30 mm above its bottom surface, so the lever arm is

$$z = 120 - 17/2 - 30 = 81.5 \text{ mm}$$

and

$$M_{p,Rm} = 431 \times 0.0815 = 35.1 \text{ kN m/m}$$

The method of calculation for the partial-interaction diagram is now considered, following *clause B.3.6(1)*. The stress blocks in *Fig. B.5* correspond to those used in *clauses 9.7.2(5)* and *9.7.2(6)* modified by *clause 9.7.3(8)*. It follows from equation (D11.11) that for any degree of shear connection $\eta \ (= N_c/N_{c,f})$, the stress block depth is 17η mm, with a line of action 8.5η mm below the top of the slab (Fig. 11.5(c)).

For any assumed value for η, the lever arm z is given by *equation (9.9)*. For typical trapezoidal sheeting, where the profile is such that $e_p > e$ (these symbols are shown in *Fig. 9.6*), the simplification given in equation (D9.4) should for this purpose be replaced by

$$z = h_t - 0.5\eta x_{pl} - e \tag{D11.12}$$

where h_t is the thickness of the slab tested. The use of e in place of e_p is because an approximation to the mean resistance M_{Rm} should over-estimate it. This moves curve FG in Fig. 11.6 upwards. For a given test resistance M, following the route ABC then gives a lower value for η_{test}, and, hence, a lower predicted τ_u, from *equation (B.2)*.

Curve FG is found by calculations for a set of values for η that covers the range of $M/M_{p,Rm}$ found in the tests. The mean bending resistance is given by

$$M_{Rm} = M_{pr} + \eta N_{c,f} z \tag{D11.13}$$

(based on equation (D9.5)). The reduced plastic resistance of the sheeting, M_{pr}, which equals $N_p z_p$ in Fig. 11.5(c), is found from *equation (9.6)*.

Calculations for the partial-interaction diagram and τ_u
For $\eta \geq 0.2$, *equation (9.6)* and equation (D11.13) give

$$M_{Rm} = \eta N_{c,f} z + 1.25 M_{p,a}(1 - \eta) \tag{D11.14}$$

Assuming $\eta = 0.7$, for example, equation (D11.12) gives for specimens 5–8

$$z = 120 - 0.7 \times 8.5 - 30 = 84.0 \text{ mm}$$

From the tests,[122] $M_{p,a} = 5.65$ kN m/m, with $e_p = 33$ mm, so $e - e_p = 3$ mm, much less than z. From equation (D11.14),

$$M_{Rm} = 0.7 \times 431 \times 0.084 + 1.25 \times 5.65 \times 0.3 = 27.48 \text{ kN m/m}$$

and

$$M_{Rm}/M_{p,Rm} = 27.48/35.1 = 0.783$$

For specimens 1–4, $h_t = 170$ mm and $M_{p,Rm} = 56.7$ kN m/m. For $\eta = 0.7$,

$$z = 170 - 0.7 \times 8.5 - 30 = 134 \text{ mm}$$

$$M_{Rm} = 0.7 \times 431 \times 0.134 + 1.25 \times 5.65 \times 0.3 = 42.5 \text{ kN m/m}$$

$$M_{Rm}/M_{p,Rm} = 42.5/56.7 = 0.750$$

Similar calculations for other degrees of shear connection give curves DE for the short-span slabs 5–8 and FG for slabs 1–4.

In *clause B.3.6(2)*, the bending moment M is defined as being '*at the cross-section under the point load*', on the assumption that two-point loading is used in the tests. Here, four-point loading was used (see Fig. 11.2). At failure, there was significant slip throughout the length of $3L/8$ between each inner point load and the nearer support, so, for these tests, M was determined at an inner point load, and L_s was taken as $3L/8$.

The calculation of M_{test} for specimen 5 is now explained. From Table 11.1, the maximum load was 94.2 kN. This included 2.2 kN that was, in effect, applied to the composite slab by the removal of the prop that was present at mid-span during concreting.[122] The loads on the composite member were thus as shown inset on Fig. 11.6, and the bending moment at point J was

$$M_{test} = 47.1 \times 0.75 - 23.0 \times 0.5 = 23.83 \text{ kN m}$$

This is for a slab of width 0.915 m, so that

$$M_{test}/M_{p,Rm} = 23.83/(0.915 \times 35.1) = 0.742$$

From Fig.11.6, $\eta_{test} = 0.646$.

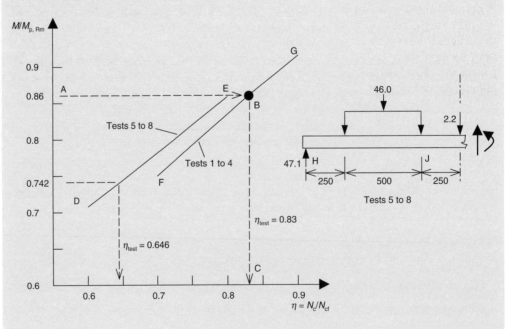

Fig. 11.6. Partial-interaction diagram from tests (units: mm and kN)

Table 11.2. Degree of shear connection, from tests on composite slabs

Test No.	Maximum load (kN)	M_{test} (kN m)	$M_{test}/M_{p, Rm}$	η
1	75.5	44.8	0.863	0.835
2	75.5	44.8	0.863	0.835
3	73.9	43.9	0.846	0.814
4	75.4	44.7	0.862	0.833
5	94.2	23.83	0.742	0.646

Corresponding results for tests 1–4 are given in Table 11.2.

Clause B.3.6(4) defines $\tau_{u, Rk}$ as the 5% lower fractile, based on the results for tests 1–4. There may be other evidence on the variance of such results. Here, it is assumed that this enables a value 10% below the mean to be used, as for the *m–k* method.

The values of η for tests 1–4 are so close that τ_u can be found from their mean value, 0.83. From *clause B.3.6(2)*,

$$\tau_u = \eta N_{c, f}/[b(L_s + L_0)] \tag{D11.15}$$

For tests 1–4, $L_s = 3 \times 4.5/8 = 1.69$ m. For all tests, $N_{cf} = 431$ kN/m, $L_0 = 0.1$ m, and b is taken as 1.0 m. Hence,

$$\tau_u = 0.83 \times 431/1790 = 0.200 \text{ N/mm}^2$$

From *clause B.3.6(6)*, with γ_{VS} taken as 1.25,

$$\tau_{u, Rd} = 0.9 \times 0.200/1.25 = \textbf{0.144 N/mm}^2$$

The interaction curve DE for specimens 5–8 is slightly higher than FG in Fig. 11.6. Its value at $\eta = 0, M_{p, a}/M_{p, Rm}$, is higher because, for these thinner slabs ($h_t = 120$ mm), $M_{p, Rm}$ is lower, at 35 kN m/m. Using the preceding method for these results gives $\tau_{u, Rd} = 0.24$ N/mm^2. This much higher result confirms the suspicion, noted above, that longitudinal shear failure was not reached in specimens 1–4.

Comments

Where the test data are in accordance with the specification in *Annex B*, determination of $\tau_{u, Rd}$ is straightforward, as values of η can be found by replacing the graphical method (used here for illustration) by direct calculation. However, where tests are being planned, or other data are being used, as here, the work requires understanding of the basis of the provisions of *Annex B*. It is of particular importance to ensure that longitudinal shear failures occur in the tests.

APPENDIX A

Lateral–torsional buckling of composite beams for buildings

This appendix supplements the comments on *clause 6.4*.

Simplified expression for 'cracked' flexural stiffness of a composite slab

The 'cracked' stiffness per unit width of a composite slab is defined in *clause 6.4.2(6)* as the lower of the values at mid-span and at a support. The latter usually governs, because the profiled sheeting may be discontinuous at a support. It is now determined for the cross-section shown in Fig. A.1 with the sheeting neglected.

It is assumed that only the concrete within the troughs is in compression. Its transformed area in 'steel' units is

$$A_e = b_0 h_p / n b_s \qquad (a)$$

where n is the modular ratio. The position of the elastic neutral axis is defined by the dimensions a and c, so that

$$A_e c = A_s a \qquad \text{and} \qquad a + c = z \qquad (b)$$

where A_s is the area of top reinforcement per unit width of slab, and

$$z = h - d_s - h_p / 2 \qquad (c)$$

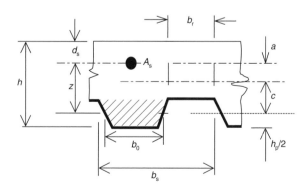

Fig. A.1. Model for stiffness of a composite slab in hogging bending

Assuming that each trough is rectangular, the second moment of area per unit width is

$$I = A_s a^2 + A_e(c^2 + h_p^2/12) \tag{d}$$

Using equations (b) to (d), the flexural stiffness is

$$(EI)_2 = E_a [A_s A_e z^2/(A_s + A_e) + A_e h_p^2/12] \tag{DA.1}$$

This result is used in Example 6.7.

Flexural stiffness of beam with encased web

For a partially encased beam the model used for the derivation of *equation (6.11)* for the flexural stiffness k_2 is as shown in Fig. A.2(a). A lateral force F applied to the steel bottom flange causes displacement δ. The rotation of line AB is $\phi = \delta/h_s$. It is caused by a bending moment Fh_s acting about A. The stiffness is

$$k_2 = M/\phi = Fh_s^2/\delta$$

The force F is assumed to be resisted by vertical tension in the steel web and compression in a concrete strut BC, of width $b_c/4$. Elastic analysis gives *equation (6.11)*.

Maximum spacing of shear connectors for continuous U-frame action

A rule given in ENV 1994-1-1 is derived. It is assumed that stud connectors are provided at spacing s in a single row along the centre of the steel top flange (Fig. A.2(b)). The tendency of the bottom flange to buckle laterally causes a transverse moment M_t per unit length, which is resisted by a tensile force T in each stud. From Fig. A.2,

$$M_t s = 0.4bT \tag{a}$$

The initial inclination from the vertical of the web, θ_0 in Fig. 6.9(b), due to the tendency of the bottom flange to buckle sideways, would be resisted by a moment $k_s\theta_0$, from the definition of k_s in *clause 6.4.2(6)*. For a design longitudinal moment M_{Ed} at the adjacent internal support, θ_0 is assumed to be increased to

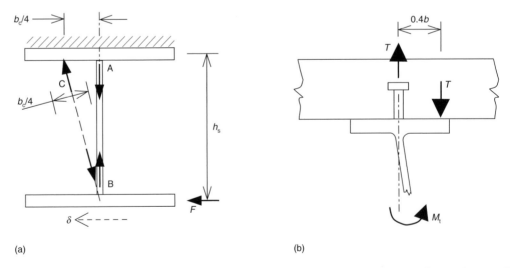

(a)　　　　　　　　　　　　　　　　(b)

Fig. A.2. Resistance to transverse bending in an inverted U-frame. (a) Flexural stiffness of encased web. (b) Spacing of shear connectors

Table A.1. Maximum spacings for 19 mm studs, and minimum top reinforcement

Serial size	Mass (kg/m)	Web thickness (mm)	s_{max} (mm)	$100A_{s,\,min}/d_s$
762 × 267 UB	197	15.6	362	0.06
610 × 305 UB	238	18.6	204	0.12
610 × 229 UB	101	10.6	767	0.02
IPE 600	122	12.0	509	0.03
HEA 700	204	14.5	452	0.05

$$\theta_0[(M_{Ed}/M_{cr})/(1 - M_{Ed}/M_{cr})]$$

where M_{cr} is the elastic critical buckling moment. This deformation causes a transverse bending moment per unit length

$$M_t = k_s\theta_0[(M_{Ed}/M_{cr})/(1 - M_{Ed}/M_{cr})] \tag{b}$$

where k_s is the stiffness defined in *clause 6.4.2(6)*.

The design procedure of *clause 6.4.2(1)* is such that $M_{Ed} \le \chi_{LT}M_{Rd}$. Here, M_{Rd} is taken as approximately equal to the characteristic resistance M_{Rk}. From *clause 6.4.2(4)*, $\bar{\lambda}_{LT}^2 = M_{Rk}/M_{cr}$, so that equation (b) becomes

$$M_t = k_s\theta_0[(\chi_{LT}\bar{\lambda}_{LT}^2)/(1 - \chi_{LT}\bar{\lambda}_{LT}^2)] \tag{c}$$

It is assumed that the resistance of the studs to longitudinal shear, P_{Rd}, must not be reduced, and that this is achieved if

$$T \le 0.1P_{Rd} \tag{d}$$

The initial slope θ_0 is taken as $L/400\,h$, where h is the depth of the steel section. A typical L/h ratio is 20, giving $\theta_0 = 0.05$. From these results,

$$\frac{s}{b} = \frac{0.4T}{M_t} \le \frac{0.04P_{Rd}(1 - \chi_{LT}\bar{\lambda}_{LT}^2)}{0.05k_s\chi_{LT}\bar{\lambda}_{LT}^2} \tag{DA.2}$$

This upper limit to the spacing of studs reduces as the slenderness $\bar{\lambda}_{LT}$ increases.

It can be evaluated where the conditions of *clause 6.4.3* for simplified verification are satisfied, because the value $\bar{\lambda}_{LT} = 0.4$ can be assumed. From Table 6.5 of EN 1993-1-1, buckling curve c should be used for rolled I-sections with a depth/breadth ratio exceeding 2.0. For $\bar{\lambda}_{LT} = 0.4$ it gives $\chi_{LT} = 0.90$. For a typical 19 mm stud, the resistance P_{Rd} is about 75 kN. The combined stiffness of the slab and the web, k_s, depends mainly on the stiffness of the web, and is here taken as $0.9k_2$ where k_2, the stiffness of the web, is given by *equation (6.10)* as

$$k_2 = E_a t_w^3/[4(1 - \nu_a^2)h_s] \tag{DA.3}$$

For a typical I-section, $h_s \approx 0.97\,h$. With $E_a = 210$ kN/mm² and $\nu = 0.3$, substitution into equation (DA.2) gives

$$s \le 6.66(b/t_w)(h/t_w)(1/t_w) \tag{e}$$

For rolled sections, the closest stud spacing is thus required for relatively thick webs. Examples are given in Table A.1. For studs in two rows, these spacings can be doubled, because the assumed lever arm for the moment M_t would increase from $0.4b$ (Fig. A.2) to about $0.8b$. For web-encased beams, ENV 1994-1-1 required the maximum spacings to be halved.

This check is not required by EN 1994-1-1. The results show that it would not govern in normal practice, but could do so where there was a need for wide spacing of studs (e.g. because precast concrete floor slabs were being used) on a beam with a relatively thick web, or where web encasement was used.

Top transverse reinforcement above an edge beam

Where the concrete flange of a beam is continuous on one side only, as in Fig. 6.9(a), top transverse reinforcement (AB) is required to prevent lateral buckling by anticlockwise rotation of the steel section, in the plane of the diagram. The preceding results for spacing of stud connectors can be used to estimate the amount required.

The reinforcement will be light, so the lever arm for transverse bending can be taken as $0.9d_s$ (notation as in Fig. 6.9(a)), even where concrete in the lower half of the slab is present only in the troughs of sheeting. From expression (d) above, the force T per unit length is $0.1P_{Rd}/s$; so from equation (a) the transverse bending moment is

$$M_t = 0.4bT/s = 0.04bP_{Rd}/s = A_s f_{sd}(0.9d_s)$$

where A_s is the area of top transverse reinforcement per unit length along the beam, at its design yield stress f_{sd}. Using expression (e) for s,

$$0.9A_s f_{sd} d_s \geq 0.0060 P_{Rd} t_w^3/h$$

Assuming $P_{Rd} = 75$ kN and $f_{sd} = 500/1.15 = 435$ N/mm^2:

$$100A_s/d_s \geq 115 t_w^3/d_s^2 h$$

The area A_s is thus greatest for a thin slab, so an effective depth $d_s = 100$ mm is assumed, giving

$$100A_s/d_s \geq 0.0115 t_w^3/h \tag{f}$$

These values are given in the last row of Table A.1. They show that although top reinforcement is required for U-frame action, the amount is small. *Clause 6.6.5.3*, on local reinforcement in the slab, does not refer to this subject, and could be satisfied by bottom reinforcement only. The requirements for minimum reinforcement of *clause 9.2.1(4)* and of EN 1992-1-1 could also be satisfied by bottom reinforcement, whereas some should be placed near the upper surface.

Derivation of the simplified expression for $\overline{\lambda}_{LT}$

The notation is as in the comments on *clause 6.4* and in this appendix, and is not redefined here.

Repeating equation (D6.11):

$$M_{cr} = (k_c C_4/L)[(G_a I_{at} + k_s L^2/\pi^2)E_a I_{afz}]^{1/2} \tag{D6.11}$$

From *clause 6.4.2(4)*,

$$\overline{\lambda}_{LT} = (M_{Rk}/M_{cr})^{0.5} \tag{a}$$

It is on the safe side to neglect the term $G_a I_{at}$ in equation (D6.11), which in practice is usually less than $0.1k_s L^2/\pi^2$. Hence,

$$M_{cr} = (k_c C_4/\pi)(k_s E_a I_{afz})^{1/2} \tag{b}$$

It is assumed that the stiffness of the concrete slab k_1 is at least 2.3 times the stiffness of the steel web, k_2. The combined stiffness k_s, given by *equation (6.8)* in *clause 6.4.2*, then always exceeds $0.7k_2$, so k_s in equation (b) can be replaced by $0.7k_2$. This replacement would not be valid for an encased web, so these are excluded.

For a steel flange of breadth b_f and thickness t_f,

$$I_{afz} = b_f^3 t_f/12 \tag{c}$$

The stiffness k_2 is given by *equation (6.10)* in *clause 6.4.2*. Using it and the equations above,

$$\overline{\lambda}_{LT}^4 = \left(\frac{M_{Rk}}{k_c}\right)^2 \frac{48\pi^2 h_s(1-\upsilon_a^2)}{0.7E_a^2 t_w^3 b_f^3 t_f C_4^2} \tag{d}$$

For sections in Class 1 or Class 2, $M_{Rk} = M_{pl, Rk}$. It can be shown that $M_{pl, Rk}$ is given approximately by

$$M_{pl, Rk} = k_c M_{pl, a, Rk}(1 + t_w h_s/4b_f t_f) \qquad \text{(e)}$$

For double-symmetrical steel I-sections, the plastic resistance to bending is given approximately by

$$M_{pl, a, Rk} = f_y h_s b_f t_f (1 + t_w h_s/4b_f t_f) \qquad \text{(f)}$$

From equations (d) to (f), with $v_a = 0.3$,

$$\bar{\lambda}_{LT} = 5.0\left(1 + \frac{t_w h_s}{4b_f t_f}\right)\left(\frac{h_s}{t_w}\right)^{0.75}\left(\frac{t_f}{b_f}\right)^{0.25}\left(\frac{f_y}{E_a C_4}\right)^{0.5} \qquad \text{(D6.14)}$$

as given in Annex B of ENV 1994-1-1.

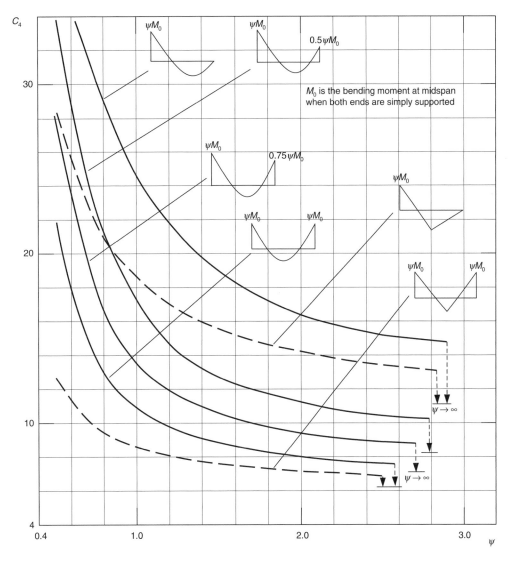

Fig. A.3. Values of the factor C_4 for uniformly distributed and centre point loading

Effect of web encasement on $\overline{\lambda}_{LT}$

The reduction in relative slenderness achieved by encasing a steel web to *clause 5.5.3(2)* can be estimated as follows. The subscript e is used for properties of the section after encasement.

From *equations (6.10)* and *(6.11)*,

$$\frac{k_{2,e}}{k_2} = \frac{(1-v_a^2)b_f^2}{4(1+4nt_w/b_f)t_w^2}$$

The modular ratio n rarely exceeds 12, and b_f/t_w is at least 15 for rolled or welded I-sections. With these values, and $v_a = 0.3$,

$$k_{2,e}/k_2 = 12.2$$

Assuming, as above, that $k_1 > 2.3k_2$ and using *equation (6.8)*, the change in k_s is

$$\frac{k_{s,e}}{k_s} = \frac{k_{2,e}}{k_1 + k_{2,e}} \frac{k_1 + k_2}{k_2} > \frac{12.2 \times (2.3 + 1)}{2.3 + 12.2} = 2.78$$

It was found above that k_s can be replaced by $0.7k_2$, so $k_{s,e}$ is now replaced by $2.78 \times 0.7k_2 = 1.95k_2$. Thus, the divisor 0.7 in equation (d) above is replaced by 1.95. Hence,

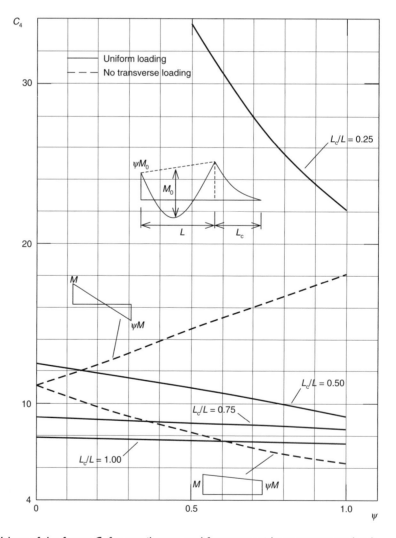

Fig. A.4. Values of the factor C_4 for cantilevers, and for spans without transverse loading

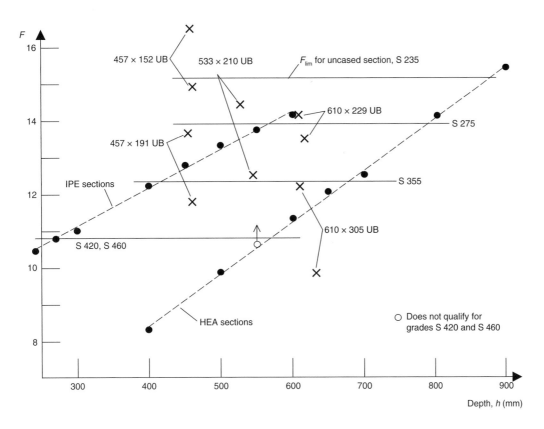

Fig. A.5. Property F (equation (D6.15)) for some IPE, HEA and UB steel sections

$$\bar{\lambda}_{LT,e}/\bar{\lambda}_{LT} = (0.7/1.95)^{0.25} = 0.77 \tag{DA.4}$$

Factor C_4 for the distribution of bending moment

The tables that were given in ENV 1994[49] relate to distributions of bending moment between points at which the steel bottom flange is laterally restrained, not necessarily to complete spans. The more commonly used values for distributed loading on internal spans are plotted in Fig. A.3. For values of ψ exceeding 3.0, values corresponding to $\psi \to \infty$ can conservatively be used. These are also shown.

The dashed lines in Fig. A.3 are for point loads at mid-span. Two other sets of values are plotted in Fig. A.4. The solid lines apply for lateral buckling of a cantilever of length L_c, where both it and the adjacent span of length L have the same intensity of distributed loading. The dashed lines are for an unloaded span with one or both ends continuous.

Criteria for verification of lateral–torsional stability without direct calculation

Unlike UB steel sections, the basic sets of IPE and HEA sections have only one size for each overall depth, h. Plots of their section properties F, from equation (D6.15), against h lie on straight lines, as shown in Fig. A.5. This enables limits on F to be presented in *Table 6.1* of *clause 6.4.3* as limits to overall depth. From equation (D6.14), F_{lim} for given $\bar{\lambda}_{LT}$ is proportional to $f_y^{-0.5}$. From this, and the qualifying sections, it can be deduced that the values of F_{lim} used in EN 1994-1-1 for the various grades of steel are as given in Table A.2.

Table A.2. Limiting section parameter F_{lim}, for uncased and web-encased sections

Nominal steel grade	S235	S275	S355	S420 and S460
F_{lim}, uncased	15.1	13.9	12.3	10.8
F_{lim}, encased web	19.5	18.0	15.8	13.9

The IPE and HEA sections shown qualify for all steel grades that have F_{lim} above their plotted value of F. The only exception is HEA 550, which plots just below the S420 and S460 line, but does not qualify according to *Table 6.1*.

For UB sections, crosses in Fig. A.5 represent the 10 sections listed in Table 6.1. The entries 'Yes' in that table correspond to the condition $F \leq F_{\text{lim}}$. It is not possible to give a qualifying condition in terms of depth only; equation (D6.15) should be used.

Web encasement

From equation (DA.4), the effect of web encasement is to increase F_{lim} by a factor of at least $1/0.77 = 1.29$. These values are given in Tables 6.1 and A.2. The additional depths permitted by *clause 6.4.3(1)(h)* are a little more conservative than this result.

APPENDIX B

The effect of slab thickness on resistance of composite slabs to longitudinal shear

Summary

A mechanical model based on ductile shear connection has been applied to the $m-k$ and partial connection methods of *Section 9* for design of composite slabs for longitudinal shear. For the $m-k$ method it was shown[124] that:

- where the assumptions of the model apply, the two sets of tests from which m and k are derived can be done on sets of slabs of different thickness but similar concrete strength
- two widely different shear spans should be used
- predictions by the $m-k$ method of EN 1994-1-1 for degrees of shear connection between those corresponding to the shear spans tested, are conservative
- predictions for degrees of shear connection outside this range are unconservative
- the percentage errors can be estimated.

For the partial-connection method it was found[124] that:

- where tests are done on slabs of one thickness only, the model gives no help in predicting the effect of slab thickness on ultimate shear strength τ_u
- slabs of at least two different thicknesses should be tested, preferably with the same shear span.

The model

The notation and assumptions are generally those of *clauses 9.7.3* and *B.3*, to which reference should be made.

Figure B.1 shows the left-hand shear span of a composite slab of breadth b and effective depth d_p, at failure in a test in accordance with *clause B.3*. The self-weight of the slab is neglected in comparison with V_t, the value of each of the two point loads at failure.

The shear connection is assumed to be ductile, as defined in *clause 9.7.3(3)*, with ultimate shear strength τ_u, as would be found by the procedure of *clause B.3.6* (except that all values here are mean values, with no partial safety factors).

The sheeting and the slab are shown separated in Fig. B.1, and the longitudinal shear force between them is

$$\eta N_{c,f} = \tau_u b L_s \qquad \text{(DB.1)}$$

where η is the degree of shear connection, ≤ 1. The value of τ_u is assumed to be independent of the shear span, so that

$$L_s = \eta L_{sf} \qquad \text{(DB.2)}$$

where L_{sf} is the length of shear span at which the longitudinal force $N_{c,f}$ equals the tensile strength of the sheeting, N_{pl}. In the absence of a partial safety factor for strength of concrete, the rectangular stress block is quite shallow, and is assumed to lie within the concrete slab. Its depth is ηx_{pl}, where x_{pl} is the depth for full shear connection.

Let the plastic bending resistance of the sheeting be $M_{p,a}$, reduced to M_{pr} in the presence of an axial force N, as shown by the stress blocks in Fig. B.1. The resistance M_{pr} is assumed to be given by

$$M_{pr} = (1 - \eta^2)M_{p,a} \qquad \text{(DB.3)}$$

The bilinear relationship given in *clause 9.7.2(6)* is an approximation to this equation, which is also approximate, but accurate enough for the present work.

For equilibrium of the length L_s of composite slab,

$$V_t L_s = \eta N_{cf}(d_p - \eta x_{pl}/2) + M_{pr}$$

Hence,

$$V_t = [\eta N_{cf}(d_p - \eta x_{pl}/2) + (1 - \eta^2)M_{p,a}]/(\eta L_{sf}) \qquad \text{(DB.4)}$$

For a typical profiled sheeting, $M_{p,a} \approx 0.3 h_p N_{pl}$. This is assumed here. The conclusions do not depend on the accuracy of the factor 0.3. Hence,

$$V_t = (N_{cf}/\eta L_{sf})[\eta d_p - \eta^2 x_{pl}/2 + 0.3 h_p(1 - \eta^2)] \qquad \text{(DB.5)}$$

For a particular sheeting and strength of concrete, it may be assumed that N_{cf}, L_{sf}, x_{pl} and h_p are constant. The independent variables are the slab thickness, represented by d_p, and the shear span in a test, represented by the degree of shear connection, η. The dependent variable is the vertical shear resistance, V_t.

The *m–k* method

The use of test results as predictors

The properties m and k are determined from the graph shown in Fig. B.2, by drawing a line through two test results. The line is

$$y = mx + k$$

For a single result, (x_1, y_1), say,

$$y_1 = mx_1 + k$$

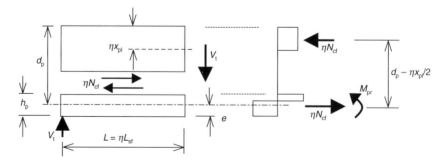

Fig. B.1. Shear span of composite slab, and stress blocks at failure in longitudinal shear

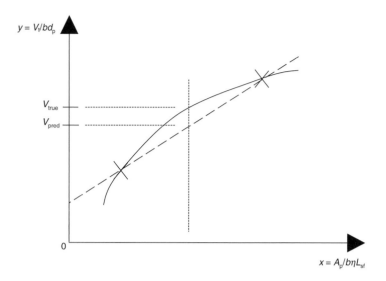

Fig. B.2. Determination of m and k from two sets of test results

From the definitions of x and y, shown in Fig. B.2, and for this test result,

$$V_{t1} = bd_{p1}(mA_p/bL_{s1} + k)$$

This is *equation (9.7)* in *clause 9.7.3(4)*. Thus, the m–k method predicts exactly the first test result. This is so also for the second test result, even if the slab thickness and shear span are different. Two test results 'predict' themselves. The basic assumption of the m–k method is that other results can be predicted by assuming a straight line through the two known results. It has been shown that it is in fact curved, so that other predictions are subject to error.

Shape of function $y(x)$

The slope of the curve $y(x)$ was found for a set of tests done with different shear spans and constant slab thickness. It was shown, by differentiation of equation (DB.5), that the curve through the two points found in tests is convex upwards, as shown in Fig. B.2.

For some degree of shear connection between those used in two tests on slabs of the same thickness, from which the m–k line was predicted, the method gives the result V_{pred}, shown in Fig. B.2. This is less than the resistance given by equation (DB.5), V_{true}, so the method is safe, according to the model.

For a degree of shear connection outside this range, the m–k method is unsafe.

Estimate of errors of prediction

As an example, suppose that for a set of tests with $d_p/h_p = 2.0$ the sheeting and concrete are such that when the shear span is L_{sf}, the depth x_{pl} of the concrete stress block is given by $x_{pl}/h_p = 0.4$. Equation (DB.5) then becomes

$$V_t = (N_{c,f}h_p/L_{sf})(0.3/\eta + 2 - 0.5\eta) \tag{DB.6}$$

Suppose that four otherwise identical tests are done with shear spans such that $\eta = 0.4, 0.5,$ 0.7 and 1.0. The (assumed) true results for $V_t L_{sf}/N_{c,f}h_p$ are calculated and plotted against $1/\eta$. They lie on a convex-upwards curve, as expected. By drawing lines through any two of the points, values for the other two tests predicted by the m–k method are obtained. Comparison with the plotted points gives the error from the m–k method, as a percentage. Typical results are given in Table B.1, for which the m–k line is drawn through the results for η_1 and η_2, and used to predict the shear resistance for a slab with $\eta = \eta_3$. The values in columns 4 and 5 of the table are proportional to V_t, so the percentage values are correct.

Table B.1. Errors in prediction of V_t by the m–k method

η_1	η_2	η_3	Prediction from m–k line	Plotted value	Error of prediction (%)
0.4	1.0	0.7	2.00	2.08	−4
0.4	0.5	1.0	1.98	1.80	+10
0.7	1.0	0.4	2.78	2.55	+9

Conclusion for the m–k method

Two sets of tests should be done, with shear spans as widely different as possible, subject to obtaining the correct failure mode. The slab thickness should be roughly central within the range of application, and can differ in the two sets; but the concrete strengths should be the same. The m–k results are applicable within the range of shear spans tested, and probably for a short distance outside it.

The partial-connection method

From Fig. B.1, the ultimate bending moment at the end of the shear span is

$$M = V_t \eta L_{sf} \tag{DB.7}$$

The overhang L_0 (*clause B.3.6(2)* and Fig. 9.2) is much less than L_{sf}. For simplicity it is assumed that $L_{sf} + L_0 \approx L_{sf}$, so that *equation (B.2)* in *clause B.3.6* becomes

$$\tau_u = \eta N_{c,f}/bL_{sf} \tag{DB.8}$$

From equations (DB.5) and (DB.7),

$$M/M_{p,Rm} = (N_{c,f}/M_{p,Rm})[\eta d_p - \eta^2 x_{pl}/2 + 0.3h_p(1 - \eta^2)] \tag{DB.9}$$

where $M_{p,Rm}$ is the plastic resistance moment with full shear connection.

For any assumed value for η, an ultimate bending moment M can be calculated from equation (DB.9). Thus, an M–η curve (*Fig. B.5* of EN 1994-1-1) can be found. If safety factors are omitted, the same curve is used to find η_{test} from a measured value M_{test}, and hence τ_u from equation (DB.8).

Equation (DB.9) is independent of shear span because ductile behaviour is assumed. It gives no information on the rate of change of η with slab thickness or shear span, so a single group of four tests gives no basis for predicting τ_u for slabs of different thickness from those tested.

Assuming that the fourth test, with a short shear span (*clause B.3.2(7)*), shows ductile behaviour, the effect of thickness can be deduced from results of a further group of three tests. The specimens and shear span should be identical with those in tests 1–3 in the first group, except for slab thickness. The thicknesses for the two groups should be near the ends of the range to be used in practice.

Let the ratios d_p/h_p for these two series be denoted v_1 and v_2, with $v_2 > v_1$, leading to the corresponding degrees of shear connection η_1 and η_2. It is likely that $\eta_2 > \eta_1$, because the longitudinal strain across the depth of the embossments will be more uniform in the thicker slabs; but the difference may be small.

Assuming that over this range the relationship between test bending resistance M and ratio v is linear, it can be shown[124] that the η–v curve is convex upwards. Hence, interpolation for η is conservative for slab thicknesses between those tested, and may be unconservative outside this range.

Conclusion for the partial-connection method

For this method, further tests at constant thickness but different shear span would only provide a check on the presence of ductile behaviour. Information on the effect of slab thickness is best obtained from tests at constant shear span and two thicknesses. It can be shown that values of degree of shear connection for intermediate thicknesses can be obtained by linear interpolation between the values for the thicknesses tested.

Simplified calculation method for the interaction curve for resistance of composite column cross-sections to compression and uniaxial bending

Scope and method

Equations are given for the coordinates of points B, C and D in *Fig. 6.19*, also shown in Fig. C.1. They are applicable to cross-sections of columns where the structural steel, concrete and reinforcement are all doubly symmetric about a single pair of axes. The steel section should be an I- or H-section or a rectangular or circular hollow section. Examples are shown in *Fig. 6.17*.

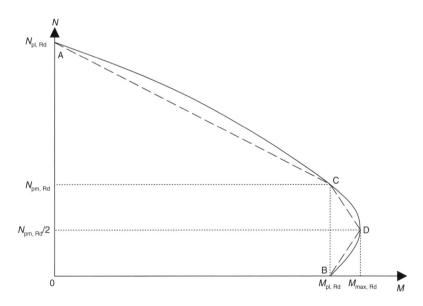

Fig. C.1. Polygonal interaction curve

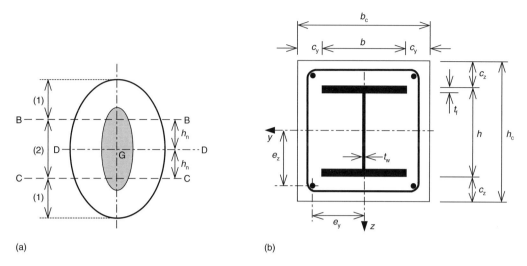

Fig. C.2. Composite cross-sections symmetrical about two axes

Plastic analysis is used, with rectangular stress blocks for structural steel, reinforcement, and concrete in accordance with *clauses 6.7.3.2(2)* to *6.7.3.2(6)*. For filled tubes of circular section, the coefficient η_c in *clause 6.7.3.2(6)* has conservatively been taken as zero.

In this annex, the compressive stress in concrete in a rectangular stress block is denoted f_{cc}, where generally, $f_{cc} = 0.85f_{cd}$. However, for concrete-filled steel sections, the coefficient 0.85 may be replaced by 1.0, following *clause 6.7.3.2(1)*.

Resistance to compression

The plastic resistance $N_{pl,\,Rd}$ is given by *clause 6.7.3.2*. The resistance $N_{pm,\,Rd}$ is calculated as follows.

Figure C.2(a) represents a generalized cross-section of structural steel and reinforcement (shaded area), and of concrete, symmetrical about two axes through its centre of area G. For bending only (point B) the neutral axis is line BB which defines region (1) of the cross-section, within which concrete is in compression. The line CC at the same distance h_n on the other side of G is the neutral axis for point C in Fig. C.1. This is because the areas of structural steel, concrete and reinforcement in region (2) are all symmetrical about G, so that the changes of stress when the axis moves from BB to CC add up to the resistance $N_{pm,\,Rd}$, and the bending resistance is unchanged. Using subscripts 1 to 3 to indicate regions (1) to (3),

$$N_{pm,\,Rd} = R_{c2} + 2|R_{a2}| \tag{C.1}$$

where R_{c2} is the resistance of the concrete in region (2), and R_{a2} is the resistance of the steel in region (2).

In the notation of *clause 6.7.3.2(1)*,

$$R_{c2} = A_{c2}f_{cc}$$

$$R_{a2} = A_{a2}f_{yd} + A_{s2}f_{sd}$$

where compressive forces and strengths f_{cc}, f_{sd} and f_{yd} are taken as positive.

From symmetry,

$$R_{a1} = |R_{a3}|$$

$$R_{c1} = R_{c3} \tag{C.2}$$

When the neutral axis is at BB, $N = 0$, so that

$$R_{a1} + R_{c1} = |R_{a2}| + |R_{a3}| \tag{C.3}$$

From eqs (C.2) and (C.3), $|R_{a2}| = R_{c1} = R_{c3}$. Substituting in equation(C.l),

$$N_{pm, Rd} = R_{c2} + R_{c1} + R_{c3} = R_c \tag{C.4}$$

where R_c is the compressive resistance of the whole area of concrete, which is easily calculated.

Position of neutral axis

Equations for h_n depend on the axis of bending, the type of cross section and the cross section properties. The equations are derived from equations (C.1) and (C.4), and are given below for some cross sections.

Bending resistances

The axial resistance at point D in Fig. C.1 is half that at point C, so the neutral axis for point D is line DD in Fig. C.2(a).

The bending resistance at point D is

$$M_{max, Rd} = W_{pa}f_{yd} + W_{ps}f_{sd} + W_{pc}f_{cc}/2 \tag{C.5}$$

where W_{pa}, W_{ps} and W_{pc} are the plastic section moduli for the structural steel, the reinforcement and the concrete part of the section (for the calculation of W_{pc} the concrete is assumed to be uncracked), and f_{yd}, f_{sd} and f_{cc} are the design strengths for the structural steel, the reinforcement and the concrete.

The bending resistance at point B is

$$M_{pl, Rd} = M_{max, Rd} - M_{n, Rd} \tag{C.6}$$

with

$$M_{n, Rd} = W_{pa, n}f_{yd} + W_{ps, n}f_{sd} + W_{pc, n}f_{cc}/2 \tag{C.7}$$

where $W_{pa, n}$, $W_{ps, n}$ and $W_{pc, n}$ are the plastic section moduli for the structural steel, the reinforcement and the concrete parts of the section within region (2) of Fig. C.2(a).

Equations for the plastic section moduli of some cross-sections are given below.

Interaction with transverse shear

If the shear force to be resisted by the structural steel is considered according to *clause 6.7.3.2(4)* the appropriate areas of steel should be assumed to resist shear alone. The method given here can be applied using the remaining areas.

Neutral axes and plastic section moduli of some cross-sections

General

The compressive resistance of the whole area of concrete is

$$N_{pm, Rd} = A_c f_{cc} \tag{C.8}$$

The value of the plastic section modulus of the total reinforcement is given by

$$W_{\mathrm{ps}} = \sum_{i=1}^{n} |A_{\mathrm{s},i} e_i| \qquad (\mathrm{C.9})$$

where e_i are the distances of the reinforcement bars of area $A_{\mathrm{s},i}$ to the relevant middle line (y-axis or z-axis).

The equations for the position of the neutral axis h_{n} are given for selected positions in the cross-sections. The resulting value h_{n} should lie within the limits of the assumed region.

Major-axis bending of encased I-sections

The plastic section modulus of the structural steel may be taken from tables, or be calculated from

$$W_{\mathrm{pa}} = \frac{(h - 2t_{\mathrm{f}})^2 t_{\mathrm{w}}}{4} + bt_{\mathrm{f}}(h - t_{\mathrm{f}}) \qquad (\mathrm{C.10})$$

and

$$W_{\mathrm{pc}} = \frac{b_{\mathrm{c}} h_{\mathrm{c}}^2}{4} - W_{\mathrm{pa}} - W_{\mathrm{ps}} \qquad (\mathrm{C.11})$$

For the different positions of the neutral axes, h_{n} and $W_{\mathrm{pa,n}}$ are given by:

(a) Neutral axis in the web, $h_{\mathrm{n}} \le h/2 - t_{\mathrm{f}}$:

$$h_{\mathrm{n}} = \frac{N_{\mathrm{pm,Rd}} - A_{\mathrm{sn}}(2f_{\mathrm{sd}} - f_{\mathrm{cc}})}{2b_{\mathrm{c}} f_{\mathrm{cc}} + 2t_{\mathrm{w}}(2f_{\mathrm{yd}} - f_{\mathrm{cc}})} \qquad (\mathrm{C.12})$$

$$W_{\mathrm{pa,n}} = t_{\mathrm{w}} h_{\mathrm{n}}^2 \qquad (\mathrm{C.13})$$

where A_{sn} is the sum of the area of reinforcing bars within the region of depth $2h_{\mathrm{n}}$.

(b) Neutral axis in the flange, $h/2 - t_{\mathrm{f}} < h_{\mathrm{n}} < h/2$:

$$h_{\mathrm{n}} = \frac{N_{\mathrm{pm,Rd}} - A_{\mathrm{sn}}(2f_{\mathrm{sd}} - f_{\mathrm{cc}}) + (b - t_{\mathrm{w}})(h - 2t_{\mathrm{f}})(2f_{\mathrm{yd}} - f_{\mathrm{cc}})}{2b_{\mathrm{c}} f_{\mathrm{cc}} + 2b(2f_{\mathrm{yd}} - f_{\mathrm{cc}})} \qquad (\mathrm{C.14})$$

$$W_{\mathrm{pa,n}} = bh_{\mathrm{n}}^2 - \frac{(b - t_{\mathrm{w}})(h - 2t_{\mathrm{f}})^2}{4} \qquad (\mathrm{C.15})$$

(c) Neutral axis outside the steel section, $h/2 \le h_{\mathrm{n}} \le h_{\mathrm{c}}/2$:

$$h_{\mathrm{n}} = \frac{N_{\mathrm{pm,Rd}} - A_{\mathrm{sn}}(2f_{\mathrm{sd}} - f_{\mathrm{cc}}) - A_{\mathrm{a}}(2f_{\mathrm{yd}} - f_{\mathrm{cc}})}{2b_{\mathrm{c}} f_{\mathrm{cc}}} \qquad (\mathrm{C.16})$$

$$W_{\mathrm{pa,n}} = W_{\mathrm{pa}} \qquad (\mathrm{C.17})$$

The plastic modulus of the concrete in the region of depth from $2h_{\mathrm{n}}$ then results from

$$W_{\mathrm{pc,n}} = b_{\mathrm{c}} h_{\mathrm{n}}^2 - W_{\mathrm{pa,n}} - W_{\mathrm{ps,n}} \qquad (\mathrm{C.18})$$

with

$$W_{\mathrm{ps,n}} = \sum_{i=1}^{n} |A_{\mathrm{sn},i} e_{\mathrm{z},i}| \qquad (\mathrm{C.19})$$

where $A_{\mathrm{sn},i}$ are the areas of reinforcing bars within the region of depth $2h_{\mathrm{n}}$, and $e_{\mathrm{z},i}$ are the distances from the middle line.

Minor-axis bending of encased I-sections

The notation is given in Fig. C.2(b).

The plastic section modulus of the structural steel may be taken from tables or be calculated from

$$W_{pa} = \frac{(h - 2t_f)t_w^2}{4} + \frac{2t_f b^2}{4} \tag{C.20}$$

and

$$W_{pc} = \frac{h_c b_c^2}{4} - W_{pa} - W_{ps} \tag{C.21}$$

For the different positions of the neutral axes, h_n and $W_{pa,n}$ are given by:

(a) Neutral axis in the web, $h_n \leq t_w/2$:

$$h_n = \frac{N_{pm,Rd} - A_{sn}(2f_{sd} - f_{cc})}{2h_c f_{cc} + 2h(2f_{yd} - f_{cc})} \tag{C.22}$$

$$W_{pa,n} = h h_n^2 \tag{C.23}$$

(b) Neutral axis in the flanges, $t_w/2 < h_n < b/2$:

$$h_n = \frac{N_{pm,Rd} - A_{sn}(2f_{sd} - f_{cc}) + t_w(2t_f - h)(2f_{yd} - f_{cc})}{2h_c f_{cc} + 4t_f(2f_{yd} - f_{cc})} \tag{C.24}$$

$$W_{pa,n} = 2t_f h_n^2 + \frac{(h - 2t_f)t_w^2}{4} \tag{C.25}$$

(c) Neutral axis outside the steel section, $b/2 \leq h_n \leq b_c/2$

$$h_n = \frac{N_{pm,Rd} - A_{sn}(2f_{sd} - f_{cc}) - A_a(2f_{yd} - f_{cc})}{2h_c f_{cc}} \tag{C.26}$$

$$W_{pa,n} = W_{pa} \tag{C.27}$$

The plastic modulus of the concrete in the region of depth $2h_n$ then results from

$$W_{pc,n} = h_c h_n^2 - W_{pa,n} - W_{ps,n} \tag{C.28}$$

with $W_{ps,n}$ according to equation (C.19), changing the subscript z to y.

Concrete-filled circular and rectangular hollow sections

The following equations are derived for rectangular hollow sections with bending about the y-axis of the section (see Fig. C.3). For bending about the z-axis the dimensions h and b are to be exchanged as well as the subscripts z and y. Equations (C.29) to (C.33) may be used for circular hollow sections with good approximation by substituting

$$h = b = d \qquad \text{and} \qquad r = d/2 - t$$

$$W_{pc} = \frac{(b - 2t)(h - 2t)^2}{4} - \frac{2}{3}r^3 - r^2(4 - \pi)(0.5h - t - r) - W_{ps} \tag{C.29}$$

with W_{ps} according to equation (C.9).

W_{pa} may be taken from tables, or be calculated from

$$W_{pa} = \frac{bh^2}{4} - \frac{2}{3}(r + t)^3 - (r + t)^2(4 - \pi)(0.5h - t - r) - W_{pc} - W_{ps} \tag{C.30}$$

$$h_n = \frac{N_{pm,Rd} - A_{sn}(2f_{sd} - f_{cc})}{2b f_{cc} + 4t(2f_{yd} - f_{cc})} \tag{C.31}$$

$$W_{pc,n} = (b - 2t)h_n^2 - W_{ps,n} \tag{C.32}$$

$$W_{pa,n} = b h_n^2 - W_{pc,n} - W_{ps,n} \tag{C.33}$$

with $W_{ps,n}$ according to equation (C.19).

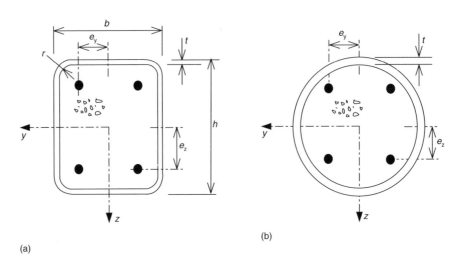

(a)

(b)

Fig. C.3. Concrete-filled (a) rectangular and (b) circular hollow sections, with notation

Example C.1: *N–M* interaction polygon for a column cross-section

The method of Appendix C is used to obtain the interaction polygon given in Fig. 6.38 for the concrete-encased H section shown in Fig. 6.37. The small area of longitudinal reinforcement is neglected. The data and symbols are as in Example 6.10 and Figs 6.37, C.1 and C.2.

Design strengths of the materials: $f_{yd} = 355$ N/mm^2; $f_{cd} = 16.7$ N/mm^2.

Other data: $A_a = 11\,400$ mm^2; $A_c = 148\,600$ mm^2; $t_f = 17.3$ mm; $t_w = 10.5$ mm; $b_c = h_c = 400$ mm; $b = 256$ mm; $h = 260$ mm; $10^{-6}W_{pa, y} = 1.228$ mm^3; $10^{-6}W_{pa, z} = 0.575$ mm^3; $N_{pl, Rd} = $ **6156 kN.**

Major-axis bending

From equation (C.8),

$$N_{pm, Rd} = 148.6 \times 16.7 = \mathbf{2482 \text{ kN}}$$

From equation (C.12),

$$h_n = 2482/[0.8 \times 16.7 + 0.021 \times (710 - 16.7)] = 89 \text{ mm}$$

so the neutral axis is in the web (Fig. C.4(a)), as assumed. From equation (C.11), the plastic section modulus for the whole area of concrete is

$$10^{-6}W_{pc} = 4^3/4 - 1.228 = 14.77 \text{ mm}^3$$

From equation (C.13),

$$10^{-6}W_{pa, n} = 10.5 \times 0.089^2 = 0.083 \text{ mm}^3$$

From equation (C.18),

$$10^{-6}W_{pc, n} = 400 \times 0.089^2 - 0.083 = 3.085 \text{ mm}^3$$

From equation (C.5),

$$M_{max, Rd} = 1.228 \times 355 + 14.77 \times 16.7/2 = \mathbf{559 \text{ kN m}}$$

From equations (C.6) and (C.7),

$$M_{pl, Rd} = 559 - (0.083 \times 355 + 3.085 \times 16.7/2) = \mathbf{504 \text{ kN m}}$$

The results shown above in bold type are plotted on Fig. 6.38.

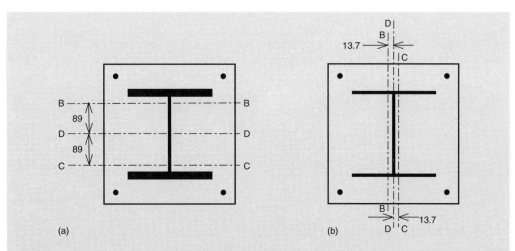

Fig. C.4. Neutral axes at points B, C and D on the interaction polygons

Minor-axis bending

From equation (C.4), $N_{pm,Rd}$ is the same for both axes of bending. Thus,

$$N_{pm,Rd} = \textbf{2482 kN}$$

Assuming that the neutral axis B–B intersects the flanges, from equation (C.24),

$$h_n = [2482 - 0.0105 \times (260 - 34.6) \times (710 - 16.7)]/[0.8 \times 16.7$$
$$+ 0.0692 \times (710 - 16.7)] = 13.7 \text{ mm}$$

so axis B–B does intersect the flanges (Fig. C.4(b)). From equation (C.21),

$$10^{-6}W_{pc} = 4^3/4 - 0.575 = 15.42 \text{ mm}^3$$

From equation (C.25),

$$10^{-6}W_{pa,n} = 34.6 \times 0.0137^2 + 0.0105^2 \times (260 - 34.6)/4 = 0.0127 \text{ mm}^3$$

From equation (C.28),

$$10^{-6}W_{pc,n} = 400 \times 0.0137^2 - 0.0127 = 0.0624 \text{ mm}^3$$

From equation (C.5),

$$M_{max,Rd} = 0.575 \times 355 + 15.42 \times 16.7/2 = \textbf{333 kN m}$$

From equation (C.7),

$$M_{n,Rd} = 0.0127 \times 355 + 0.0624 \times 16.7/2 = 5.03 \text{ kN m}$$

From equation (C.6),

$$M_{pl,Rd} = 333 - 5 = \textbf{328 kN m}$$

These results are plotted on Fig. 6.38, and used in Example 6.10.

References

1. British Standards Institution (2004) *Design of Composite Steel and Concrete Structures. Part 1.1: General Rules and Rules for Buildings*. BSI, London, BS EN 1994 (in preparation).
2. Gulvanessian, H., Calgaro, J.-A. and Holický, M. (2002) *Designers' Guide to EN 1990. Eurocode: Basis of Structural Design*. Thomas Telford, London.
3. British Standards Institution (2002) *Eurocode: Basis of Structural Design*. BSI, London, BS EN 1990.
4. British Standards Institution (2004) *Design of Concrete Structures. Part 1.1: General Rules and Rules for Buildings*. BSI, London, BS EN 1992 (in preparation).
5. British Standards Institution (2004) *Design of Steel Structures. Part 1.1: General Rules and Rules for Buildings*. BSI, London, BS EN 1993 (in preparation).
6. Beeby, A. W. and Narayanan, R. S. (2004) *Designers' Guide to EN 1992. Eurocode 2: Design of Concrete Structures. Part 1.1: General Rules and Rules for Buildings*. Thomas Telford, London (in preparation).
7. Nethercot, D. and Gardner, L. (2004) *Designers' Guide to EN 1993. Eurocode 3: Design of Steel Structures. Part 1.1: General Rules and Rules for Buildings*. Thomas Telford, London (in preparation).
8. European Commission (2002) *Guidance Paper L (Concerning the Construction Products Directive – 89/106/EEC). Application and Use of Eurocodes*. EC, Brussels.
9. British Standards Institution (2002) *Actions on Structures. Part 1.1: Densities, Self Weight and Imposed Loads*. BSI, London, BS EN 1991 [Parts 1.2, 1.3, etc., specify other types of action].
10. British Standards Institution (2004) *Design of Structures for Earthquake Resistance*. BSI, London, BS EN 1998 (in preparation).
11. British Standards Institution (2004) *Design of Composite Steel and Concrete Structures. Part 2: Bridges*. BSI, London, BS EN 1994 (in preparation).
12. International Organization for Standardization (1997) *Basis of Design for Structures – Notation – General Symbols*. ISO, Geneva, ISO 3898.
13. European Commission (1989) *Construction Products Directive 89/106/EEC*. EC, Brussels, OJEC No. L40, 11 Feb.
14. British Standards Institution (2004) *Geotechnical Design*. BSI, London, BS EN 1997 (in preparation).
15. Johnson, R. P. and Huang, D. J. (1994) Calibration of safety factors γ_M for composite steel and concrete beams in bending. *Proceedings of the Institution of Civil Engineers: Structures and Buildings*, **104,** 193–203.
16. Johnson, R. P. and Huang, D. J. (1997) Statistical calibration of safety factors for encased composite columns. In: C. D. Buckner and B. M. Sharooz (eds), *Composite Construction in Steel and Concrete III*. American Society of Civil Engineers, New York, pp. 380–391.

17. British Standards Institution (1997) *Structural Use of Concrete. Part 1: Code of Practice for Design and Construction.* BSI, London, BS 8110.

18. Stark, J. W. B. (1984) Rectangular stress block for concrete. Technical paper S16, June. Drafting Committee for Eurocode 4 (unpublished).

19. Anderson, D., Aribert, J.-M., Bode, H. and Kronenburger, H. J. (2000) Design rotation capacity of composite joints. *Structural Engineer*, **78**, 25–29.

20. Morino, S. (2002) Recent developments on concrete-filled steel tube members in Japan. In: J. F. Hajjar, M. Hosain, W. S. Easterling and B. M. Shahrooz (eds), *Composite Construction in Steel and Concrete IV*. American Society of Civil Engineers, New York, pp. 644–655.

21. Wakabayashi, M. and Minami, K. (1990) Application of high strength steel to composite structures. *Symposium on Mixed Structures, including New Materials, Brussels.* IABSE, Zurich. *Reports*, **60**, 59–64.

22. Hegger, J. and Döinghaus, P. (2002) High performance steel and high performance concrete in composite structures. In: J. F. Hajjar, M. Hosain, W. S. Easterling and B. M. Shahrooz (eds), *Composite Construction in Steel and Concrete IV*. American Society of Civil Engineers, New York, pp. 891–902.

23. Hoffmeister, B., Sedlacek, G., Müller, Ch. and Kühn, B. (2002) High strength materials in composite structures. In: J. F. Hajjar, M. Hosain, W. S. Easterling and B. M. Shahrooz (eds), *Composite Construction in Steel and Concrete IV*. American Society of Civil Engineers, New York, pp. 903–914.

24. British Standards Institution (2004) *Design of Steel Structures. Part 1-8: Design of Joints.* BSI, London, BS EN 1993 (in preparation).

25. British Standards Institution (2004) *Design of Steel Structures. Part 1-3: Cold Formed Thin Gauge Members and Sheeting.* BSI, London, BS EN 1993 (in preparation).

26. British Standards Institution (1998) *Welding – Studs and Ceramic Ferrules for Arc Stud Welding.* BSI, London, BS EN 13918.

27. Trahair, N. S., Bradford, M. A. and Nethercot, D. A. (2001) *The Behaviour and Design of Steel Structures to BS 5950*, 3rd edn. Spon, London.

28. Johnson, R. P. and Chen, S. (1991) Local buckling and moment redistribution in Class 2 composite beams. *Structural Engineering International*, **1**, 27–34.

29. Johnson, R. P. and Fan, C. K. R. (1988) Strength of continuous beams designed to Eurocode 4. *Proceedings of the IABSE*. IABSE, Zurich, P-125/88, pp. 33–44.

30. British Standards Institution (2004) *Design of Steel Structures. Part 1-5: Plated Structural Elements.* BSI, London, BS EN 1993 (in preparation).

31. British Standards Institution (1990) *Code of Practice for Design of Simple and Continuous Composite Beams.* BSI, London, BS 5950-3-1.

32. Haensel, J. (1975) Effects of creep and shrinkage in composite construction. *Report 75-12*. Institute for Structural Engineering, Ruhr-Universität, Bochum.

33. Johnson, R. P. and Hanswille, G. (1998) Analyses for creep of continuous steel and composite bridge beams, according to EC4: Part 2. *Structural Engineer*, **76**, 294–298.

34. Johnson, R. P. (1987) Shrinkage-induced curvature in cracked composite flanges of composite beams. *Structural Engineer*, **65B**, 72–77.

35. British Standards Institution (2004) *Actions on Structures. Part 1-5: Thermal Actions.* BSI, London, BS EN 1991 (in preparation).

36. British Standards Institution (2002) *Eurocode: Basis of Structural Design. Annex A1: Application for Buildings.* BSI, London, BS EN 1990.

37. Johnson, R. P. and Buckby, R. J. (1986) *Composite Structures of Steel and Concrete*, 2nd edn, Vol. 2. *Bridges*. Collins, London.

38. Johnson, R. P. and Huang, D. J. (1995) Composite bridge beams of mixed-class cross-section. *Structutural Engineering International*, **5**, 96–101.

39. ECCS TC11 (1999) *Design of Composite Joints for Buildings*. European Convention for Constructional Steelwork, Brussels. *Reports*, **109**.

40. Johnson, R. P. (2003) Cracking in concrete tension flanges of composite T-beams – tests and Eurocode 4. *Structural Engineer*, **81,** 29–34.

41. Ahmed, M. and Hosain, M. (1991) Recent research on stub-girder floor systems. In: S. C. Lee (ed.), *Composite Steel Structures*. Elsevier, Amsterdam, pp. 123–132.

42. Lawson, R. M. (1987) *Design for Openings in the Webs of Composite Beams*. Steel Construction Institute, Ascot, Publication 068.

43. Lawson, R. M., Chung, K. F. and Price, A. M. (1992) Tests on composite beams with large web openings. *Structural Engineer*, **70,** 1–7.

44. Johnson, R. P. and Anderson, D. (1993) *Designers' Handbook to Eurocode 4. Part 1: Basis of Design*. Thomas Telford, London.

45. Ansourian, P. (1982) Plastic rotation of composite beams. *Journal of the Structural Division of the American Society of Civil Engineers*, **108,** 643–659.

46. Johnson, R. P. and Hope-Gill, M. (1976) Applicability of simple plastic theory to continuous composite beams. *Proceedings of the Institution of Civil Engineers, Part 2*, **61,** 127–143.

47. Johnson, R. P. and Molenstra, N. (1991) Partial shear connection in composite beams for buildings. *Proceedings of the Institution of Civil Engineers, Part 2*, **91,** 679–704.

48. Aribert, J. M. (1990) Design of composite beams with a partial shear connection [in French]. *Symposium on Mixed Structures, including New Materials, Brussels*. IABSE, Zurich. *Reports*, **60,** 215–220.

49. British Standards Institution (1994) *Design of Composite Steel and Concrete Structures. Part 1.1: General Rules and Rules for Buildings*. BSI, London, DD ENV 1994.

50. Johnson, R. P. and Willmington, R. T. (1972) Vertical shear in continuous composite beams. *Proceedings of the Institution of Civil Engineers*, **53,** Sept., 189–205.

51. Allison, R. W., Johnson, R. P. and May, I. M. (1982) Tension-field action in composite plate girders. *Proceedings of the Institution of Civil Engineers, Part 2*, **73,** 255–276.

52. British Standards Institution (2004) *Design of Composite Steel and Concrete Structures. Part 1–2: Structural Fire Design*. BSI, London, BS EN 1994 (in preparation).

53. Andrä, H.-P. (1990) Economical shear connection with high fatigue strength. *Symposium on Mixed Structures, including New Materials, Brussels*. IABSE, Zurich. *Reports*, **60,** 167–172.

54. Studnicka, J., Machacek, J., Krpata, A. and Svitakova, M. (2002) Perforated shear connector for composite steel and concrete beams. In: J. F. Hajjar, M. Hosain, W. S. Easterling and B. M. Shahrooz (eds), *Composite Construction in Steel and Concrete IV*. American Society of Civil Engineers, New York, pp. 367–378.

55. Lindner, J. and Budassis, N. (2002) Lateral distortional buckling of partially encased composite beams without concrete slab. In: J. F. Hajjar, M. Hosain, W. S. Easterling and B. M. Shahrooz (eds), *Composite Construction in Steel and Concrete IV*. American Society of Civil Engineers, New York, pp. 117–128.

56. Johnson, R. P. and Fan, C. K. R. (1991) Distortional lateral buckling of continuous composite beams. *Proceedings of the Institution of Civil Engineers, Part 2*, **91,** 131–161.

57. British Standards Institution (2000) *Design of Steel Bridges*. BSI, London, BS 5400: Part 3.

58. Johnson, R. P. and Molenstra, N. (1990) Strength and stiffness of shear connections for discrete U-frame action in composite plate girders. *Structural Engineer*, **68,** 386–392.

59. Hanswille, G. (2002) Lateral torsional buckling of composite beams. Comparison of more accurate methods with Eurocode 4. In: J. F. Hajjar, M. Hosain, W. S. Easterling and B. M. Shahrooz (eds), *Composite Construction in Steel and Concrete IV*. American Society of Civil Engineers, New York, pp. 105–116.

60. Hanswille, G., Lindner, J. and Münich, N. D. (1998) Zum Biegedrillknicken von Stahlverbundträgern. *Stahlbau*, **7.**

61. Roik, K., Hanswille, G. and Kina, J. (1990) Background to Eurocode 4 clause 4.6.2 and Annex B. University of Bochum, Bochum, Report RSII 2-674102-88.17.

227

62. Roik, K., Hanswille, G. and Kina, J. (1990) Solution for the lateral torsional buckling problem of composite beams [in German]. *Stahlbau,* **59**, 327–332.

63. Lawson, M. and Rackham, J. W. (1989) *Design of Haunched Composite Beams in Buildings.* Steel Construction Institute, Ascot, Publication 060.

64. British Standards Institution (2004) *Design of Steel Structures. Part 2: Bridges.* BSI, London, BS EN 1993 (in preparation).

65. British Standards Institution (2000) *Code of Practice for Design in Simple and Continuous Construction: Hot Rolled Sections.* BSI, London, BS 5950-1.

66. Johnson, R. P. and Chen, S. (1993) Stability of continuous composite plate girders with U-frame action. *Proceedings of the Institution of Civil Engineers: Structures and Buildings,* **99**, 187–197.

67. Johnson, R. P. and Oehlers, D. J. (1981) Analysis and design for longitudinal shear in composite T-beams. *Proceedings of the Institution of Civil Engineers, Part 2,* **71**, 989–1021.

68. Li, A. and Cederwall, K. (1991) *Push Tests on Stud Connectors in Normal and High-strength Concrete.* Chalmers Institute of Technology, Gothenburg, Report 91:6.

69. Mottram, J. T. and Johnson, R. P. (1990) Push tests on studs welded through profiled steel sheeting. *Structural Engineer,* **68**, 187–193.

70. Oehlers, D. J. and Johnson, R. P. (1987) The strength of stud shear connections in composite beams. *Structural Engineer,* **65B**, 44–48.

71. Roik, K., Hanswille, G. and Cunze Oliveira Lanna, A. (1989) *Eurocode 4, Clause 6.3.2: Stud Connectors.* University of Bochum, Bochum, Report EC4/8/88.

72. Stark, J. W. B. and van Hove, B. W. E. M. (1991) *Statistical Analysis of Pushout Tests on Stud Connectors in Composite Steel and Concrete Structures.* TNO Building and Construction Research, Delft, Report BI-91-163.

73. British Standards Institution (1998) *Welding – Arc Stud Welding of Metallic Materials.* BSI, London, BS EN ISO 14555.

74. Kuhlmann, U. and Breuninger, U. (2002) Behaviour of horizontally lying studs with longitudinal shear force. In: J. F. Hajjar, M. Hosain, W. S. Easterling and B. M. Shahrooz (eds), *Composite Construction in Steel and Concrete IV.* American Society of Civil Engineers, New York, pp. 438–449.

75. Grant, J. A., Fisher, J. W. and Slutter, R. G. (1977) Composite beams with formed metal deck. *Engineering Journal of the American Institute of Steel Construction,* **1**, 27–42.

76. Johnson, R. P. and Yuan, H. (1998) Existing rules and new tests for studs in troughs of profiled sheeting. *Proceedings of the Institution of Civil Engineers: Structures and Buildings,* **128**, 244–251.

77. Johnson, R. P. and Yuan, H. (1998) Models and design rules for studs in troughs of profiled sheeting. *Proceedings of the Institution of Civil Engineers: Structures and Buildings,* **128**, 252–263.

78. Lawson, R. M. (1993) Shear connection in composite beams. In: W. S. Easterling and W. M. K. Roddis (eds), *Composite Construction in Steel and Concrete II.* American Society of Civil Engineers, New York, pp. 81–97.

79. Johnson, R. P. and Oehlers, D. (1982) Design for longitudinal shear in composite L-beams. *Proceedings of the Institution of Civil Engineers, Part 2,* **73**, 147–170.

80. Najafi, A. A. (1992) End-plate connections. PhD thesis, University of Warwick, Warwick.

81. Johnson, R. P. (2004) *Composite Structures of Steel and Concrete: Beams, Columns, Frames, and Applications in Building,* 3rd edn. Blackwell, Oxford.

82. British Standards Institution (1987) *Design of Composite Bridges.* BSI, London, BS 5400: Part 5.

83. Lam, D., Elliott, K. S. and Nethercot, D. (2000) Designing composite steel beams with precast concrete hollow core slabs. *Proceedings of the Institution of Civil Engineers: Structures and Buildings,* **140**, 139–149.

84. Roik, K. and Bergmann, R. (1990) Design methods for composite columns with unsymmetrical cross-sections. *Journal of Constructional Steelwork Research,* **15**, 153–168.

85. Wheeler, A. T. and Bridge, R. Q. (2002) Thin-walled steel tubes filled with high strength concrete in bending. In: J. F. Hajjar, M. Hosain, W. S. Easterling and B. M. Shahrooz (eds), *Composite Construction in Steel and Concrete IV*. American Society of Civil Engineers, New York, pp. 584–595.

86. Kilpatrick, A. and Rangan, V. (1999) Tests on high-strength concrete-filled tubular steel columns. *ACI Structural Journal*, **96-S29**, 268–274.

87. May, I. M. and Johnson, R. P. (1978) Inelastic analysis of biaxially restrained columns. *Proceedings of the Institution of Civil Engineers, Part 2*, **65**, 323–337.

88. Roik, K. and Bergmann, R. (1992) Composite columns. In: P. J. Dowling, J. L. Harding and R. Bjorhovde (eds), *Constructional Steel Design – An International Guide*. Elsevier, London, pp. 443–469.

89. British Standards Institution (2004) *Design of Steel Structures. Part 1-9: Fatigue Strength of Steel Structures*. BSI, London, BS EN 1993 (in preparation).

90. Atkins, W. S. and Partners (2004) *Designers' Guide to EN 1994. Eurocode 4: Design of Composite Structures. Part 2: Bridges*. Thomas Telford, London (in preparation).

91. Johnson, R. P. (2000) Resistance of stud shear connectors to fatigue. *Journal of Constructional Steel Research*, **56**, 101–116.

92. Oehlers, D. J. and Bradford, M. (1995) *Composite Steel and Concrete Structural Members – Fundamental Behaviour*. Elsevier, Oxford.

93. Gomez Navarro, M. (2002) Influence of concrete cracking on the serviceability limit state design of steel-reinforced concrete composite bridges: tests and models. In: J. Martinez Calzon (ed.), *Composite Bridges – Proceedings of the 3rd International Meeting*. Spanish Society of Civil Engineers, Madrid, pp. 261–278.

94. Johnson, R. P. and May, I. M. (1975) Partial-interaction design of composite beams. *Structural Engineer*, **53**, 305–311.

95. Stark, J. W. B. and van Hove, B. W. E. M. (1990) *The Midspan Deflection of Composite Steel-and-concrete Beams under Static Loading at Serviceability Limit State*. TNO Building and Construction Research, Delft, Report BI-90-033.

96. British Standards Institution (2004) *Draft National Annex to BS EN 1990: Eurocode: Basis of Structural Design*. BSI, London (in preparation).

97. British Standards Institution (1992) *Guide to Evaluation of Human Exposure to Vibration in Buildings*. BSI, London, BS 6472.

98. Wyatt, T. A. (1989) *Design Guide on the Vibration of Floors*. Steel Construction Institute, Ascot, Publication 076.

99. Randl, E. and Johnson, R. P. (1982) Widths of initial cracks in concrete tension flanges of composite beams. *Proceedings of the IABSE*, *P-54/82*, 69–80.

100. Johnson, R. P. and Allison, R. W. (1983) Cracking in concrete tension flanges of composite T-beams. *Structural Engineer*, **61B**, 9–16.

101. Johnson, R. P. (2003) Cracking in concrete flanges of composite T-beams – tests and Eurocode 4. *Structural Engineer*, **81**, 29–34.

102. Roik, K., Hanswille, G. and Cunze Oliveira Lanna, A. (1989) *Report on Eurocode 4, Clause 5.3, Cracking of Concrete*. University of Bochum, Bochum, Report EC4/4/88.

103. Moore, D. B. (2004) *Designers' Guide to EN 1993. Eurocode 3: Design of Steel Structures. Part 1-8: Design of Joints*. Thomas Telford, London (in preparation).

104. Couchman, G. and Way, A. (1998) *Joints in Steel Construction – Composite Connections*. Steel Construction Institute, Ascot, Publication 213.

105. Bose, B. and Hughes, A. F. (1995) Verifying the performance of standard ductile connections for semi-continuous steel frames. *Proceedings of the Institution of Civil Engineers: Structures and Buildings*, **110,** November, 441–457.

106. Nethercot, D. A. and Lawson, M. (1992) *Lateral Stability of Steel Beams and Columns – Common Cases of Restraint*. Steel Construction Institute, Ascot, Publication 093.

107. British Standards Institution (1994) *Code of Practice for Design of Floors with Profiled Steel Sheeting*. BSI, London, BS 5950-4.

108. British Standards Institution (2004) *Actions on Structures. Part 1-6: Actions During Execution*. BSI, London, BS EN 1991 (in preparation).

109. Couchman, G. H. and Mullett, D. L. (2000) *Composite Slabs and Beams Using Steel Decking: Best Practice for Design and Construction*. Steel Construction Institute, Ascot, Publication 300.

110. Bryan, E. R. and Leach, P. (1984) *Design of Profiled Sheeting as Permanent Formwork*. Construction Industry Research and Information Association, London, Technical Note 116.

111. Stark, J. W. B. and Brekelmans, J. W. P. M. (1990) Plastic design of continuous composite slabs. *Journal of Constructional Steel Research*, **15**, 23–47.

112. ECCS Working Group 7.6 (1998) *Longitudinal Shear Resistance of Composite Slabs: Evaluation of Existing Tests*. European Convention for Constructional Steelwork, Brussels. *Reports*, **106**.

113. Bode, H. and Storck, I. (1990) *Background Report to Eurocode 4 (Continuation of Report EC4/7/88). Chapter 10 and Section 10.3: Composite Floors with Profiled Steel Sheet*. University of Kaiserslautern, Kaiserslautern.

114. Bode, H. and Sauerborn, I. (1991) Partial shear connection design of composite slabs. In: *Proceedings of the 3rd International Conference*. Association for International Cooperation and Research in Steel–Concrete Composite Structures, Sydney, pp. 467–472.

115. British Standards Institution (1997) *Falsework. Performance Requirements and General Design. Standard 97/102975DC*. BSI, London, prEN 12812.

116. Huber, G. (1999) *Non-linear Calculations of Composite Sections and Semi-continuous Joints*. Ernst, Berlin.

117. COST-C1 (1997) *Composite Steel–concrete Joints in Braced Frames for Buildings. Report: Semi-rigid Behaviour of Civil Engineering Structural Connections*. Office for Official Publications of the European Communities, Luxembourg.

118. Aribert, J. M. (1999) Theoretical solutions relating to partial shear connection of steel–concrete composite beams and joints. In: *Proceedings of the International Conference on Steel and Composite Structures*. TNO Building and Construction Research, Delft, 7.1-7.16.

119. Patrick, M. (1990) A new partial shear connection strength model for composite slabs. *Steel Construction Journal*, **24**, 2–17.

120. Oehlers, D. J. (1989) Splitting induced by shear connectors in composite beams. *Journal of the Structural Division of the American Society of Civil Engineers*, **115**, 341–362.

121. British Standards Institution (2001) *Tensile Testing of Metallic Materials. Part 1: Method of Test at Ambient Temperature*. BSI, London, BS EN 10002.

122. van Hove, B. W. E. M. (1991) *Experimental Research on the CF70/0.9 Composite Slab*. TNO Building and Construction Research, Delft, Report BI-91-106.

123. Elliott, J. S. and Nethercot, D. (1991) *Non-composite Flexural and Shear Tests on CF70 Decking*. Department of Civil Engineering, University of Nottingham, Report SR 91033.

124. Johnson, R. P. (2004) The m–k and partial-interaction models for shear resistance of composite slabs, and the use of non-standard test data. In: *Composite Construction in Steel and Concrete V* [Proceedings of a Conference, Kruger National Park, 2004]. American Society of Civil Engineers, New York (in preparation).

Index

Note: references to 'beams' and to 'columns' are to composite members